FRUIT GROWING

NECTARINES—*Pine-apple* and *Pitmaston Orange* (*top*)
PEACHES—*Waterloo* and *Royal George* (*bottom*)

FRUIT GROWING

MODERN CULTURAL METHODS

Edited by

N. B. BAGENAL, B.A.(Cantab.)
East Malling Research Station, Kent

8 *PLATES IN COLOUR*
60 *PHOTOGRAPHIC ILLUSTRATIONS*
and *MANY DIAGRAMS*

WARD, LOCK & CO., LIMITED
LONDON AND MELBOURNE

First Impression	.	1939
Revised Edition	.	1945
Reprinted	. .	1946
Reprinted	. .	1948

MADE IN ENGLAND
Printed in Great Britain by Butler & Tanner Ltd., Frome and London

CONTENTS

CONTENTS

COLOUR PLATES

7

LIST OF ILLUSTRATIONS

9

LIST OF ILLUSTRATIONS

DIAGRAMS IN TEXT

DIAGRAMS IN TEXT

PREFACE

THE aim of this book has been to give both to the amateur and to the professional fruit grower accurate and up-to-date information which will enable him to produce fruit successfully.

The principles of fruit culture apply equally to fruit growing in the private garden, and to production on a large scale for market ; it is only in certain practical details that differences are to be found.

The methods advocated here are those that have been tested over a long period and found to be of proved value.

Special attention has been paid to the selection of the best and most suitable varieties of each particular fruit for the form in which it is to be grown, and for the purpose for which it is needed. The pruning of each particular fruit has been dealt with in considerable detail, pollination and the correct practice in regard to propagation, planting, training and staking, grading, packing, and marketing are all fully but concisely explained. Finally, with regard to that important subject the checking of diseases and pests, the latest methods of control are given.

Here, therefore, is a work that will, I hope, prove of the greatest value to the novice and even to the experienced nurseryman ; to both student and instructor ; indeed, to all interested in the subject of fruit growing.

In editing this book I have drawn largely from the information contained in the reports and bulletins published by the Ministry of Agriculture, East Malling and Long Ashton Research Stations, and the Imperial Bureau of Fruit Production. In the description of varieties of fruits with which I am not personally familiar, I have consulted the two Handbooks of Hardy Fruits by the late Edward A. Bunyard. The information on diseases and pests and their control has been supplied by W. Steer, University of Manchester, and M. H. Moore of East Malling Research Station.

In this revised edition I have included an important new chapter on the forming and training, and pruning of the " delayed open-centre " tree by Mr. C. R. Thompson of Kent Education Committee.

The fruit illustrated on four of the eight colour plates are reproduced by courtesy of the late Edward Bunyard.

N. B. BAGENAL,
East Malling Research Station,
Kent.

13

VEITCHBERRY (*top*) LOWBERRY and WINEBERRY (*bottom*)

[*Facing page* 14

FRUIT CULTURE

CHAPTER I

GENERAL CONSIDERATIONS

Hardy fruits can be grown over a wide range of soils and of climatic conditions in England. Success in growing them is based on two main principles, the first to maintain in the tree a balanced and steady rate of growth, and the second to keep the tree free from diseases and pests. If growth is too slow, the tree becomes stunted and crops prematurely ; if growth is too fast, the tree becomes unbalanced : it produces more leaf and wood growth and less fruit than it should, and as a result of growing too fast, it becomes more liable to certain functional and parasitic diseases. Selection of soil, site and aspect, choice of kinds, varieties and forms of trees and bushes, and methods of planting, pruning, cultivating, manuring and spraying, are important in so far as they help to keep the trees in a state of balanced and healthy growth.

SOIL

The soil, naturally, has an important part to play in the life of any plant whose roots are growing in it. Moreover, for fruit trees and bushes, the subsoil, no less and sometimes even more than the surface soil, needs to be carefully considered. It has been shown, for instance, that the roots of a comparatively weak-growing variety of apple tree on a very dwarfing rootstock (see illustration on plate facing page 32) can penetrate 10 feet below ground in as many years under certain soil conditions, and in a sandy loam the roots of gooseberries (see illustration on plate facing page 241) may penetrate more than 8 feet.

This shows that fruit soils cannot be judged by the same standards as those employed in choosing a site for flowers and vegetables. There are, for instance, many shallow soil series overlying solid chalk or sticky clay with as little as 9 to 12 inches of surface soil which in the process of digging or ploughing have been brought into a comparatively fertile and friable condition. In such soils certain vegetables and flowers might be made to flourish, but if fruit trees

15

or bushes were planted, their roots would very soon penetrate to the solid chalk or clay layers in the subsoil and perish.

Other soil series which may appear most disappointing on the surface have a layer of better soil lower down, and as soon as the roots reach this layer, the trees begin to grow more strongly. When setting out to examine the suitability of the soil for fruit growing the wise man will arm himself with a soil auger, which can easily be made by a local blacksmith, or he will take with him a good spade with which to penetrate at least 3 feet below the surface.

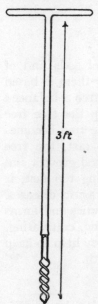

3 ft

SOIL AUGER.

In subsequent chapters mention will be made of the special soil requirements of different kinds and varieties of fruits. It might be noted here that what may prove admirable for one kind or variety may be by no means desirable for another. The richest soil is not always the most suitable. A deep, fertile soil is good in so far as it will always give the young tree or bush a better start than it would get in a thin, sandy loam or in a wet, sticky clay. There is always the danger, however, that too rich a soil may produce too rapid growth, and this is bad for the tree.

SITUATION AND ASPECT

Some shelter from severe or prolonged winds is important for all fruits, however hardy. In exposure to the south-west there is a double danger; in the late summer the fruits may be blown from the trees, and in the autumn a heavy strain is put on the anchorage, especially of newly-planted trees which are not yet firmly rooted in the ground. A few years ago a wind of gale force blowing from the south-west in different parts of England uprooted hundreds of fruit trees, most of which were staked, and were not in exceptionally exposed situations.

Shelter from east winds is important for quite another reason. These winds are usually at their worst in March and April, and sometimes last well into May. This is the flowering time for most fruit trees and bushes, and it is, therefore, one of the most critical periods in the whole season. Many kinds of fruits depend on insects for cross-pollination, and if the trees or bushes are exposed to the full force of the easterly gales, the pollinating insects cannot fly freely from flower to flower. Apart from this, the force of the

F.G.

Copyright Photos]

STANDARD APPLE TREE " LORD DERBY."

YOUNG STANDARD CHERRY TREE.

[*N. B. Bagenal.*

B

BUSH APPLE ON MALLING NUMBER IX STOCK.

BUSH PEAR "CONFERENCE."

[N. B. Bagenal.

wind may be so great as to bruise the flower petals, thus making them less attractive to insects. Then, again, easterly winds, if prevalent for any length of time during the period after blossoming, may seriously upset the balance of the plants by causing a sudden check to growth, which should at this period be continuous. The tiny fruitlets, instead of making steady development, remain small, often change colour, shrivel up and drop to the ground. This frequently happens in the case of black currants, gooseberries and cherries, and although such " running-off " is often attributed to insufficient pollination or to frost damage, the check to growth caused by cold east winds is all too frequently an important contributory factor.

Thus, at almost any season of the year there is risk of damage of one sort or another from undue exposure to wind, whether it comes from the south-west, the east or the north-east. Nevertheless, when looking for a sheltered situation, it is important not to choose the lowest altitude available, since there is always a danger of selecting a spot which, although well out of the wind, may be dangerously subject to frost. It is no use making the orchard safe for insects if the flowers are to be frost-bitten before they open or just as they come into bloom. To escape frost the situation should have free air drainage beyond and below it, and should not be too closely overtopped by higher land whence frosts or cold mists can descend upon it.

Having, then, successfully compromised between undue exposure to winds and to frost and cold mists, the next important consideration is to choose a situation with as much sunlight as possible, a matter which naturally becomes more and more important as the fruit grower moves northwards or to districts in the neighbourhood of large manufacturing towns where sunshine is likely to be diminished. At all costs a site directly overshadowed by tall trees or buildings should be avoided, since it is impossible for healthy fruit-bud formation to take place under such conditions. Where there is little likelihood of the trees being exposed to gales from the south-west or from the east, there is no doubt that a southern slope is desirable, because it gets more direct sunlight per day than any other, but where these winds have to be reckoned with, a gentle slope to the north or north-east is by no means to be despised.

Two other general considerations should be mentioned in connection with the choice of a site. A plentiful water supply will be required for spraying, and this should be easily accessible to the orchard or fruit garden, and there must be a good hard path or roadway on which the fruit can be carried smoothly and securely to the packing shed and store.

TYPES OF FRUIT CULTURE

THE WALLED GARDEN

From the above, it is easy to appreciate the popular belief that a really good walled-in garden is the best place for growing fruit. The soil, whatever it may have been to start with, has been transformed by generations of digging, manuring and the decay of vegetable matter, into a friable loam, full of humus. The garden is sheltered on all sides from winds ; as a rule water has already been laid on, and there are good paths. The one real risk is that in seeking a sheltered situation for flowers and vegetables, the original planner of the garden may have unwittingly provided a frost-trap. Apart from this risk there is little doubt that outdoor fruit culture in a walled garden devoted solely to that purpose is the system which will give the best quality fruit of all kinds under conditions which from the point of view of the cultivator are the most pleasurable.

Let it be said at the outset, however, that if fruit is to be grown successfully and economically in a walled garden, then all other crops, be they flowers, vegetables or shrubs, must play second fiddle. If the trees are to be grown at their normal rate and kept free from disease, the grower must be free to cultivate or grass down just where and when he wishes ; to apply the kinds of manure which the trees want, and to withhold those which they do not want. Above all, he must be free to take his spraying machine where he will, and use the sprays that are most likely to control the diseases and pests of fruit without worrying about what effect they will have on delphiniums or lettuces or anything else.

At present, for most of us, such a fruit-garden is more a subject for dreams than for reality, since the vast majority of walled gardens are already planted up with many other crops besides fruit. Because of these other crops in the garden, there must always be some compromise between the varying requirements of the fruit trees and bushes, and of the flowers, vegetables and shrubs. So long as this situation is accepted from the outset, and a certain amount of give and take is provided for, there is no reason why all the crops should not do reasonably well.

The fruit in any walled garden has an advantage over that in orchards or plantations, in that it is well sheltered from wind and can be trained along the walls to receive the maximum amount of sun and air.

THE KITCHEN GARDEN

The kitchen garden, as its name implies, is primarily devoted to the growing of fresh vegetables for use in the kitchen. Fruit is bound to be a secondary consideration here, and spraying and manuring are possible only in so far as they can be made to fit into the scheme of vegetable culture. Tar-oil sprays in the winter and lime-sulphur sprays in the spring or early summer are usually out of the question in a kitchen garden ; and such manures as are generally used for vegetables, whilst they may be suitable for some kinds of fruits, are not desirable for others. So that in the kitchen garden as in the mixed wall garden, the two cardinal principles of fruit-growing, the growing of the plants at their normal rate and keeping them free from disease, are always going to be difficult so long as vegetables continue to be the main consideration.

Nevertheless, since there must be thousands of keen amateur fruit-growers who have no other site for their fruit, let it be said at once that the kitchen garden has certain obvious advantages. It is fairly certain to be more sheltered than an open field, and since the trees and bushes are likely to be confined in a comparatively small space, it is possible to give them much more individual attention than they could ever hope to receive in a large orchard or plantation.

THE FRUIT GARDEN

The fruit-garden pure and simple, where only fruit is grown without vegetables or flowers, is undoubtedly the next best thing to the " dream " walled garden already mentioned, and for many people a more practical proposition.

In the fruit-garden the distribution of the kinds and varieties of fruits can be planned to ensure that spraying, pruning, manuring and cultivating can be carried out economically and efficiently. Top fruits such as plums and cherries, which need fairly heavy dressings of organic nitrogenous manures, can be planted with bush fruits such as black currants, loganberries and blackberries, which have similar manurial requirements. Fruits such as apples, which require a large amount of potash, and may have to be grassed down for a time to reduce nitrogen, can be planted by themselves. A third part of the garden can be left for such fruits as strawberries, gooseberries, red currants and raspberries, which require potash and nitrogen and constant cultivation to produce well-balanced growth.

FRUIT CULTURE

In the fruit-garden, small to medium-sized trees will usually be found planted fairly closely on dwarfing or semi-dwarfing stocks according to the kind and variety of fruit, and in various forms—bushes, pyramids, espaliers, and the different forms of wall-trained trees and cordons. Since space is bound to be more or less limited, the standard and half-standard trees will not usually be welcomed in the fruit-garden. Such trees are almost invariably grafted or budded on vigorous or very vigorous rootstocks, and are certain to grow into very large trees whose branches will rob the garden of sunlight, whilst their roots will monopolize the plant foods underground.

THE PLANTATION

The plantation might be defined as any unit of fruit trees larger than that usually contained within the boundaries of a private garden ; and it is intended primarily for the production of fruit for market. The term " plantation " usually implies that some degree of cultivation is being given, however intermittently, to the soil. It is this last characteristic which distinguishes the plantation from the orchard in which the trees should have the greater part of their root area covered with a permanent sward of grass. In a plantation there may be fruit of all kinds and sizes : bush, half-standard, three-quarter standard or standard trees, on various types of stock, may be planted with or without an undercrop, or soft fruits may be planted by themselves. Among commercial growers there is an increasing tendency to keep the different kinds of fruit separate as much as possible, because this makes it easier to give to each the best manurial, pruning, cultural and spraying treatment, instead of having to be content with a compromise.

When planting-up fruit for market in this way, one of the most difficult things to decide is what constitutes an economic unit of production. In other words, which pays best ? To plant up a comparatively small acreage on a highly intensive system of cordon, espalier or dwarf-pyramid culture, or to spread the same amount of capital over a comparatively large area on a more extensive system of fruit culture ? There is, of course, no simple answer to this question, but it is safe to say of fruit-growing, as of any other branch of agriculture or horticulture, that the smaller the unit, the more will success depend upon the skill and industry of the individual cultivator.

There is no more fascinating form of hobby-farming than a small area devoted to intensive fruit plantations of one kind or another, provided the owner has independent means and plenty of reserve capital. Such a form of hobby-farming can be undertaken under a surprisingly large range of conditions, if precautions are taken to secure beforehand the services of a really competent manager who has had experience in this particular type of fruit culture. As a means of supplementing a pension or small fixed income, intensive fruit-growing, or, indeed, any form of farming, must be regarded as highly speculative, especially for a man who has had no previous experience.

The most important factor in deciding the success of such a venture is the temperament and business ability of the man who is going to run the concern. If he can contemplate with equanimity the idea of giving up most of his time throughout the year to the problems of growing and marketing his fruit to the best advantage, he will probably make a success of it ; if not, he would be well-advised to put what spare cash he has into gilt-edged securities rather than invest it in the roots of fruit trees.

When it comes to the question of planting fruit on a more extensive scale, the problem is not so much whether it pays to plant fruit under these conditions, as the extent to which it is profitable to invest capital in the business.

There are those who say that a unit of fifty acres of fruit under one management is likely to produce the highest gross income, because such an acreage is large enough to allow of certain important economies of large-scale production in the way of spraying machines, tractors and grading machines, and yet small enough to allow of specialization in fruit-quality, packing and marketing. Others maintain that, over a long period, the biggest profits per acre are made by the factory fruit farms, run either privately or by limited companies, where the acreage is so large that the overhead expenses are cut to a minimum, and economies are effected in all the most expensive factors of production.

There can be no doubt that extensive fruit plantations on any scale from fifty acres upwards can be made to pay a profit at the present time provided there is enough capital available to buy and plant the land with fruit under reasonably favourable growth-conditions, and to keep it going under good management until the trees or bushes come into bearing.

After that period, the question of how much interest it will yield on the capital invested is, as in all farming enterprises, partly a matter of luck, but still more a question of business ability on the part of the farmer or farm manager.

21

The main point of interest for the prospective planter is that some reserve capital will be necessary in addition to what is required for buying and planting the land with fruit.

THE ORCHARD

In a grass orchard, the trees, of whatever kind of fruit they may be, are usually planted at greater distances apart than in a plantation, being strong-growing varieties grafted or budded on vigorous or very vigorous stocks. Standard or three-quarter standard forms are most often used, the head of the tree being formed between 5 and 7 feet above ground level. In the west and west midlands, where a grass orchard is to be found on most farms, the custom has been to graze cattle and horses in the orchards, and this has led to the adoption of a very high-headed form of " standard " tree to make it more difficult for the animals to feed on the branches.

In Kent sheep are the recognized grazers of orchard land, cattle being seldom seen in the orchards.

It has always been a tradition of grass orchardists that the condition of the grass is the acid test of a good orchard, the assumption being that stock will not graze closely unless there is good herbage, and unless the grass is kept closely grazed the fruit trees will suffer. Be this as it may, one of the main points to be remembered is that grass management is an art in itself, and one which can at times be very troublesome. If the grass is left to grow ungrazed and uncut, the finer and sweeter grasses are soon displaced by those which are more vigorous in growth, but which are usually coarse and rank. If the grass is cut for hay and then carried off, the soil tends gradually to become impoverished and the fruit trees suffer.

Grazing itself automatically introduces a new set of farming problems all connected with the management of stock. A flock of sheep at the rate of about ten to the acre is probably the most efficient form of stock for close grazing, but at the present time a very expensive one. Horses and cattle will keep the grass from growing too long, but are apt to be uneven grazers and seldom get the grass down as close as sheep. Pigs are often run in old orchards, but more as cultivators of the soil than as grazers.

Lastly, poultry, if run in sufficiently large numbers, will keep the grass down quite as short as sheep, but they in their turn introduce a new problem in connection with manuring, to which reference will be made later.

There is, however, a method of grass-management which does not involve the use of livestock and which, partly for that reason, is becoming increasingly popular with fruit-growers. This has been in use in some of the fruit-growing districts in America and Canada for some years under the name of *sod mulching*. The grass is cut two or three times in the course of each season, and after each cutting it is spread in wide circles round the trees and left to rot. On acid soils it may be necessary to apply ground-lime every few years to encourage the bacterial activity by which the rotting process is brought about.

With the *sod mulch system*, since cutting is done whilst the grass is still green and comparatively tender, a motor-mowing machine can be used. When the cut grass eventually rots, it will supply a good deal of humus to the soil, but, in addition, it will be necessary to feed the trees with artificial manures to replace what would have been supplied by grazing stock (see information in chapter on manuring).

As a system of fruit culture the grass orchard has certain obvious advantages. It requires a comparatively small number of trees, the number varying from 27 to 34 per acre according to the distance of planting. After a few years no digging or cultivating should be necessary, and a certain amount of labour is thus saved. As an adjunct to stock farming the grass orchard has its advantages, providing, if required, a shelter for lambing as well as pasture for all forms of stock. Again, where poultry is kept in any quantity, a grass orchard of plums or cherries may be extremely useful to provide both shade and herbage for the birds (see page 94).

One disadvantage of the orthodox orchard of standard trees on grass is that the trees are normally standards on very vigorous stocks. This means that they will take a long time to come into cropping, and also that they will make large trees very unwieldy to prune, spray and thin, and which, if not carefully looked after, may prove an expensive form of white elephant. It is impossible to spray large standard trees efficiently without some form of power spraying plant which will give a pressure of 350 to 400 lb. per square inch, and if the trees are not properly sprayed they become not only useless themselves but a menace to the rest of the fruit on the farm.

Then, again, the question of keeping a properly balanced growth in grass orchard trees is not as simple as it might appear. Unless care is taken when planning the layout to see that the different kinds of fruit are grouped according to their manurial requirements, it may be difficult to regulate their feeding. The dessert apple is best kept to one part of the orchard, where it can be given plenty of potash, the cooking apples in another, where potash and nitrogen may be applied together, while the nitrogen-loving stone fruits, the plums and cherries, may be planted together. Possibly, the most satisfactory form of grass orchard consists of standard plums or cherries under which poultry are kept in light portable houses which can be moved daily up and down the tree rows. This practice is not advisable where apples are concerned, because the high nitrogen content of poultry manure may soon upset the balance in the trees; but with plums or cherries, provided the manure is spread evenly and the orchard is not overstocked, the results are usually very good.

The chief difficulty is to prevent the fowls from scratching the earth away from the tree roots in early years, but this can be prevented by surrounding each tree with a wire-netting frame placed flat on the ground (see illustration).

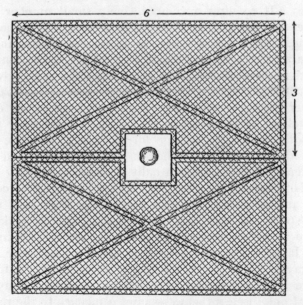

A WIRE-NETTING PLANTING FRAME.
To prevent fowls scratching the earth away from the tree roots.

CHAPTER II

SOILS IN RELATION TO FRUIT GROWING

Reference has been made in Chapter I to the fact that the roots of fruit trees and bushes penetrate much deeper into the soil than used to be imagined.

In the fruit soil surveys which were carried out in this country under the auspices of the Ministry of Agriculture this point has been kept in mind, and the soil surveyors, in taking their samples, have invariably screwed their augers some three feet down into the ground.

Broadly speaking, the aim of these surveys is to find out as much as possible about the soil in its relation to the growth and cropping of fruit, and at the same time to make careful records of the behaviour of the fruit already planted there.

The soils are grouped into series based on their geological origin, and their method of formation, position, drainage and profile.

GEOLOGICAL ORIGIN

The geological material underlying the soil is marked on the Ordnance Survey Geological Maps. Its importance in determining the nature of the soil depends on the original mode of formation of that soil.

METHOD OF FORMATION OF SOIL

The soil may be formed in different ways. It may weather away naturally from the parent rock as in the case of *sedentary* soils. It may be washed gradually downhill by rain in the process known as erosion, and accumulate at the foot of a slope in a *colluvial* form, leaving a shallow *eroded* soil behind it on the hillsides. Or again, in the course of thousands of years soil may be transported for long distances in the bed of a stream or river, gradually being sifted out and deposited far from its place of origin in beds of gravel, silt, or loam, in a form which has come to be called *alluvial*. As a result of these varying methods of formation, the finished products, be they sedentary or transported, retain certain marked characteristics which can easily be recognized, and which have an important influence on plant growth.

POSITION

The position or topography of a soil series, whether high or low, flat or sloping, is important mainly because it gives an indication of the kind of geological formation underneath and of the method by which the soil has been formed.

NATURAL DRAINAGE

This is one of the most important characteristics of soil in relation to fruit culture on account of its great influence on root growth. A soil may have insufficient natural drainage, when waterlogging will occur at some period during the year and roots will rot away. Another soil may have excessive natural drainage so that the roots will die for want of water in a dry season. Yet another soil may have perfect natural drainage in one place but impeded drainage in another. The best soil will have just the right amount of natural drainage throughout.

SOIL PROFILE

When the auger bores vertically downwards a few inches at a time, the face of the soil is revealed in profile as each successive layer is brought to the surface and examined. The different bands or horizons tell their own story to the soil surveyor, who can thus follow point by point the depth, colour, drainage and general make-up of each horizon and so decide on the particular series into which the soil is to be grouped.

Meanwhile the pomologist takes records of the fruit trees and bushes in the area, and finds out the history of their management, so that he may correlate the performance of the fruit with the nature of the soil on each series. In this way he discovers which kinds and varieties of fruit do best on each different soil, and in cases of marked failure or success, he can often trace the cause to some peculiarity which the soil surveyor has revealed in the make-up of the soil. In certain cases it may be possible to suggest treatment which will overcome the defect, but perhaps the chief advantage of the surveys is in providing a reliable guide for future planting. Whereas in the past the fruit-grower has had to buy his experience by planting up fruit and waiting to see how it will behave, the surveys will provide him in future with well-authenticated information on what to plant and where to plant it.

SOIL TYPES

In places where there have been no fruit soil surveys the fruit-grower has nothing to guide him as to the nature of his own particular soil, beyond what he can learn from the 6-inch Geological Survey and Drift Maps, and from his own observations or those of the county horticultural advisory officer. As we have explained, the geological maps will show him the nature of the underlying rock, and if his soil is a sedentary one, he may learn a good deal about it from knowing something of its parentage. If his soil is a transported one, it should be included in a special series of Drift Maps also issued by the Ordnance Survey, which show the approximate boundaries of some, though not all, of the transported soils. Having learnt as much as possible from these two kinds of map, he will go into the garden, plantation or orchard with his soil auger or a good spade to see what the soil profile has to tell him, the best time being when the soil is wet but not sodden. In making these observations the following points about the chief soil types should be borne in mind :

Clay.—As everyone knows, the term clay is used in a general way as a term of abuse, "a nasty sticky wet clay" being universally and justly condemned as the most difficult soil in which to make any fruit grow well. If the geological map indicates London Clay, Gault, or Weald Clay as the geological formation, there will be no difficulty in recognizing it in the chunks of grey, yellow or bluish clay of cheese-like texture which may be reached at any depth from 10 or 12 inches to 3 feet below the surface. The soil particles in this type of clay are so fine, and they stick together so closely, that the soil very quickly becomes impermeable in rainy weather, and remains waterlogged for long periods ; moreover, in the summer such soils crack badly, so that the roots of plants are subjected to the two-fold danger of rotting in winter and of being torn apart in summer.

There is great difference between clay soils on sloping ground and those on the flat. In both cases the upper horizons can be made friable and open-textured by digging in or ploughing in lime or some bulky organic manure, and by constant cultivation. But whereas clay soils on level ground can seldom be properly drained, those on a slope can have a system of pipe-drains inserted at a depth of from 2 to 3 feet to drain the winter rains away into the ditches before the soil becomes entirely waterlogged.

Some of the best-grown fruit trees in this country are on sloping clay soils which have been pipe-drained in this way and kept carefully cultivated. In general, however, from an economic aspect, clay soils stand condemned, since so much money has to be spent and so much skill is required to improve their drainage and texture.

27

They can be made very good at a price, but as natural fruit soils they are to be avoided.

Chalk.—Chalk on the geological map covers a wide range from thin bare chalks on the top of the Downs, through chalk loams of varying depth and texture to chalk marls overlying clay at the bottom of the escarpment.

When the auger strikes solid rocky chalk at a depth of anything under 18 inches, fruit of any kind, with the possible exception of strawberries, is almost bound to be a failure. When roots penetrate the chalk layer, a condition known as lime-induced chlorosis is set up in the plant and this is due to the large quantities of lime present in the chalk. The leaves turn a sickly yellow colour, and, being deprived of chlorophyll, are unable to perform their natural functions on which the health of the tree depends.

Where local deposits of clay-with-flints are found over the chalk on the top of the Downs, there are often 3 feet or more of red clay loam above the solid chalk. Here fruit of all kinds can be grown successfully if the drainage is good enough. But when solid chalk occurs at anything less than 3 or 4 feet below the surface, top fruits are always liable to chlorosis, although bush fruits may prosper. When chlorosis does occur the trees should be grassed down and generously manured through the grass; under such conditions they have been known to recover and to remain healthy.

Chalk loams on the more gradual slopes of the Downs where erosion has not been too severe, and chalk marls, often overlying Gault clay, on the foothills are by no means to be despised. The chalk loams are apt to dry out in dry summers, especially under grass, and the chalk marls, unless very well drained, are apt to be waterlogged, but on deep chalk loams, plums, cherries and dessert apples can all be made to do well, and on chalk marls, plums, especially greengages and damsons, can be grown.

To sum up, the thin chalk soils should be avoided, but deep chalk loams and well-drained chalk marls will grow good quality fruit under skilled management, especially plums and to a less extent cherries.

Brick Earth.—The term brick earth is generally applied to soils which contain a moderately high percentage of clay particles and are thus fairly retentive of moisture. They have also a nicely balanced proportion of the coarser soil particles, fine silt, sand, and coarse sand which provide perfect natural drainage. Being for the most part transported soils, they may be encountered over a wide range of situations, usually in rather small patches, and frequently in the valleys formed by existing or by prehistoric rivers.

The auger bores easily into brick earths, revealing a brown or reddish soil with a distinctly soft and silky texture. On really deep soils of this type fruit trees and bushes of all kinds grow with remarkable vigour. Cherries and pears in particular seem to revel in it, and for vigorous growth in all fruits it is, perhaps, the best natural soil in the country.

From the economic aspect also it is desirable, since no money need be spent on draining it or on improving the texture, and less money than usual has to be spent on manures. For dessert apples brick-earth soils produce rather too much growth to be altogether ideal, but this can easily be rectified.

To sum up, in looking for soils in this country on which to grow hardy fruits with the minimum of effort, the first thing is to buy Drift Maps of the district and discover all the soils of a brick-earth type shown on them. Many of these, by nature of their alluvial origin, are liable to be in low-lying situations peculiarly susceptible to late spring frosts, and this point must be carefully borne in mind when selecting the site for fruit.

Gravel.—If the auger or spade strikes a solid bed of gravel with nothing but coarse sand between the pebbles, it should be realized that in such a soil every drop of rain-water will rapidly drain away in winter, and there will be little or no chance of moisture being drawn upwards from below during the summer. It will, in fact, be too well drained.

Gravels of this kind are bound to be fatal to successful tree growth if they occur in beds of any depth and they should accordingly be avoided.

The word "gravel," however, includes much more than the gravel that is used for ballast, or for putting on garden paths. In assessing the value of any gravelly soil for fruit-growing, the most important points to consider are the nature of the gravel itself, and the amount and nature of the soil between the gravel.

Plateau gravels are found in high places, and valley gravels in any place where rivers run or have run in the past. In many districts a bed of any kind of stones not larger than tennis balls is alluded to as gravel, whatever its origin may have been. As a rule, however, the word is more correctly taken to refer to small, round, hard pebbles which have been worn smooth in the course of years by being swirled round and round in a river bed by fast-moving water.

The amount and nature of the soil between the gravel depends on how the beds came ultimately to be deposited. Some of the valley gravels which have plenty of soil of a medium to stiff texture between the stones form ideal soils for fruit-growing. The stones provide a natural drainage system, while the soil between the stones contains sufficient clay particles to retain the moisture in a dry summer.

To sum up, a soil containing a fair proportion of small gravelly stones is suitable for fruit-growing, whereas a soil in which there seems to be more gravel than earth, or in which the earth between the gravel consists of nothing but coarse sand, is to be avoided on account of its poor drought-resisting qualities.

Sand.—Fruit trees can be grown in pure sand, provided they are fed periodically with nutrient solutions dissolved in rain water. This has been done experimentally with trees in pots in order to test the effect on growth of depriving the plant of some particular element of food.

From the economic point of view, however, sandy soils are to be condemned on account of the money which must be spent to make them retentive of moisture in drought, and to provide the plant foods which the trees require. Apart from these two very important considerations, sandy soils have numerous advantages. Cultivation is easy and roots can penetrate freely. White, silvery sands are very much to be avoided, for they produce the poorest growth of any.

Generally speaking, the darker the colour of the sand the more likely it is to contain a fair amount of organic matter. Contrary to general belief, apple and pear canker are found on many sandy soils.

From the manurial point of view it is important to remember that sandy soils are, as a rule, deficient in potassium, and if apples are to be successfully grown on such soils, regular applications of sulphate of potash will be necessary.

As was pointed out at the beginning of this chapter, the fruit-grower is concerned to know the nature of his soil as far down as the roots of his trees are likely to penetrate. In the majority of cases, an examination of the profile will reveal one or more bands or horizons of different types of soil of the kinds we have described, rather than a solid mass of any one of them.

Enough has been said to show that clay, gravel, chalk and sand have all got certain definite advantages and, provided no one type is present in excess, it is fairly certain that fruit trees and bushes can be made to grow successfully without too much money being spent on soil improvement.

Soils most naturally suitable for fruit culture are those which combine depth with good but not excessive drainage, and which have a smooth, silky texture. Soils naturally unsuitable are those which are shallow, badly drained or excessively drained, and which have a texture which is either too close or too open. Reference has already been made to the preference shown by certain kinds of fruit for certain soil characters. For example, when the brick earths were being described it was stated that cherries and pears revelled in this particular soil type. The principles underlying these preferences are not yet fully understood, but that they do exist is well established.

If balanced and healthy growth is to be maintained, it is important that fruit trees and bushes should be planted, wherever a choice is possible, in the soil conditions most suitable to their kind. Further reference will be made to this when dealing with the different kinds of fruit.

SOIL CULTIVATION IN RELATION TO GROWTH

Before planting any fruit the soil should be thoroughly well cultivated by means of ploughing, subsoiling where necessary, digging, double-digging, or trenching. And for the first few years after planting, digging or ploughing in early winter, levelling in early spring with cultivators, and hoeing in early summer seldom fails to benefit all young fruit trees and bushes. Thereafter there is no hard and fast rule to guide the grower in deciding on the amount of cultivating that should be done to the soil. Bush fruits and strawberries will always do best under conditions of " clean " cultivation, which means keeping the surface soil loose and free from weeds or grass. Some top fruits will do best when no attempt is made to cultivate the soil, and when weeds or grass are allowed to grow over the tree roots. The governing principle underlying successful soil management is that cultivating tends to encourage shoot growth, and lack of cultivation tends to check it. Thus between clean cultivation at one end of the scale, and grass or weeds at the other, the fruit-grower has at his disposal an extremely wide range of controlling factors which he can apply in maintaining a correct balance between shoot growth and fruit-bud formation.

CHAPTER III

MANURING

In the past there has been a tendency to regard manuring as the main if not the sole factor in the nutrition of fruit trees. Since 1918, however, as a result of research work in this and other countries, it has been shown that fruit-tree nutrition is a complex process in which many factors other than manuring are concerned. Undoubtedly the most important individual contribution to the study of fruit nutrition since the war of 1914–18 has been that of Dr. T. Wallace of Long Ashton Research Station. Dr. Wallace started his experiments by planting trees in pots containing pure sand devoid of plant foods, and feeding them with solutions containing the elements nitrogen, potassium and phosphorus, singly and in combination. By carefully observing the effect of these different manurial treatments on the plants, Dr. Wallace succeeded in showing that by starving the tree of any one of the most important elements of plant food he could make it produce certain symptoms which would be easily recognizable in the field. For instance, when he starved an apple or a gooseberry bush of potassium, the leaves turned brown at the edges and gave the appearance of having been scorched by fire. The next step was to plant out trees and bushes in experimental plantations and to apply nitrogen, potassium, phosphorus and one or two other elements in the form of inorganic fertilizers singly and in combination. This brilliant series of investigations opened a new chapter in the study of the manuring of fruit trees in this country. Dr. Wallace's early experiments were repeated and extended at Long Ashton, at East Malling, and at numerous other centres throughout the country under different growth conditions, and during the last twenty years a substantial mass of experimental evidence with regard to the nutrition of fruit trees has been gradually built up. In the course of these further experiments Dr. Wallace and other workers were able to show the importance which other factors besides the mere application of fertilizers played in the nutrition of fruit trees.

SOIL IN RELATION TO MANURING

At the outset there is the question of soils. When trees were grown experimentally in pure sand, it was possible, for instance, by

32

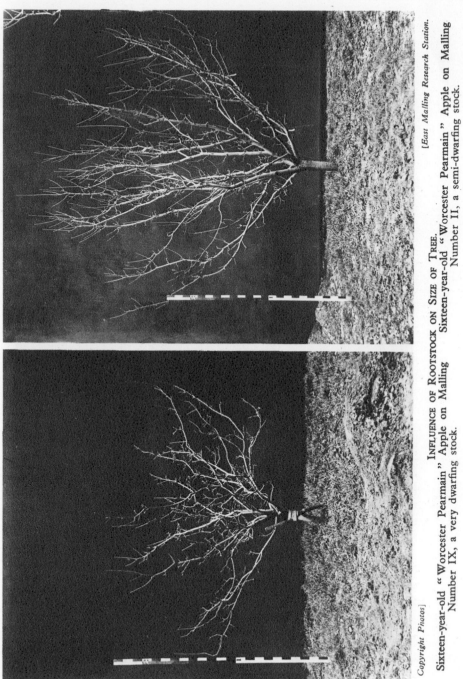

[East Malling Research Station.

INFLUENCE OF ROOTSTOCK ON SIZE OF TREE.

Sixteen-year-old "Worcester Pearmain," Apple on Malling Number IX, a very dwarfing stock.

Sixteen-year-old "Worcester Pearmain" Apple on Malling Number II, a semi-dwarfing stock.

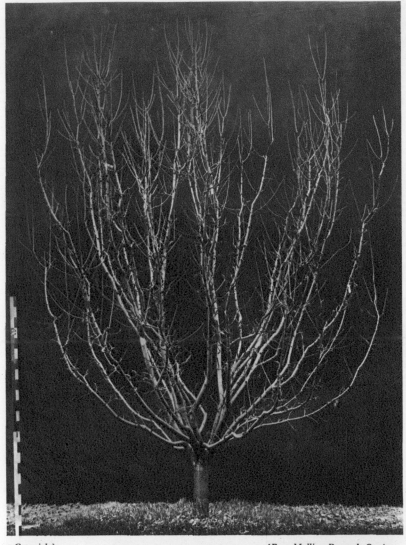

 [East Malling Research Station.
INFLUENCE OF ROOTSTOCK ON SIZE OF TREE.
Sixteen-year-old "Worcester Pearmain" Apple on Malling Number XVI, a very vigorous stock.

withholding phosphorus, to produce certain definite symptoms of phosphorus deficiency. But when trees were planted under field conditions, it was found impossible to prove a case of phosphorus deficiency, a result which has since been repeated in many different soils in this country, and which tends to show that our soils already contain sufficient phosphorus for the needs of fruit trees. On the other hand, in certain other countries it is easy to prove that phosphorus deficiency is one of the main limiting factors to plant growth.

Then, again, the fruit soil surveys have shown that while certain soils are very rich in nitrogen, others are lacking in potassium.

DRAINAGE IN RELATION TO MANURING

There is also the question of drainage to be considered. On a badly drained soil, the waterlogged conditions during the winter may cause some of the roots to rot, so that whatever plant foods may be applied in the form of manures, the nutrition of the tree will be incomplete because there will be a shortage of healthy roots to pass up the various raw materials of plant food to the branches. On the other hand, if the soil is too well drained, it will not retain sufficient moisture in the dry months of the year, and the nutrition of the tree will be incomplete for lack of moisture.

CLASSES OF FRUIT IN RELATION TO MANURING

One of the most important discoveries in regard to manuring is that different classes of fruits require different proportions of two very important elements of plant foods, nitrogen and potassium.

Broadly speaking, it may be said that the main manurial requirement of dessert apples, red currants and gooseberries is potassium. For this class of fruit, although nitrogen is necessary at certain periods in their life, the plants can never use that nitrogen to the best advantage unless potassium is available at the same time.

Cooking apples, pears, raspberries, loganberries, blackberries and strawberries form a second class which, although requiring potassium as a permanent part of their manurial treatment, will nevertheless respond to much heavier applications of nitrogenous manures than is the case with those of the first class.

The third class consists of plums, damsons, peaches, nectarines, apricots, cherries, black currants, cobnuts and filberts. These all require plentiful supplies of nitrogen to keep up a regular supply of annual shoot growth and to give size and quality to the fruit. They fare all the better for regular applications of potassium in moderate quantities, but primarily they are nitrogen lovers.

C—F.G.

33

VARIETIES IN RELATION TO MANURING

Another new and interesting discovery of modern times is that within the same class of fruit there are differences in varictial habit in regard to manuring. Thus among cooking apples there are varieties, such as *Grenadier*, which are notoriously dependent on ample supplies of potassium, whilst other cooking varieties, such as *Bramley's Seedling*, have been found to provide the finest crops of fruit when they are given fairly heavy dressings of nitrogenous manures *after the necessary basis of potassium has been secured.*

Again, among dessert apples *Worcester Pearmain* will give its best-coloured fruits only when receiving very low amounts of nitrogen in proportion to potash, while *Cox's Orange Pippin* when in full bearing responds to moderately high amounts of nitrogen in proportion to potassium. These preferences have been discovered in the course of experiments carried out on a field scale with varieties commonly grown for market. Similar preferences probably exist in a number of other varieties commonly grown in gardens.

Doubtless, in course of time it will be possible to group varieties according to such preferences, but for the present fruit trees, like human beings, must be studied individually.

PRUNING IN RELATION TO MANURING

That there is a definite connection between pruning and manuring should be mentioned at this point, since the degree of severity of pruning needs to be taken into account. Briefly, it may be said that very severe pruning tends to promote new shoot growth, and in this respect it has much the same effect as heavy dressings of nitrogenous fertilizers.

It follows that when the process is reversed and little or no pruning is done, the trees will tend to produce a relatively small amount of new growth. Thus, where new growth is required to keep the balance, more nitrogen will be necessary than in the case of the severely pruned tree in order to produce the same result.

CULTIVATION IN RELATION TO MANURING

Dr. Wallace has shown that stirring the soil in the course of ordinary cultivation has the same effect as an application of nitrogen. This is important in more than one respect. It means that trees under cultivation cannot be treated manurially in the same way as trees under grass to produce the same results. When trees are grown under grass, there is always a tendency towards what may be called a " low-nitrogen " condition, but when they are grown under clean cultivation, there is the reverse tendency.

MANURING

It is now widely recognized that potassium is one of the main requirements of fruit plants. It is not so generally recognized, however, that if trees are suffering from want of potassium, it will make matters worse to apply nitrogen.

Hence, whenever potash is greatly needed, nitrogen should be withheld until the potash requirement of the trees has been satisfied.

In grass orchards where, as noted above, there is always a tendency towards a lower nitrogen condition than in a cultivated plantation, the manurial problem is usually comparatively simple. Once a potassium basis has been determined, the balance can usually be adjusted by one or more of the three methods of increasing shoot growth, i.e., by the application of nitrogenous manures, by hard pruning, or by ploughing up and cultivating under the trees.

In cultivated plantations the problem is generally not so simple. When a serious deficiency of potassium must be rectified for trees with well-established root systems, the first difficulty is that of getting the potassium down to the deeper parts of the soil where the roots are, and the second, of having to wait for several years before the trees get enough potassium to have any marked effect. The main symptom of the lack of potassium is a burnt-up appearance of the margins of the leaves, and this is known as " leaf-scorch." There are various forms of leaf-scorch, as, for instance, the damage caused by sprays used at too high a concentration, or that caused by severe and sudden droughts, or by growing the trees under water-logged conditions, or through a deficiency of available magnesium in the soil. By far the most common form of leaf-scorch, however, is that seen on apples, gooseberries and red currants as a result of lack of potassium.

Leaf-scorch seldom occurs on trees growing in grass, and this is generally attributed to the " low-nitrogen " condition of such trees.

Hence, with apple trees in an established plantation where leaf-scorch is severe, an obvious remedy is to give up clean cultivation either partly or wholly, and to apply heavy dressings of potassium as sulphate of potash. With gooseberries and red currants, however, this is out of the question, since such comparatively shallow-rooting plants soon succumb under these conditions from lack of moisture. This is one of the main arguments against growing top fruits and bush fruits together if they can possibly be kept separate.

Magnesium deficiency is seen mainly on apples in sandy soil. The chief symptom is severe scorching of the central part of the leaf between the ribs towards the close of the growing season. The leaf may sometimes show a yellowing between the ribs and again

35

sometimes there may be a purpling. At leaf fall the leaves nearest the base of the terminal shoots fall first. In cases of severe magnesium deficiency the fruits may fail to ripen on the tree.

Magnesium deficiency may be corrected by the application of magnesium limestone at the rate of 1-2 tons per acre or by Epsom salts (magnesium sulphate), when obtainable, at the rate of from 2-4 cwt. per acre. It should be added that over-heavy application of potash on soils inclined to be short of magnesium may intensify the symptoms of magnesium deficiency.

ROOTSTOCKS IN RELATION TO MANURING

Trees on very vigorous rootstocks have a natural urge to make strong growth, while those on dwarfing or semi-dwarfing rootstocks are much less inclined to do so. Again, it has been shown for apples that one or two rootstocks produce trees which suffer severely from potassium or nitrogen deficiency unless very well looked after in this respect. Thus, in planning the manurial programme, it is always well to know something about the rootstocks.

DISEASE CONTROL IN RELATION TO MANURING

If the leaves of an apple tree are badly eaten by caterpillars, curled up by aphis or blackened by the scab fungus, they cannot perform their natural function of manufacturing food for the tree. In consequence, growth is checked and the nutrition of the tree suffers, whatever the manurial programme may be. There is also evidence to show that manuring has a direct influence on the incidence of diseases and of spray damage.

To sum up, modern research has shown that the study of the manuring of fruit trees cannot be limited to mere consideration of the kinds and amounts of manures to apply, but must be regarded as part of the much larger subject of nutrition. In the complex process of fruit-tree nutrition, many different factors play their part, and if trees are to be kept in a condition of healthy and balanced growth, each one of these factors must be taken into consideration.

We have seen how such important elements as nitrogen and potassium ought not to be distributed in equal quantities to all classes and varieties of fruit under all conditions, but should be given in their right proportions.

Some indication of what these proportions should be will be given in the sections dealing with the individual fruits.

NOTE 1.—2¼ cwt. per acre is equal to 2 lb. per square rod or 1 oz. per square yard.
2. Readers should also consult " Manuring Fruit Crops in War Time " (Growmore Bulletin No. 4 M.O.F.) and " The Diagnosis of Mineral Deficiencies in Plants " (H.M. Stationery Office), both by Dr. T. Wallace, Long Ashton.

CHAPTER IV

PROPAGATION OF FRUIT TREES AND BUSHES

Where large numbers of trees or bushes are to be planted, and when early cropping is the main requirement, the best source of supply for planting material is a reliable nursery.

On the other hand, for those with plenty of time, leisure and money, or for those who wish to try their hand at raising new varieties, or who require only a few trees or bushes of very select varieties, the propagation of fruit trees and bushes is a fascinating hobby.

HYBRIDIZATION AND PROPAGATION FROM SEED

With few exceptions, all new varieties of fruit are obtained as the result of hybridizing, i.e., the transferring of pollen from the stamens of the flower of one variety to the style of another. This may be done naturally through the passing of insects from flower to flower, collecting pollen from one and brushing it off against another. This is known as " open pollination." Or again, artificial cross-fertilization may be carried out in the following way : first decide on the trees on which to carry out the cross-fertilization, choosing varieties which blossom at the same time. A very popular cross is that between the apples *Cox's Orange Pippin* and *Gladstone*. Assuming that the pollen of Gladstone is to be transferred to the flower of Cox, Gladstone will be the male parent and Cox the female parent. When the flower buds are about to unfold, cover over a few blossom buds of the two varieties with little bags made of specially prepared paper or muslin to keep out insects. When the petals begin to open, take off the bags from the Cox tree, and remove the stamens with a pair of forceps, leaving only three or four buds to a truss, and then put the bags on again. When the flowers of both parents are fully open, remove the bags and examine the styles on the Cox flowers. If the styles look sticky, they are in the right condition to receive the pollen from the Gladstone flowers. These may be cut off and the stamens rubbed gently against the styles of the Cox flowers. Another method is to collect the pollen from the Gladstone stamens with a soft camel's-hair brush, and then to pass the brush gently backwards and forwards, over the style of the Cox flower. Now put the bags on again and

37

PROPAGATION

keep them on until the fruits of the Cox's Orange Pippin are completely ripe and ready to pick. The apple pips should then be sown in shallow wooden boxes or earthenware pans containing one-third leaf-mould, two-thirds good loam and a little sharp silver sand. The boxes or pans must be well drained with plenty of broken crocks at the bottom. They are placed in cold frames and need not be pampered in any way until after the seeds have germinated the following spring, when they will need protection from frost. The seedlings are potted up when a few inches high and gradually hardened off ready for planting out when the late frosts are over. The seedlings can either be left to grow on their own roots or, after two or three seasons' growth, their shoots may be cut off and grafted in the spring on to apple rootstocks, or the buds may be inserted into stocks in the summer. In our present state of knowledge there is no actual certainty as to what sort of apple will result from such a cross. There is a likelihood that the seedling will display one or more of the characteristics of either or both parents, but further than that, it would not be safe to forecast. Nor does it appear to make any difference which of the two parents supplies the pollen to the flower of the other.

This method of hybridizing can be used with minor modifications for raising new varieties of all our hardy fruits.

Where opportunity allows, it is advisable to pot up the parent plants and bring them under glass some months before they are due to flower. This is comparatively easy in the case of the soft fruits such as strawberries, raspberries, currants and gooseberries; in the case of apples, pears, plums, peaches, nectarines, apricots, cherries and walnuts, if the parent plants are too big to be potted up, hybridizing can be done out of doors. To ensure germination, the seeds of all hardy fruits require a resting period of from three to four months in fairly low temperatures. Seeds of the stone fruits which find it difficult to break through the hard outer shell are sometimes deliberately cracked at the time of sowing. Or alternatively the outer shell can be softened by half burying the seeds in moist sand for periods, varying with the hardness of the shell, of from three to nine months. This process is known as " stratification."

PROPAGATION FROM HARDWOOD CUTTINGS

Currants and gooseberries are raised in thousands every year by fruit-growers from hardwood cuttings, and are very easy to propagate in this way provided a few important points are borne in

38

mind. The ideal growth conditions for hardwood cuttings are those which encourage quick rooting and unchecked growth through the growing season. The best results are obtained from soil of a brick-earth type, well aerated, well drained and yet retaining ample moisture throughout the summer. But with early autumn planting and constant hoeing throughout the growing season a good " strike " of cuttings may be obtained on practically any soil that is not either pure sand or solid clay. Since the technique of taking and inserting cuttings is not quite the same for all kinds of currants and gooseberries, they will be considered separately in the sections dealing with each fruit.

VEGETATIVE PROPAGATION—ROOTSTOCKS

Apples, pears, plums, peaches, nectarines, apricots and cherries are usually budded or grafted on to rootstocks belonging to the same species as the scion or to some closely-related species of plant. These rootstocks can be raised either from seed by the methods we have described or by means of vegetative propagation. Both methods have been used for generations, and both have their advantages and disadvantages. Rootstocks are generally raised from seeds more easily and more cheaply than by vegetative propagation. When they are raised from seeds of " open-pollinated " flowers it is impossible to know for certain what their parentage is and what their effect will be when used as rootstocks. At the present time most rootstocks raised in this country are produced vegetatively either from stoolbeds or from layers. By these methods a single rooted stock can be planted, and from it almost any number of " clonal " rootstocks can ultimately be produced, everyone of which will be perfectly true to type, since each contains the same genetical characters as the parent " clone." This is an advantage in the case of any particular rootstock which is known to possess certain desirable characteristics. On the other hand, both the stooling and layering methods are comparatively expensive in that they involve the moving of a great deal of earth in the course of the season, as will be seen from the following descriptions :

METHOD OF STOOLING

Most of the commonly-used apple and quince rootstocks can be raised quite easily by this method. The rooted stocks which are to form the stoolbeds are planted upright in the autumn in rows 3 feet apart, leaving one foot between the stocks in each row. The stocks are cut down to within 2 feet of ground level and are left

39

to grow for one year, the ground being kept well hoed throughout the season. In the following spring, about February, the stocks should be cut down level to the ground. The buds at the base will push out young shoots, and as soon as these are 5 or 6 inches long, earth should be mounded up in a stool to a depth of 2 or 3 inches around their base. This process is repeated again after a further flush of growth has been made, the base of each shoot being ultimately buried in 6 or 8 inches of soil. From this buried portion adventitious roots are formed in the mounded soil which forms the stoolbed. In November the soil is scraped away from the stool, and the young stocks are cut off at the point from which they started growth in the spring. Those which are well rooted can then be planted out in nursery rows in readiness for budding the following summer. Any stocks which are not sufficiently well rooted to be worth planting in the nursery for budding can be bedded out an inch or two apart in nursery rows. Quite a large percentage of these, after remaining a year in the beds, will be found to have developed sufficiently good root-systems to be planted out for budding or grafting. These are known to nurserymen as " bedded " stocks.

METHOD OF LAYERING

This is the method used for the vegetative propagation of most of the plum, cherry and pear rootstocks. The stocks are planted in the autumn, sloping at an angle of about 45 degrees, about 3 feet apart in the row, leaving about 4 feet between the rows. For the first season there is nothing to do beyond keeping the ground well hoed. At the end of the year, during the winter, any weak side shoots that may have grown out are cut back to within an inch of their base, leaving the main stem and strong laterals full length. Then a shallow trench a few inches deep is made down the middle of the row, as though for sowing peas, and into this trench the stocks are bent down in a horizontal position and held in place by strong wooden pegs or wire hoops. Fine soil is heaped over the entire length to the depth of about one inch above the layers just before buds are due to open in the spring. The essential difference between the stooling and layering methods of vegetative propagation of rootstocks, is that in layering the parent stocks must receive a covering of earth in the dormant season before growth begins, whereas in normal stooling no earthing up takes place until the young shoots have made 5 or 6 inches of growth from the base of the stool. In layering, success depends on preventing the base of the shoot from becoming hard by exposure to light, and on forcing the young shoots to push through the soil as in natural suckers. When these young shoots have grown 4 or 5 inches, the layer beds are earthed again, taking care to leave at least 2 inches of growth above soil level. Earthing up continues periodically throughout the season until the layers are covered to a depth of at least 6 or 7 inches of soil, care being taken to see that after earthing, the soil does not get washed off again by heavy rains. In November the soil is removed with a fork, and the rooted layers are cut off and planted out in the nursery for budding the following summer. Any coarse unrooted shoots are pegged down again alongside the parent layer and the whole bed is earthed over again during the winter to a depth of one inch in preparation for next year's crop of layers.

BUDDING AND GRAFTING

THE OBJECT OF BUDDING AND GRAFTING

It is by no means obvious why grafting or budding should ever have been invented, since neither is a natural process, and nearly all forms of fruit trees will eventually come into fruiting if left on their own roots.

However, the fact that trees come into bearing much more quickly when " worked " in this way on a rootstock belonging to the same botanical species probably provides the main reason for the long-continued use of this technique by tree raisers. It is now generally recognized, moreover, that apart from the period of time which it takes a tree to come into bearing, the ultimate size of the tree and the quality of the fruit can also be influenced in varying degrees by careful choice of rootstocks. This is especially the case with apples, and to a less extent with pears, plums and cherries. Hence the choice of rootstock is a matter of great importance and one which will be discussed more fully in the chapters devoted to the various fruits.

BUDDING

Budding is in itself a simple operation, but one which needs a good deal of practice to make perfect. The percentage of buds which take will depend partly on weather conditions during and after budding, and partly on the speed and dexterity with which the operation is carried out.

The principle underlying budding and grafting is the same,

namely, to bring into close contact portions of the cambium layer of stock and scion and to keep them together until fresh tissue forms to unite them into a single unit of growth.

TIME FOR BUDDING

Budding of fruit-tree stocks is usually done some time in July or August, the order of budding roughly corresponding with the date of flowering. Thus cherries, plums and pears come first and apples follow after. Much the best way to decide if the stocks are fit for budding is to run the budding knife lightly down the base of one of the stocks and insert the knife handle under the bark. If it lifts easily and comes clean away from the wood, budding can be begun at once. If the bark sticks or tears when lifted, the stock is not fit for budding.

CHOOSING THE BUDS

In selecting the buds, care must be taken to make sure that the buds are wood buds, from which a shoot will start, and not fruit buds, which will not make wood. These two kinds of bud are more easily distinguished in some kinds of trees than in others, but as a general rule it may be taken that the wood buds are more pointed than are the fruit buds. The buds of some fruit trees, most usually in dry seasons, are troublesome to peel away from their wood, the wood very frequently pulling out the middle of the bud with it. When this is very marked, it is a good plan to pierce the wood just behind the bud with the point of the knife, so as to cut it away from the bud at that point, before beginning to peel it from the bark. Shoots selected for budding should be plump, firm, and well ripened. Watery shoots or buds are valueless.

A good well-matured shoot of current year's growth having been chosen (Fig. A), the leaves should all be removed from it close to the leaf-stalk, only a piece of the latter being left on (Fig. B). If the leaves are left on, they will draw and pass out the moisture from the bark and the bud, causing the latter to shrink. With a sharp knife the bud is then cut out of the wood, the knife making a curve behind it, leaving the bud midway on a thin strip of bark and wood. The knife should enter the wood some half an inch above the bud, and come out an equal distance below it, leaving a piece of bark of the shape of a long shield, whence the name of " shield-budding " sometimes given to the operation (Fig. C). The woody part of this may now be removed, and in order to do this, the piece is held by the leaf-stalk and bud, while the bark is started

42

away from the wood at the top end with the tip of the knife, and is then given a sharp pull, when the bark should peel cleanly off the slip of wood. Occasionally, and generally when the bud is too forward when cut, the wood, when it pulls away, will leave a small hole in the bark behind the bud, as if it had pulled out a little bit of the inside of the bud with it. When this has occurred the bud is spoilt, and will shrivel and die before it has time to build up new cells. Such a bud should be thrown away and a fresh one, less developed, taken.

Experiments have shown that removing the woody portion of the bud in this way is n o t always essential, and should it prove difficult to do so without spoiling the bud, it would probably be

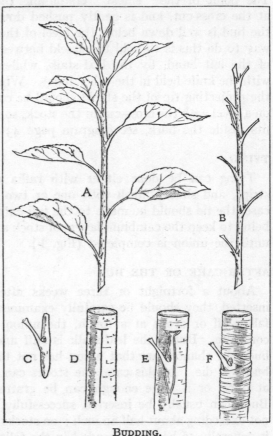

BUDDING.

as well to make the cut as thin as possible with a very sharp knife and to leave the wood in. In some seasons, however, and with some kinds of buds, the wood comes away so easily that no difficulty is found in performing the full operation.

PREPARING THE STOCK

The bud being ready, the stock must next be dealt with. A clean, smooth spot on the stem is chosen, and with the budding knife a cut about $1\frac{1}{2}$ inches long is made, only just sufficient pressure to pierce the bark without penetrating the wood beneath being employed. At the top of this a cross-cut half an inch long should

43

be made with equal care (Fig. D), the bark on either side of the first cut then being raised from the wood by means of the blade of the knife, or its thin handle, slipped in between bark and wood. The point of the " shield " containing the bud is then inserted at the cross-cut, and is gently pushed down under the bark until the bud is well down below the level of the cross-cut. The easiest way to do this is to hold the shield between the finger and thumb of the left hand, by the leaf-stalk, while holding the bark open with the knife held in the other hand. When the bud is well down, the projecting tip of the shield should be cut off with a cut exactly on a level with the cross-cut in the stock, so that the tip of the shield fits inside the bark, see diagram page 43 (Fig. E).

TYING

Tying can be done either with raffia or with narrow rubber strips, and should finish with one or two half-hitches. In either case, the tie should be made to the full extent of the slit, its object being to keep the cambium layers of stock and scion in close contact until the union is completed (Fig. F).

AFTER-CARE OF THE BUD

About a fortnight or three weeks after the buds have been inserted, they should be carefully examined. If the leaf-stalk has fallen off or drops at a touch, the union is pretty certain to be complete. But if the leaf-stalk is stiff and adheres firmly to the bud, the chances are that union has not taken place and that the bud will die. In this case, the stocks can either be budded again at once, or if large enough can be grafted the following spring. Buds can usually be inserted successfully on stocks of diameters not exceeding about half an inch ; on stocks larger than this grafting is generally to be recommended in the following spring.

If raffia is used for tying in the buds, there is always a certain risk of its causing constriction if the stem swells rapidly. Should there appear to be any risk of this, it is a good thing three or four weeks after budding to run a sharp knife down the raffia on the side furthest from the bud, severing the strands of raffia without cutting the bark. With rubber strips there is no risk of constriction, since the rubber expands with the stem and rots away during the winter.

The buds that are inserted remain dormant until the following spring. In February the stocks are cut back either to the bud or leaving a " snag " of 3 or 4 inches above the bud. The only object in leaving this snag is to have a natural stake to which to tie the young " maiden " shoot as it grows out from the bud. The stock buds which are left on the snag have to be rubbed out three or four times in April, May and June, or they will start growing strongly at the expense of the scion. Many people prefer to cut the stock right back to the bud at the beginning of the growing season. By the end of the growing season the bud will have grown out and become a shoot of any-thing from 3 to 8 feet of " maiden " growth according to the kind of fruit and the stock in which it was in-serted.

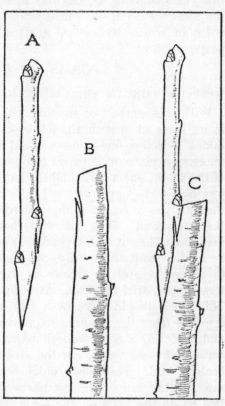

WHIP OR TONGUE GRAFTING.

Plum and cherry buds have been known to make as much as 7 or 8 feet of growth in their first season, the average growth for apples and pears being from 2 to 4 or 5 feet according to the variety and stock.

By the autumn these are known as " maidens " and should be quite strong enough to be planted out in their permanent positions. If growth has been poor and the maiden trees are less than 2 feet high, they cer-tainly ought not to be planted out until they have spent another year in the nursery. Sometimes poor maiden trees make a re-markable recovery in their second year, but if they still continue weak, they ought to be dug up and burnt, because in all probability they will never make good trees.

GRAFTING

There are a number of different ways of grafting, all depending for success mainly on bringing together portions of the cambium layer in stock and scion and keeping these in close contact until they unite, and the rootstock and scion shoot become one plant. In grafting, as in budding, speed and neatness in performing the operation both play an important part. It is, therefore, just as well to practise preparing and inserting the graft beforehand, but best of all is to see the operation being done by an expert.

April is the best month for most kinds of grafting in this country, but it can sometimes be started earlier and carried on later than this. All splitting or clefting methods can be started earlier in the season than those which involve lifting the bark. The usual order in which stocks are grafted is: plums, cherries, quinces, pears, apples.

FORMS OF GRAFTING

WHIP OR TONGUE GRAFTING (Diagram, page 45)

With this method of grafting, the stock must be more advanced in its state of growth than the scion. The scion is prepared by taking a well-ripened one-year-old shoot some 6 inches long, and selecting a place on it where two good buds come on opposite sides of the shoot, one a little higher than the other (Fig. A). Beginning just below the upper of the buds, make a clean cut at one sweep through the wood in a downward slope, coming out just below the lower bud. It is essential that there should be a good bud just above the cut at each end. It is important that this cut should be made firmly and evenly, otherwise the scion will not fit closely to the stock and its chance of a perfect union will be lessened. Having prepared the scion, attention should be turned to the stock. This stock should have been cut back late in January to about 8 inches from the ground. Remove all side growth from the base and, selecting a good smooth place about 3 or 4 inches from the surface of the ground, cut the stock cleanly off just above a good healthy bud. This bud's chief function will be to draw up the sap into the top of the cut parts while they are healing together, just as do the buds on the scion, but while the latter are allowed to grow and, indeed, become the real tree, the former should not be permitted to outlive its utility, and when perfect union has taken place, it should only be allowed to grow two or three leaves, and then should be stopped out. Having cut down the stock, its top should be carefully measured against the scion. The important thing to arrive at is that the cut surfaces of the inner bark of both stock and scion shall touch as much as possible. If it is found impossible to make these layers of bark meet on both edges, make them meet perfectly on the one. The tail of the scion should not

46

in any case come below the end of the peeled piece of the stock, if anything it should err very slightly on the other side.

When both scion and stock fit perfectly, a further security may be obtained by making a small upward cut in the tail of the scion, in order to obtain a slip projecting towards the stock (Fig. A). In the stock itself, opposite this slip, should be made an incision (Fig. B) into which the slip will exactly fit, thus holding stock and scion together (Fig. C) during the operations of tying and covering with wax. This slip should be thin, or it may cause the junction to bulge, and the scion to be pushed away from the stock. When these two latter are fitted closely together, and it is found that their layers of inner bark are fitting closely and neatly, the junction should be made firm by tying tightly with raffia.

The last process is the secure covering of the whole junction— scion and stock, with grafting wax—and the graft is complete. The label should always be attached to the stock, not to the scion, as otherwise there would be an added risk of the scion being caught accidentally and pulled off before a union has been effected.

SADDLE GRAFTING

Saddle grafting can be used for stocks of about the same thickness as the scion. The scion is cut with two tails, the one below the upper bud being shorter than that below the lower bud. The whole of the inner part of the wood below the buds is removed, and at the top the cuts are ended by a cross-cut beginning just behind the upper bud and sloping

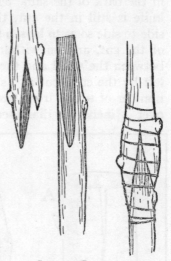

SADDLE GRAFTING.

slightly upwards. The scion will now have two tails of unequal length, the shorter one having a bud at its upper extremity, and the longer one having a bud midway up its length. The stock should then be taken, and its top cut to slope slightly, at an angle corresponding with that of the cross-cut of the scion. A slip should be peeled corresponding with the long tail of the scion, and the latter laid over the stock, saddle-wise, the long tail fitting its peeled slip, and the top angle of the stock fitting into the top angle of the cross-cut. The short tail of the scion

47

will be found to cross the top of the stock and project a little. A slip should be cut off the side of the stock to fit this projecting piece of the tail, which should then be bent down on to it, and the graft is ready for tying and waxing. This system has the advantage that the scion unites on both sides of the stock, and is therefore not so liable to an accidental break during the healing process.

RIND OR CROWN GRAFTING

This is one of the most popular and easiest methods of grafting on to mature trees when the stock is comparatively large, especially when renovating old fruit trees. In this system the scion is prepared much as for tongue grafting, with a sloping cut about $1\frac{1}{2}$ inches in length. The tail is quite thin, too much wood often being left by beginners when preparing scions for grafting. The stock should be cut off cleanly, and with a sharp knife a slit should be made in the bark of the same length as the tail of the scion. While the knife is still in the cut, the blade should be gently pressed from side to side so as to loosen the bark in the immediate neighbourhood of the cut, and on withdrawing the knife, the scion is slipped in between the wood and the bark, and pressed down until the surface left by the cross-cut at its head lies on the top of the stock. Any number of scions from two to four may be placed on each branch over 4 inches in diameter so treated, for the more scions there

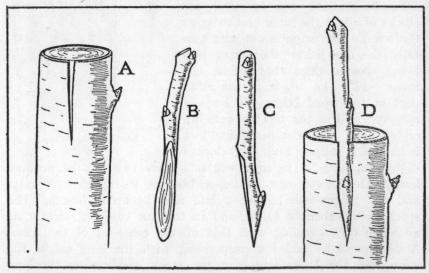

RIND OR CROWN GRAFTING.
A. The prepared stock. B and C. The scion. D. The scion inserted in the stock.

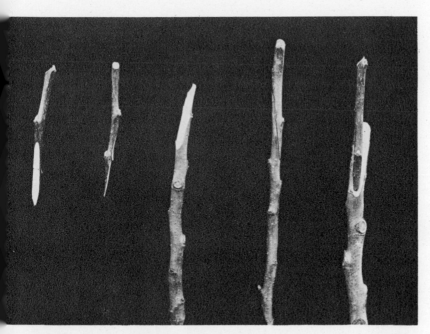

WHIP OR TONGUE GRAFTING.

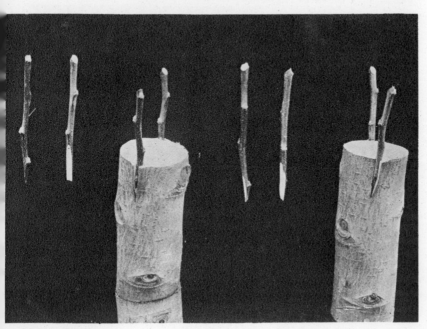

RIND GRAFTING.

[*East Malling Research Station.*

F.G.

D

DWARF PYRAMID APPLE.

are, the better and more strongly will the sap be drawn up, and the quicker and better will the stock heal and effect a junction. When the grafts are growing well, they may be supported by being tied to sticks fastened securely to the branches of the

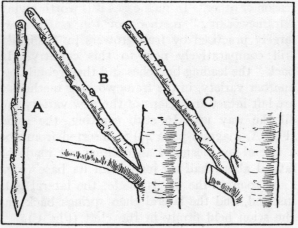

STUB GRAFTING.

stock. Until the grafted tree has developed a good head of new grafted wood, it is a great mistake to remove all the shoots and twigs of the old stock.

OTHER METHODS OF TOP GRAFTING

Three other methods of top grafting mature trees may be briefly mentioned here.

OBLIQUE CLEFT GRAFTING

Cleft grafting, in which the branch to be grafted is cleft down the middle, has always been popular for cherries, plums and old trees of apples and pears in which the bark is rough and difficult to lift. This method, however, is open to criticism because of the dangers of infection from fungus diseases in the deep gash made by the cleft. In oblique cleft grafting instead of splitting the branch straight down through the middle, one or more small splits are made with a special grafting tool at a tangent at equal distances round the circumference of the branch. The scion is cut to the shape of a thin wedge and inserted cambium to cambium at the outside edge of the cleft, where it is held firmly without having to be tied. A piece of clay or " pug " is generally pushed into the cleft behind the scion before all the cut surfaces are waxed over.

FRAMEWORKING—STUB AND BARK GRAFTING

Many gardens contain one or more established trees of anything between ten and twenty years old that are unsatisfactory for some

D—F.G.

reason or other. In such cases it is worth trying one of the so-called " frameworking " methods of top grafting, which, although now largely practised by fruit-growers in Tasmania and Australia, are still comparatively new to this country. Instead of "heading back " the leading branches and then rebuilding the framework with another variety, in the frameworking methods the leading branches are left intact and scions of the new variety are grafted on to them all the way up. In stub grafting, the scion, cut wedge shape (Fig. A, diagram page 49) is inserted from above into the base of a lateral by means of an oblique cut made half-way through the lateral about half an inch from its base (Fig. B).

As soon as the cut is made, the lateral is bent back, the scion inserted, and the lateral then springs back and is cut off, leaving the scion held firmly in the cleft (Fig. C).

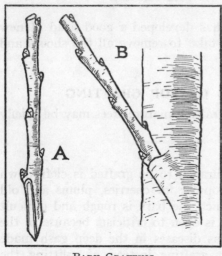

BARK GRAFTING.

In bark grafting the main branches are completely stripped of everything, including all the laterals, and the scions are inserted actually into these main branches. The scion is cut with a long, slanting cut as for rind grafting on one side and with a short cut on the other side. At the point of insertion on the main branch two cuts are made, one vertically downwards, corresponding in length with the long cut on the side, and the other at an angle of about 150°, making the letter L upside down on the branch (see diagram page 50, Figs. A and B).

The rind is then lifted and the scion pushed home and held in place by driving a small, thin nail through the rind and the scion into the branch, and waxing over.

The various frameworking methods are still largely in an experimental stage in this country, and it is too early yet to say which method is the best or whether any modifications of the methods are likely to be found more suitable to English conditions. The results obtained, however, have so far been very encouraging.

INARCHING AND BRIDGE GRAFTING

If a fruit tree has been partly or wholly girdled by canker, or if the stem has been badly gnawed by cattle, sheep, rabbits, etc., or if the tree is unduly stunted as a result of being grafted on an unsuitable rootstock, or because it has been planted in an unsuitable soil, it is always worth trying to restore its vigour.

A tree that has been injured by canker or by gnawing can be inarched. If there are one or more strong shoots growing out from below the injury, or stock suckers growing from ground level close to the stem, one or more of these can be inarch grafted above the injury, in late March or any time in April. Press the selected shoot inwards against the stem in a vertical position, and mark a place on the stem well above the injury, where it can conveniently be inserted. Next prepare the top end of the shoot or sucker for grafting by making a long sloping cut about $1\frac{1}{2}$ inches long on the under side, and a similar cut about one inch long on the upper side, forming a wedge (Figs. 1 and 2, page 52). At the place on the stem already marked, make a vertical incision downwards, about three-quarters of an inch long, and at the base of this draw the knife away to the right, at an angle of about 150 degrees, cutting obliquely into the bark. This cut is also about three-quarters of an inch long (Fig. 3). Lift the bark under these two cuts with the handle of a budding knife, or old filed-down handle of a toothbrush, and push the top end of the scion gently into place under the bark. To hold the graft in position, a small-headed nail, known technically as a " gimp pin," No. 20 gauge, is driven clean through the bark and scion into the wood, at the point of insertion under the bark (Fig. 4). Finally seal the graft thoroughly at the point of insertion with a good grafting wax.

For badly stunted trees, and for trees on which there are no low-growing shoots or rootstock suckers suitable for inarching, it will be necessary to dig up rootstock suckers from elsewhere, or to buy some rootstocks. These must be of the same species, i.e., apple for apple, and should be as vigorous as possible. One or more of these stocks is planted in autumn or winter close to the base of the tree to be inarched. If the tree stem is over 3 inches in diameter, it may be necessary to plant more than one stock, at equal intervals round the base of the tree. The inarch grafting is then done the following spring as described above. Where there is an injury in the stem, the inarch will be made a few inches above the injured area. Where there is no injury, but the tree is stunted, the inarch should be made about 9 to 12 inches above ground level.

51

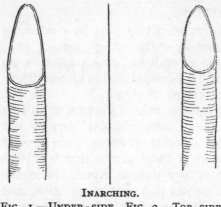

INARCHING.

FIG. 1.—UNDER-SIDE
OF SCION.

FIG. 2.—TOP-SIDE
OF SCION.

Bridge Grafting.—Another way of saving a tree stem that has been badly girdled is by means of bridge grafting. Scions long enough to span the girdled area with ease are cut in winter as described on page 46. The scions can be of any variety, but must be the same species as the tree into which they are to be bridge-grafted, i.e., a *Cox's Orange Pippin* can be bridge-grafted with a *Bramley* or any other variety of apple, but not with a pear.

In April inarch the bottom end of the scion into the stem below the injured area, and the top end of the scion into the stem above the injured area, nail in position and seal as already described. In making the bottom graft the L-shaped cut should be made in the reverse position to that for the top graft described on page 51 under inarching (Fig. 3). It is not an easy operation, and requires a good deal of practice to make perfect. A stem of 3 inches or more in diameter will require more than one scion, and these should be inserted at equal intervals round the

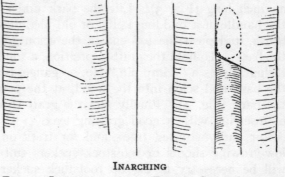

INARCHING

FIG. 3.—INCISION ON
STEM.

FIG. 4.—SCION INSERTED
AND NAILED.

stem to make an effective bridge across the girdled area. If the girdle has been caused by canker, the diseased tissue should be cut out as described on page 166 before the grafting is done.

NOTE.—For a detailed description of different methods of grafting see " Grafting Established Fruit Trees " by R. J. Garner, published by East Malling Research Station in 1942.

CHAPTER V

PRUNING

PRUNING A DIFFICULT ART

The pruning of the bush fruits is a comparatively straightforward operation, which can soon be mastered with a little practice. Nor do the stone fruits present much difficulty when grown in the more natural forms, though when trained on walls or wires they are by no means simple trees to prune. But with all forms of apples and pears, pruning is a difficult art and one which can never be fully learnt from a book.

In the course of centuries of trial and error, a few underlying principles have emerged, but for the details we must turn to the trees themselves, since each variety has its own habits which can be learnt only by careful observation.

THE OBJECTS OF WINTER PRUNING

For the pruner there are three main stages in the life of the tree. In the first stage he aims at building up a branch framework for the fruit by *hard* pruning, in the second stage he encourages the tree to come into fruiting by *light* pruning, and in the third stage he has to keep the tree balanced in a state of healthy growth combined with regular cropping, by hard or light pruning according to circumstances.

FIRST STAGE—FORMING AND SHAPING THE FRAMEWORK

Hard Pruning for Shoot Growth.—To form the framework of the tree strong extension shoots are needed from which to select the main branches or "leaders." Thus, the first object of the pruner in this stage is to promote healthy growth of strong wood shoots. This is done by the hard pruning back of all the shoots on the young tree to within a few inches of their base, since *the first general principle of winter pruning is that hard cutting back encourages the growth of strong new shoots from all parts of the trees.*

The pruner's second object is to shape the framework according to the form required, by cutting out unwanted shoots, and making the others grow in the right direction. This is comparatively

53

simple in the case of the more natural shapes such as bush and standard, but espalier, pyramid and other artificial forms of trees require a good deal of skill, and for this reason it is usually cheaper in the long run to buy three- or four-year-old trees which have been trained by a nurseryman. Naturally, the price of such trees is higher than that of one- or two-year-olds, but for those who have not the time nor the inclination to carry out the shaping of these more complicated frameworks, it is worth paying the extra price to get well-trained trees to begin with.

SECOND STAGE—BRINGING THE TREE INTO BEARING

Light Pruning for Fruit-Bud Formation.—In this stage the second general principle of pruning must be borne in mind, namely, that

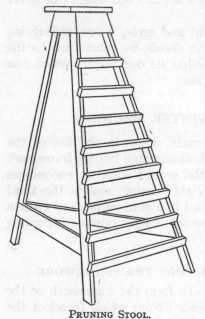

PRUNING STOOL.

the less winter pruning a young tree receives, the more quickly it will come into bearing.

Hence, at this stage pruning should be as light as possible consistent with healthy growth. The extension shoot at the end of each " leader " should either be left full length or only " tipped " lightly, according to kind and variety, and the lateral or side shoots should be left as long as possible. The treatment of these lateral shoots must depend to a large extent on the kind of fruit and on the form of the tree. With the stone fruits, most of them are best left full length, those which are actually touching each other being merely cut off at the point of contact. In the case of bush and standard forms of apples and pears, the shoots on the inside of the tree must be shortened back to let the light in, whilst those on the outside of the tree can safely be left quite long for a year or two until the tree comes into fruiting.

With the more artificial forms of tree, cordon, espalier, etc., in which the number of main branches is limited, the second stage of pruning is immensely important if quick fruiting is required. Only too often the period of fruiting is delayed indefinitely because, in order to preserve the trim appearance of the tree, all the shoots are clipped off close at the very time when they should be left long for a season or two.

THIRD STAGE—PRUNING THE FRUITING TREE

Hard or Light Pruning, according to Growth and Cropping.—When the tree has come regularly into bearing, the degree of pruning has to be decided in accordance with what the tree is doing. If it has carried a normal crop of good-sized fruits, and at the same time has made a fair amount of new wood-growth during the season, the winter pruning should aim at keeping this balance. With apples and pears, the extension shoots will need shortening in differing degrees according to variety, and lateral shoots will be " spurred back " or shortened to visible fruit buds reasonably close to their base.

If the tree has carried an abnormally large crop, and has made little or no fresh wood-growth, the winter pruning must be definitely severe. With the idea of restoring the balance of growth, the extension shoot on each main branch should be cut hard back to within a few inches of the base, and all lateral shoots or spurs which are then showing numerous fruit buds must be drastically shortened.

On the other hand, if the tree has carried little or no fruit or flowers, and has made a large number of strong new shoots, then the less winter pruning that is done, the better. In such cases, if the tree continues to make strong growth even when unpruned, it is clear that some other method of checking growth must be tried, such as summer pruning, ringing, or rootpruning (in the case of stone fruits) or grassing down to check nitrogen supply to the tree.

With stone fruits, pruning in this third stage is best confined to cutting clean out at the base any shoots that are badly placed and shortening back crossing branches to allow free passage of light and air between them.

It is very seldom necessary or desirable to shorten the extension shoot on the main branches of plums, cherries, peaches or any of the stone fruits once the tree is established. And since these fruits bear short natural spurs with mixed wood and fruit buds arising on two-year-old shoots, there is no need for regular shortening back of the side shoots in order to form artificial spurs as in the case of apples and pears.

PRUNING

When fruit trees have become too tall and straggly for pruning, spraying, thinning and picking, they may be dehorned. This operation consists of cutting back the main branches in the winter, each to a small branch terminating in a strong young shoot of the previous season's growth, pointing in the required direction. In this way it is possible to remove two or three storeys from the top of the tree and at the same time to preserve the framework in its proper shape.

PRUNING VERY OLD TREES

Fruit trees over fifty years of age have to be treated with caution when pruning. If they are dehorned too drastically, they may die back, a branch or two at a time. If the trees have been long neglected, the first thing to do is to cut out all the dead branches. After that, the actual pruning back of the straggling main branches is an operation which in a very old tree is best spread over two or three winters so as not to cause too severe a shock to the roots of the tree.

SUMMER PRUNING

There is an important distinction between winter and summer pruning. Winter pruning is done when there are no leaves on the tree, and provided the root-system is not disproportionately small, the result will be to stimulate the growth of strong shoots from well-developed wood buds on the pruned parts of the tree in the following spring.

Summer pruning, on the other hand, is done when the tree is in full leaf.

The removal of green shoots and leaves is bound to result in an immediate check to the food supply going down to the roots, because there are less leaves to do the work. A check in the growth of new roots means a check in the growth of new shoots, so that the net result of summer pruning must always be a check to shoot growth. How long the check will continue and what the effect will be on the rest of the tree will depend on the time of summer pruning, the severity of pruning, the weather following the pruning, and other conditions such as cultural and manurial treatments.

It is no wonder that the subject of summer pruning is highly controversial, and one which commercial fruit-growers of bush and

56

standard trees are inclined to fight shy of, except as a means of letting light in to colour up the fruit. Summer pruning, however, is of the utmost importance as a means of preserving a healthy balance of shoot and root growth in the more artificial forms of tree such as cordons, pyramids, fans and espaliers, or even in very closely-planted bush trees.

The main point to note is that summer pruning tends to *check growth* of roots and shoots, whereas the chief object in winter pruning is to stimulate the growth of new shoots.

The three methods most worth describing are what may be described as the orthodox English method of the Single Summer Pruning and the two Multi-Summer Pruning Methods of Long and Short Summer Pruning of Apples and Pears.

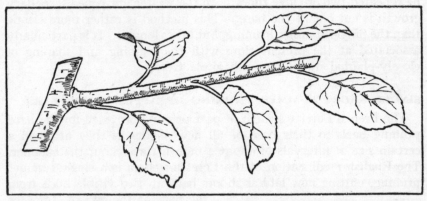

SINGLE LONG SUMMER PRUNING (APPLES AND PEARS).

SINGLE LONG SUMMER PRUNING OF APPLES AND PEARS

This consists of shortening all lateral shoots of any size to within about 5 or 6 inches of their base in July (see diagram), pears usually being done in the first half, and apples in the second half of the month. The one certain effect of this is to let the sun and air into the tree to colour the fruit and ripen the wood. Some contend that the check to growth resulting from this wholesale reduction of the leaf area has the effect of producing fruit buds more quickly at the base of the pruned lateral shoots than if those shoots had been allowed to grow unchecked throughout the season. Whether this is so or not, it often happens that if the weather continues wet, one or even two buds at the end of the summer-pruned shoots start growing out into weak secondary shoots, which often become

57

infected with one or other of the bad fungus diseases, such as canker, scab or mildew.

Single summer pruning of this kind is usually followed in the winter by the cutting back of the summer-pruned shoots to whatever length of spur is considered suitable.

MULTI-SUMMER PRUNING—LONG PRUNING OF APPLES AND PEARS

Beginning about June, all strong shoots that are going woody at the base and are a foot or more in length, are pruned back to within 5 or 6 inches of the base. This operation is continued or repeated as and when shoots or secondary shoots reach this stage. In a dry summer it may have to be done only once, if rain sets in or if the tree is growing very strongly in an off season, it may have to be repeated two or three times. In the winter unripened secondary growth is cut out at the base. This method is rather more elastic than the Single Summer Pruning, but takes longer. It is particularly associated at the present time with the training and shaping of closely-planted dwarf pyramid apple trees.

SINGLE SHORT SUMMER PRUNING OF APPLES AND PEARS

The French Lorette system of pear pruning provided for the hard pruning back to their base of all new shoots as they attained a certain size at intervals of about a month throughout the summer. The English modification of the Lorette system is a single summer pruning, cutting new lateral shoots back to two visible buds from the base at the end of June for pears and about three weeks later for apples (see diagram). Secondary growth, where it occurs, is pruned back to within one or two buds from the base the following winter.

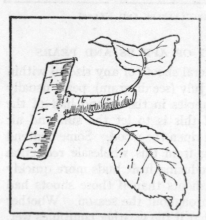

SINGLE SHORT SUMMER PRUNING (APPLES AND PEARS).

Summer pruning in relation to the other fruits is dealt with in the paragraphs devoted to the individual fruits.

PRUNING INSTRUMENTS

For the winter pruning of extension shoots where a clean cut without bruising is desirable, a

58

sharp pruning knife of really
good steel is to be recommended. The blade should
be slightly curved. A knife
that shuts up is the more
handy for the pocket ; on
the other hand, a knife with
a fixed handle and a sheath
is much stronger and more
durable. For winter prun-
ing of lateral shoots and for

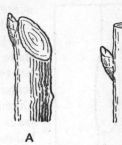

A   B   C

MAKING THE CUT.

all summer pruning the modern forms of secateurs are very popular.

Parts of these secateurs wear out rather quickly and have to
be replaced, but spare parts are easily got and should be bought
with the secateurs.

For cutting off branches which are too big for the knife or
secateurs, a small pruning saw is useful. This may be either
straight or curved, but should be fairly coarse in the teeth for
cutting green wood across the grain.

PRUNING CUTS

The perfect pruning cut begins on the side of the shoot opposite
to the selected bud, and slants slightly upwards across the shoot,
to end above the base of the bud as in the diagram above
(Fig. A). The cut should be straight, clean and unbruised. In
Fig. B, the cut is made too far above the bud, leaving a snag which
may die back to the bud. In Fig. C, the cut is too slanting, and
begins too far up the stem on the side next to the bud. In removing
an entire branch from a fruit tree it is best to cut back flush with
the main stem, since the stump is apt to decay. The cut should
be made as nearly perpendicular as possible, and should be pared
over and slightly bevelled. When the cut surface is large, it should
be covered over with a good lead paint or with some shellac preparation such as painter's knotting to keep out the wet, while
the surface is callousing over. When sawing off large branches,
it is wise to undercut first by making a small cut on the underside
before starting to saw through from the top (see diagram, page 60).

EXCESSIVE WOOD GROWTH

Restoring the Balance by Bark Ringing or by Root Pruning.—The
balance between shoot-growth and fruit-bud formation may be
upset in the other direction. In this case, owing to excessive

59

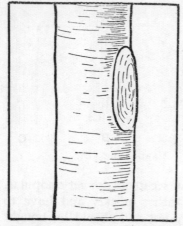

REMOVAL OF BRANCH : CUT FLUSH
WITH TRUNK, SO THAT NO STUB
IS LEFT.

winter pruning or cultivating, or to unbalanced manuring, or because the tree is on a very vigorous rootstock, there is a tendency for growth to be too strong with a consequent scarcity of fruit buds. Mention has already been made of the different ways of attempting to restore the balance in a case of this kind, either by leaving the extension shoots unpruned or lightly " tipped," by withholding all nitrogenous manures, and by giving up cultivation and letting the ground go down to weeds or grass. Where it is impossible to try these remedial measures, or in cases where they have all been tried unsuccessfully, the practice of *Stem or Branch Ringing* may often be worth trying as a last resort with apples and pears. In the case of the stone fruits, which are liable to gum when ringed, the same result may be obtained by means of different degrees of *Root Pruning*.

BARK RINGING ON STEM OR BRANCH

The operation of " ringing " has long been familiar to cultivators of the vine in Europe, and the principle underlying the practice is made use of by gardeners in many different ways to check growth and induce fruitfulness.

A fruit tree may be accidentally ringed when we forget to remove a label which has been tied round the stem with wire, or when a rabbit gnaws right round the stem on a cold winter's night, or again, when the canker fungus gets in and girdles the stem com-

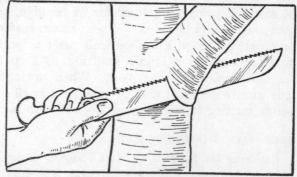

MAKING AN UNDERCUT BEFORE REMOVING A LARGE
BRANCH, TO PREVENT SNAPPING.

pletely. In all three cases the nutrition of the tree is interfered with in such a way as to cause a distinct decrease in growth and increase in fruit-bud formation above the ring, and the reverse tendency below the ring, in the season immediately following the ringing.

The reason for this sudden change is ascribed to the removal in the process of ringing of a complete band of bark tissue together with the living cambium cells immediately below the bark.

When only a narrow band of bark tissue is removed, for instance, by the tying round of a piece of wire or by a single incision with the edge of a knife, the check to growth lasts only for a very short time because the gap soon callouses over. But when a wide band of bark tissue is removed, the check to growth may be so severe as to cause the death of the tree. From this it may be seen that ringing is a dangerous operation and only to be used as a last resort, and when there is a reasonable chance that the

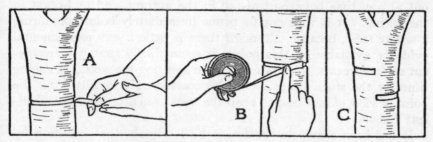

BARK RINGING AND PROTECTING THE CUT.

gap will callous over the same season. The safest way is to remove two half-rings on opposite sides of the stem or branch a few inches apart (Fig. C). The width of the band to be removed varies with the diameter of the stem or branch to be ringed, but for safety it is probably best that the band taken out should not exceed half an inch in width (Fig. A).

In the case of an extremely vigorous young tree it is usually safe to take out a complete ring provided the wound is immediately covered with adhesive tape (Fig. B). This prevents the exposed tissue from drying out and encourages rapid callousing. The operation is best performed with a sharp pruning knife some time in May when the bark lifts easily from the wood.

ROOT PRUNING

The simplest form of root pruning for young trees which are growing too strongly is to dig the tree up in the winter, prune back the roots to within about 2 feet of the stem and replant. With older trees the operation is performed by digging a deep trench half-way round the tree in the winter and severing the main roots about 4 or 5 feet from the stem, completing the process the following winter round the other half of the tree.

When root pruning " scion-rooted " trees, it is best to dig a trench all round the tree first to discover the position of the scion roots and the condition of the original root-system. In the case of pears on quince stocks, for instance, the pear may have sent out one or two very large roots, and the quince roots may be dead. In such a case care should be taken not to root-prune too severely or the tree may lose its grip and fall down in the next high wind that blows.

THE BEST TIME TO PRUNE

In this country winter pruning of apples and pears can be carried out at any time between leaf-fall in the autumn and bud-burst in the spring. It is wise not to prune immediately before or during a severe frost, because, although there is little if any experimental evidence available on this point, it seems likely that if a freshly-cut surface freezes, there is a chance of splitting the wood. Pruning time for the stone fruits should be considered primarily from the point of view of how best to keep the trees from attacks of the silver-leaf fungus.

It has been shown by Professor F. T. Brooks that infection by spores of silver-leaf fungus can occur most readily in the winter months. In summer the trees are able to resist fungal invasion of wounds by the rapid formation of a gum barrier. Branch thinning of plums, cherries, and other stone fruits is therefore best done in June, July, or August, when large wounds so made are not vulnerable to this fungus. Leader tipping, which makes small wounds, should be done in spring when the growth buds are pushing out.

PRUNING AND PLANTING

There is an old controversy on this subject between those who maintain that if you do not prune the first season, the tree will make insufficient new shoot growth, and others who say that if you do prune the first season, the tree will make insufficient new root growth.

Since, in either case the question becomes important only in the case of four- or five-year-old trees which have had a large part of their root system cut off at time of lifting, the obvious solution is to plant maidens and two-year-olds whenever possible. Trees of this age are not likely to have lost a large proportion of their root-system, and it should, therefore, be quite safe to prune them at or soon after planting with the idea of getting strong new shoot growth.

When trees over three years old are brought in or transplanted, there will be a certain check whether they are pruned or not, and since the weather conditions cannot be foreseen, it seems best to leave the question of whether they ought or ought not to be pruned at planting unanswered until the plant physiologists can provide further experimental evidence on the subject.

FRUIT THINNING

Where size of fruit is an important consideration, fruit thinning is to be recommended. Dessert apples may be spaced from 4 to 6 inches apart, and cooking apples from 6 to 9 inches. Plums on a tree which has set a very heavy crop may be spaced from 1 to 2 inches apart. Pears of most varieties grow large enough without any thinning, but when they are to be exhibited on plates at a Show, or in the case of such small-fruited varieties as *Doyenné d'Eté, Fertility, Hessle* and *Seckle*, it is as well to thin out the young fruits, spacing them from 5 to 6 inches apart.

Hand thinning may be done by hooking the first two fingers round the fruit and pushing it gently but firmly off its stalk with the thumb.

There can be no doubt that the removal of a proportion of the young fruits of a tree in this way usually results in an increase in the size and evenness of the ripe fruits, and in improving their colour, but there is very little experimental evidence as to the exact stage in the development of the fruitlets at which thinning should take place.

In commercial practice, pears, plums and apples on bush or standard trees are usually thinned out some time in June.

In the case of apples there is some evidence to show that the centre fruit of each cluster, sometimes called the " king " apple, is an abnormal fruit, less likely to keep well than the others, and one which it is, therefore, advisable to remove when thinning. Needless to say, dessert varieties such as *Charles Ross* apple, which normally grow very large, are best left unthinned.

The thinning of peaches and nectarines on trained trees and in pots has been developed by generations of expert practical gardeners into a fine art, the fruits being thinned drastically but gradually at certain well-marked stages in their growth. The technique for this thinning is given in the chapter dealing with Peaches and Nectarines (page 276).

There is some evidence to show that the thinning of certain varieties of large-fruited gooseberries such as *Leveller*, *White Lion* and *Careless*, when about half an inch in diameter, will give good results in increased size of ripe fruit, and this may make all the difference when it comes to a question of exhibiting these at fruit shows.

How far fruit thinning can be said to influence regularity ot cropping in fruit trees it is difficult to say in the absence of reliable experimental evidence, but it is probably worth doing with certain kinds and varieties if only for its effect on ultimate fruit size.

FRUITS AND THEIR METHOD OF BEARING

Fruit	On One-year-old Wood	On Wood more than One Year Old	Best Time to Prune
Apple		*	Winter and sometimes Summer
Apricot	*		Late Spring or Early Autumn
Blackberry and hybrids	*		Late Spring or Early Autumn
Bullace	*		Late Spring or Early Autumn
Cobnut		*	Winter and Summer
Currants	*		Winter and Summer (for Reds only)
Damson		*	Late Spring or Early Autumn
Fig	*		Late Spring
Filbert		*	Winter and Summer
Gooseberry	*		Late Spring or Winter
Loganberry	*		Autumn
Medlar		*	Winter
Mulberry		*	Winter
Nectarine	*		Late Spring or Early Autumn
Peach	*		Late Spring or Early Autumn
Pear		*	Winter and Summer
Plum	*		Late Spring or Early Autumn
Quince		*	Winter
Raspberry	*		Winter and Late Spring
Veitchberry	*		Winter
Walnut	*		Winter

NOTE.—For detailed instructions for pruning the different kinds and varieties of fruit trees, see under the various headings, Apple, Pear, etc. See also Chapter VII.

ESPALIERS.

Photos]

[R. A. Malby.

FAN-TRAINED TREES OF APRICOT AND GREENGAGE.

BRANCH OF A "WORCESTER PEARMAIN" APPLE SHOWING "TIP-BEARING" HABIT.

BRANCH OF A "COX'S ORANGE PIPPIN," SHOWING CLOSE SELF-SPURRING HABIT.

CHAPTER VI

FORMS OF FRUIT TREES

Fruit trees may be trained in different forms or shapes according to the conditions under which they are to be grown. Indications as to which forms are most suitable for varying conditions are given in the sections devoted to each fruit. In this chapter is given a brief description of some of the leading forms for fruit trees, together with notes on the pruning treatment required in early years to produce each individual form. For amateurs the most certain way to procure trees in any of the artificial forms is to buy them already trained from the nursery. The training of a fruit tree in any but the simplest artificial form is a comparatively long process, needing skill and experience. This accounts for the fact that trees trained in these forms are always more expensive to buy than maiden or two-year-old trees, or than the more natural forms, and are also older trees. This last point should be borne in mind when planting. Trees which have stood in the nursery for four or five years whilst in process of training in the shape of an espalier, fan or other artificial form, are likely to feel the shock of transplanting more than a young tree, and will need all the greater care for a year or two after they are transplanted into their permanent quarters.

THE MORE NATURAL FORMS OF FRUIT TREE NOT NEEDING SUPPORTS

BUSH OPEN CENTRE

This form is suitable for all the hardy fruits with the possible exception of the apricot and nectarine, and may be used for all sizes of tree in garden, plantation or orchard. Distance of planting varies from 10 to 40 feet, according to the kind and variety of fruit, the rootstock, the soil and other growth conditions. The usual tendency is to plant all forms of fruit trees much too close.

Shaping and Pruning in Early Years.—A well-grown maiden *
is cut or " headed " back in the winter to a wood bud about 30 inches above ground-level (Fig. A). The result of this hard pruning is to produce several strong shoots that season, arising from wood buds

* A maiden tree is one which has made a single season's growth from the bud or graft.

E—F.G.

65

placed spirally round the stem, just below the terminal bud. The following winter three or four of these shoots are selected to make a symmetrical, open, vase-shaped framework, and the remainder are cut clean out at the base. The framework branches or " leaders " are then cut hard back to within a few inches of their base to wood-buds pointing either outward or upwards, according to whether the variety is drooping or upright in its natural habit of growth (Fig. B).

The following winter the extension shoots from each of the leaders, together with any others that may be required to complete the framework of the tree, are again cut back to within 6 or 8 inches

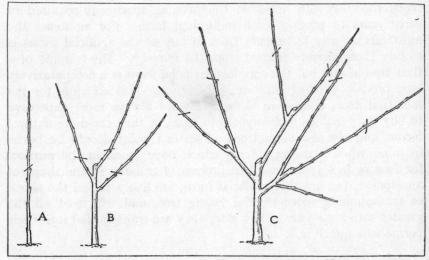

BUSH FORM : SHAPING AND TRAINING IN EARLY YEARS.

of their base (Fig. C). Shoots arising from these main branches or leaders in early years are treated differently according to the kind or variety of fruit. Notes on the pruning of these side shoots or " laterals " are given in the sections dealing with the various fruits.

HALF-STANDARD, THREE-QUARTER-STANDARD AND FULL-STANDARD OPEN CENTRE

In the standard forms the head of the tree is formed well above ground level at heights varying from about 4 feet 6 inches for the Half-standard, to about 7 feet for the tallest Full-standard, see diagrams, page 67. These forms are used mainly for trees worked on vigorous rootstocks to be planted in the orchard or plantation.

66

In general, they are not to be recommended for tree fruits in any but the largest gardens, but it is sometimes convenient to grow gooseberries and red and white currants as standards in gardens. Distances of planting for the tree fruits in the Half-standard, Three-quarter-standard and Standard forms vary from 15 to 40 feet, according to the kind and variety of fruit, rootstock, soil and other growth conditions. Standard forms of gooseberries and currants may be planted at from 6 to 8 feet apart.

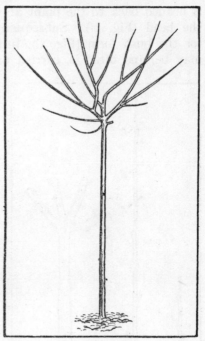

STANDARD.

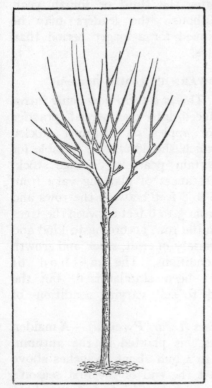

HALF-STANDARD.

Shaping and Pruning in Early Years.—To shape the standard forms, heading back is delayed until the stem is well above the height at which the head is to be formed. During the years in which the single stem is growing to the required height the leading or extension shoot is left unpruned (Fig. A, page 68) and all side shoots are kept spurred back in winter to within an inch or two of their base (Fig. B). This provides additional leaf area and ensures proper thickening of the stem during the nursery stage. In the winter after the stem has reached the required height, it

67

is headed back to the point at which it has been decided to form the head (Fig. B). Subsequent treatment is the same as that for the bush form (Fig. C), but the hard pruning of the leaders may be, and often is, carried on for a considerably longer period than in the case of the bush, in order to make sure of providing a rigid framework of leading branches. It is to be noted, however, that with the more vigorous sorts of apples, such as *Bramley's Seedling* and *Blenheim Orange*, a distinction should be made between the treatment of the leaders and the laterals. The laterals, in strong-growing varieties, may safely be left full length on the outside of the tree, after the third or fourth year, although the leaders may be tipped for a longer period than this.

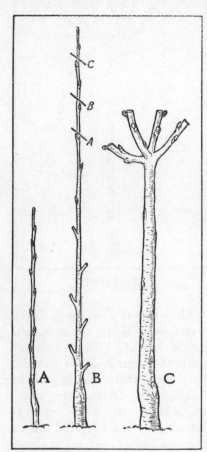

STANDARD : SHAPING AND PRUNING IN EARLY YEARS.

DWARF PYRAMID (Fuseau)

This is a form now being introduced into commercial practice for apples on dwarfing stocks, which should also be suitable for certain pears on quince stock. Distances of planting vary from 6 to 8 feet between the rows and from 3 to 6 feet between the trees in the row, according to kind and variety of fruit, stock and growth conditions. The method of shaping and pruning has not yet been standardized, but the following method can be adapted to suit varying conditions of tree growth.

Shaping and Pruning in Early Years (Dwarf Pyramid).—A maiden tree, preferably without " feathers," is planted in the autumn, and cut back the following spring to a bud about 30 inches above ground level (Fig. A, page 69). At the end of the first season's growth the terminal bud should have developed into a strong shoot

68

growing vertically upwards in extension of the stem of the " central leader." This extension shoot should be cut back in winter to about one-half its length to a bud on the other side of the stem from that to which the maiden tree had originally been cut. The object of this is to keep the central leader as straight as possible. In the summer, four or five strong lateral shoots should have grown out spirally round the stem. These are cut back in the winter to a bud on the under side of each shoot, about 5 or 6 inches from their base. The tree should then appear as in Fig. B. The following summer any strong lateral shoots arising from the original four or five side branches should be summer-pruned, cutting each back to a leaf about 5 or 6 inches from the base of the shoot. In the following winter the central leader extension shoot is again cut back by about a half, and the terminal extension shoots on

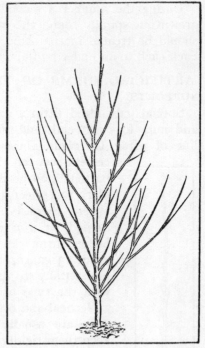

PYRAMID.

the original tier of side branches are also cut back to an under bud about 5 or 6 inches from their base. Should any secondary shoots have grown out from the summer-pruned laterals, these should be cut right back in winter to the point from which they came.

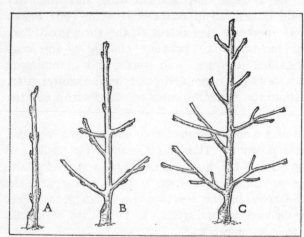

PYRAMID : SHAPING AND TRAINING IN EARLY YEARS.

69

During the summer a second tier of side branches should have grown out spirally round the stem above the first tier, and these should be treated in the same way as their predecessors and cut back each to an under bud about 6 inches from their base (Fig. C).

ARTIFICIAL FORMS OF TREES REQUIRING SUPPORTS
SUPPORTS

Special galvanized fittings can be bought with straining bolts and nuts for each end, and intermediate eyes to fix along each line of wire. On walls, these fixtures may be driven into the cement between the bricks, or two-inch-wide wooden battens may be fixed upright to the wall at intervals of 12 to 15 feet, to which the wires may be fastened. Where there is no wall or fence, the wires are carried on iron or wooden posts, which should be bedded firmly in the ground. The straining wire, 12 or 13 gauge, should be galvanized, and is fastened horizontally to the uprights at distances varying with the type of training to be adopted.

SINGLE VERTICAL CORDON.

Vertical and oblique branches of artificially-trained trees are usually tied to bamboo canes in order to keep them rigidly in position and to prevent rubbing against the wire. The canes may be fastened to the supports with thin wire or with a new form of paper-covered wire, and the branches fastened to the canes with soft fillis-string, or with raffia. Good raffia should be at least half an inch wide, and when dry it should be soaked in water and wrung out before use. If trees are tied direct to the wire, great care should be taken to prevent chafing as this may cause canker in apples and pears, and gumming in stone fruits. The ties should be examined yearly in the winter, after winter washing, and should be either re-tied or replaced with a new tie.

SINGLE CORDON

This form consists of a single-stemmed tree trained in a vertical, oblique, or horizontal position. It is used mainly for apple and pear trees, and sometimes for gooseberries and red and white currants. The trees are planted in rows 6 to 8 feet apart, the distance between the trees in the row varying from 2 to 3 feet for vertical and oblique cordons, and from 5 to 15 feet for horizontal cordons, according to circumstances.*

* Gooseberry and Currant vertical and oblique cordons should be spaced one foot apart in the row.

Shaping and Pruning in Early Years (Single Cordon).—A maiden tree, either clean stemmed or feathered, forms the cordon and no shaping is required for this form. The central leader extension shoot should require no pruning, at any rate in early years, but if the young tree m a k e s abnormally weak growth, it would be wise to prune the leader, shortening i t b y about one-half. All lateral s h o o t s arising from the stem should be summer-pruned from the first season.

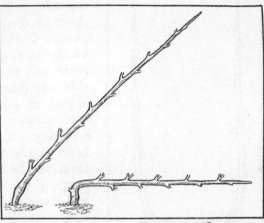

TRAINING OBLIQUE AND HORIZONTAL CORDONS.

The most usual method of summer pruning cordons is to cut the laterals back to a leaf 5 or 6 inches from the base when they are about 12 inches long. (See section on Summer Pruning, page 56.)

Training of Single Oblique Cordons.—The tree is planted in a vertical position and allowed to grow thus for one season. A bamboo cane is then fixed to the horizontal wires at an angle of 45 degrees, and the tree is tied to the cane in its new position, keeping the stem straight throughout its whole length. The tree may be kept at this angle until the central leader extension shoot has reached the top of the wire, about 6½ feet above ground level. After that, the tree is untied, and the position of the cane is adjusted to allow of the whole tree being brought down to a more horizontal position.

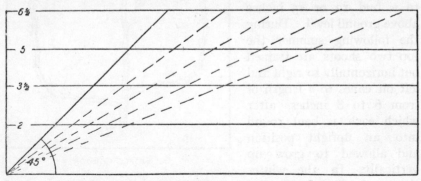

SHOWING SUCCESSIVE POSITION FOR OBLIQUE CORDONS.

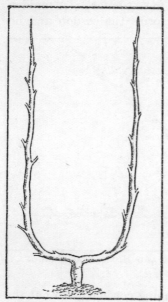

DOUBLE VERTICAL CORDON.

In this new position the tree is allowed to continue until it again reaches the top wire, when yet another alteration must be made in the position of the cane. The object of bringing the whole tree gradually down into a more and more horizontal position in this way (page 71), keeping the stem always in a straight line, is to keep the balance between growth and cropping. If the tree is allowed to bend in the middle or near the top, there will be too much growth in one part of the tree, and all the fruit will come in the other.

DOUBLE VERTICAL CORDON OR SIMPLE U-FORM

This form is suitable for apples and pears, in garden or plantation, and for

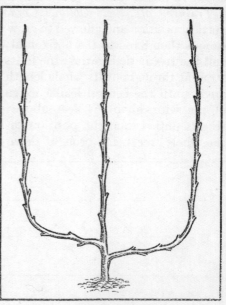

TRIPLE CORDON.

gooseberries and red currants in gardens. Apples and pears in this form should be planted at 6 to 8 feet between the rows, and at from 5 to 6 feet between the trees in the row.

Shaping and Pruning in Early Years.—The single maiden shoot is headed back to a bud 12 or 15 inches above ground level. During the following summer the top two shoots are trained out horizontally to right and left on canes to a length of from 6 to 8 inches, after which each is bent round into an upright position and allowed to grow up vertically. In the winter the two leading shoots are pruned back, removing about one-third

72

of the growth of each to an upward bud. The next year these leading shoots are again allowed to grow unrestricted through the season, being tied in to upright canes as they grow. Should one leading shoot be seen to be growing more vigorously than the other, it should be tied slightly outwards and downwards in order to check its growth and allow the other one to catch it up. The following winter both leaders are again tipped, the degree of severity of tipping being regulated in accordance with the vigour of their growth. Meanwhile all side shoots are spurred back in the normal way.

TRIPLE VERTICAL CORDON OR GRID IRON

This form is suitable for apples on dwarfing stocks, pears or quince, gooseberries and red currants.

Shaping and Pruning in Early Years.—The single maiden shoot

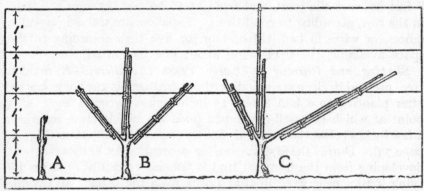

ESPALIER : SHAPING IN EARLY YEARS. FIG. 1.

is headed back to a bud pointing vertically upwards, 12 to 15 inches above ground level, care having been taken in planting the maiden tree to see that there was such a bud in the required position. When the terminal bud and the buds immediately below it, on the right and left, have each made about 6 inches of growth, the terminal shoot is trained vertically upwards by tying it to a cane, while the other two are tied out either horizontally or better still to two canes bent each in the shape of a bow. If the central shoot grows much more vigorously than the other two, the tip should be pinched out when it is about 2 feet long. At the end of the growing season, the two side branches are untied and trained more or less vertically, equidistant from and parallel to the central shoot and at a distance of from 6 to 8 inches from it. In the winter all three leaders are tipped by between one-third and one-half their length. Subsequent treatment is the same as for Double Cordons.

73

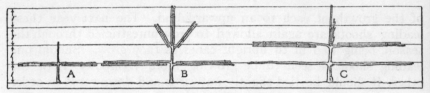

ESPALIER : SHAPING IN EARLY YEARS. FIG. 2.

ESPALIER *

This is one of the most popular forms for apples and pears grown in borders in the garden, and is also used for red and white currants and for gooseberries. Apples on dwarfing and semi-dwarfing stocks should make suitable-sized espalier trees for most varieties. For all but weak-growing varieties of pear, Quince A should be a strong enough stock ; but weak growers ought to be on pear stock. Distances of planting for apple and pear espaliers vary from 6 to 8 feet between the rows, and from 15 to 20 feet between the trees in the row, according to conditions. Espaliers are trained on walls, fences, or wires in two, three, four, or five tiers according to the space available, the tiers being about one foot apart.

Shaping and Pruning in Early Years (Espaliers).—A maiden tree, preferably clean stemmed, without feathers, is cut back shortly after planting to a bud about 15 inches above ground level, at a point at which two well-developed buds are visible close together, a few inches below the terminal, one on each side of the stem (Fig. A, page 73). During the first season, the central leader extension shoot developing from the terminal bud is trained vertically upwards by tying it to a cane fixed in that position on the wires. Meanwhile the shoots growing from the two buds below the terminal are trained out to right and left. In order to encourage them to grow strongly, they are not trained horizontally during their first season, but are tied, as they grow, to canes fixed to the wires at an angle of about 45 degrees (Fig. B). If any other shoots grow out from the main stem, their tips are pinched out when they are about 5 inches long, and any secondary growths from these are pinched out when they are about an inch long. This is done to weaken them and so ensure strong growth in the three principal shoots. Should the two shoots to right and left of the central leader grow unevenly, the weaker shoot should be raised to a more vertical position, and the stronger one lowered to a more horizontal position (Fig. C). This helps to even up the growth of the two shoots, which are to form the first tier of the espalier.

At the end of the first season's growth, these two shoots are

---

* " Espalier " is the French word for a paling or fence.

untied, the canes lowered to a horizontal position, and retied to the first line of wire about a foot above ground level. The two shoots are then retied to the canes in their new position. The central leader extension shoot is cut back to an upward-pointing bud just above the second wire, about 2 feet above ground level. See diagram, page 74 (Fig. A).

During the second season's growth, the central leader extension shoot is treated as in the first season, as also are the two second-tier shoots growing out just below it (Fig. B). Any new laterals which grow out from the first-tier shoots are generally summer-pruned (see section on Summer Pruning, page 56).

At the end of the second season the second-tier shoots are lowered to a horizontal position, and retied on their canes along the second wire. The central leader extension shoot is again cut back as in the previous winter (Fig. A). By this method the espalier can be trained to the number of tiers required, taking one season to build each new tier.

FAN

This form is used mainly for the stone fruits trained on walls,

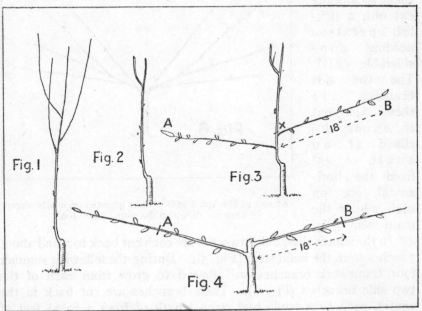

FAN.

Fig. 1.—Maiden Peach (1 year from bud or graft). Fig. 2.—First winter pruning. Fig. 3.—When (A and B) are about 18 inches long in early summer cut out middle at x. Fig. 4.—Second winter pruning cut at A and B.

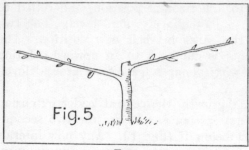

Fig. 5

at distances of from 12 to 18 feet apart according to kind and variety of fruit. The following is one of various methods used for shaping and pruning in early years.

Shaping and Pruning in Early Years (Fan).— The maiden tree as soon as it is planted, should be " tipped " by cutting off the top few inches to a bud (see diagram, page 75, Fig. 2). As the remaining buds start to break in the spring, they are removed until only two strong buds are left about 12 inches above the " union." When these two buds have each made about 18 inches of shoot growth (Fig. 3), the main stem of the tree above them is carefully cut out, a ticklish operation needing considerable skill. The two side branches are then tied out to canes, inclined at an angle of 45° from the horizontal, one on each side of the main stem (Fig.

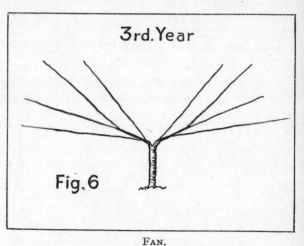

3rd. Year

Fig. 6

FAN.
At end of the third year : Four growths each side along canes. (See also diagram, page 400.)

4.) In the winter these side branches are each cut back to a bud about 7 inches from the main stem (Fig. 5). During the following summer four framework branches are allowed to grow from each of the two side branches (Fig. 6). These branches are cut back in the winter, each to a triple bud, to a length of from 2 to 2½ feet of well-ripened wood. The framework of the fan is thus completed in three seasons from the time of planting. It is a long and complicated process, needing practice and skill to be successful.

For pruning and disbudding of established fan trees, see page 272.

CHAPTER VII

FORMING AND TRAINING

THE " DELAYED OPEN-CENTRE " TREE

In recent years a form of tree that has come to be known as the " Delayed Open-Centre " or " D.O.C." has attracted the attention of fruit-growers, and several acres, comprising apples, pears, plums, and cherries, are now devoted to the system.

FORM OF TREE

As the term " Delayed Open-Centre " suggests, this form has something in common with the ordinary open centre. In the early stages of developing the D.O.C. a centre stem is purposely kept in, and from it shoots are formed that eventually become the main branches. These branches are spaced out over a length of centre stem which may be anything from 2 to 4 feet according to the size of tree required (see Fig. 1). Big trees may have a longer stem than dwarf trees, whereas in the open-centre tree all the branches have more or less a common point of origin at the

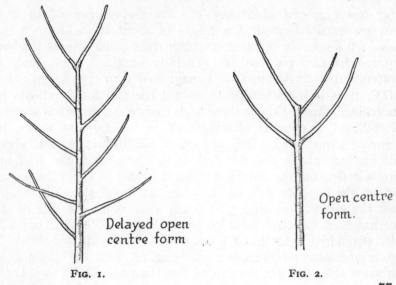

Delayed open centre form

Open centre form.

FIG. 1.   FIG. 2.

77

top of the stem (see Fig. 2). With D.O.C. trees, when the grower decides that no further extension of the centre stem is needed, all the young branches are directed outwards, away from the centre, as in the open-centre system.

SPECIAL FEATURES

The special features of the D.O.C. that attract growers to the system are as follows:

(I) The trees are strong. This is because all the shoots that are chosen as branches come out at a wide angle to the main stem, and these are strong by nature. Further, since the branches are spaced out over a length of centre stem, it follows that the strain of carrying crops is not concentrated at one point as is the case with open-centre trees.

(II) Big trees are formed quickly because little is pruned away in the early years.

(III) A good supply of blossom buds is readily formed because the branches lie almost flat, and are therefore well supplied with light.

(IV) Young growth is more evenly distributed over the entire surface of flat branches than in branches that are vertically inclined.

(V) Low-lying branches may be removed without detriment to the tree as a whole.

PRUNING TREATMENT FOR MAIDEN TREES

(a) *Non-Feathered Maidens.*—The lowest branches of all bush trees are usually formed at a height of about 18 inches to 2 feet above soil level. In open-centre bush trees young shoots that are required for this purpose are generally obtained as a result of shortening the single stem of a maiden tree to this height. For D.O.C. trees it is preferable to obtain the two lowest shoots by " notching " directly above those buds from which growth is wanted. " Notching " is done at pruning time in the dormant season by removing a small wedge-shaped piece of bark from the stem, about half an inch above the selected buds. Supposing one bud has been selected, and the notching done, it is wise to select the second bud on the opposite side of the stem, at about the same height from the ground (see Fig. 3). When a shoot on one side of the tree has been matched by a corresponding shoot on the opposite side, the initial steps have been taken to provide a balance in the arrangement of branches. Continuing with the pruning of the same tree, the top portion of the stem should be completely cut away, directly above a bud about 9 to 12 inches higher up the stem than where the notching is done. This bud (see Fig. 4 (1)) is likely to grow more or less erect. The bud directly below this (see Fig. 4 (2)) should be completely removed, because if allowed to grow it would form a shoot that would be too erect for a suitable branch. Supposing buds three and four come at right angles to the two notched buds (see Figs. 4 and 5), and they can easily do this if carefully selected, no further pruning need be done at this stage. But should either of these buds be found to occupy a position *directly above* either of the notched buds, it should be removed to prevent a shoot being formed where one is not wanted. Where one bud is removed for this reason, it is more than likely that the next bud to it will be found to occupy a position more

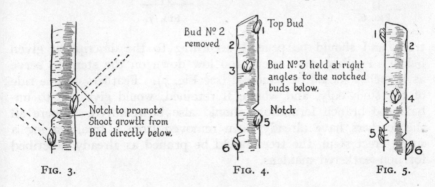

Bud Nº 2 removed

Top Bud

Bud Nº 3 held at right angles to the notched buds below.

Notch to promote Shoot growth from Bud directly below.

Notch

FIG. 3.   FIG. 4.   FIG. 5.

or less at right angles to the notched buds, and a shoot will be formed where one is wanted. Thus provision is made for the development of five shoots, the top one to continue the extension of the centre stem, and the other four to form side shoots. These four side shoots are spaced over a short stem and they are held roughly at right angles to each other.

With half-standard and standard trees the lowest branches will be wanted at about 4 to 6 feet respectively above soil level, and no pruning will be done to the centre stem until it has reached the required height. The pruning will then be identical with that described for bush trees.

(b) *Feathered Maidens.*—Some maiden trees have, in addition to the erect centre stem, one or more side shoots; such trees are spoken of as "feathered maidens," the side shoots being referred to as "feathers" (see Fig. 6). When two or more feathers occur at suitable positions they may be used to form principal branches. Such trees should be regarded as the equivalent of two-year-old

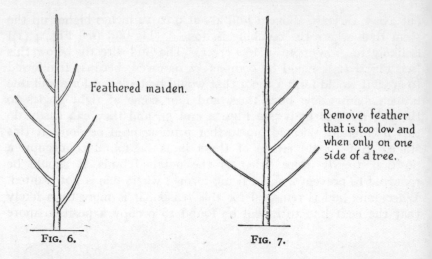

Feathered maiden.

Remove feather that is too low and when only on one side of a tree.

FIG. 6.   FIG. 7.

trees, and should be pruned according to the description given below. Feathers that occur too low down on the stem to serve as branches should be removed (see Fig. 7). Feathers on one side of the stem only, and which, if retained, would give rise to un-balanced branch formation, should also be removed. Where all the feathers have already been removed from a tree, leaving a single erect stem, the tree should be pruned as already described for non-feathered maidens.

TWO-YEAR-OLD TREES AND FEATHERED MAIDENS

The ideal two-year-old bush or a feathered maiden that has been pruned to form a delayed open-centre tree should consist of an erect centre stem with three to six side shoots, each of which is 18 inches or more in length. The centre stem should extend well above the side shoots, and these in turn should form a wide angle—45 to 60 degrees—with the centre stem. The side shoots should be evenly spaced around the centre stem, and should not be all on one side.

It is hardly to be expected that every two-year-old tree will be the ideal picture-book specimen ; there will in fact be all kinds, from those with very poor growth to those with an excessive number of vigorous side shoots. And some may be two-year-old trees originally intended for open centres, but which are to be trained as D.O.C. trees.

CURRANTS—*Laxtons No.* 1 (*Red*) and *Baldwin* (*Black*)

PRUNING TREATMENT

(a) *Treatment of Side Shoots.*—When there are plenty of side shoots, any number of these up to six may be chosen to form branches. None of these should lie directly over, or point in identically the same direction as any of the others. Two shoots, one on one side, and one on the opposite side, should be chosen to form the lowest pair of branches ; higher up the stem a second pair should be chosen, held between the first pair so that the four shoots are roughly at right angles to each other. The remaining pair should point in directions in between the right angles formed by the first two pairs (see Fig. 8). For preference, all the selected shoots should be held at a wide angle to the main stem. All side shoots in excess of those selected to become branches should be removed. It is hardly likely that all the side shoots will be the same length, even on the same tree. When one shoot is shortened, the corresponding one on the opposite side of the main stem should be shortened to leave it the same length. When a pair of wide-angled shoots are more than 18 inches long they should be reduced to a length of from 12 to 15 inches by pruning them to buds pointing in the direction in which further extensional growth is required (see Fig. 9). Shoots that are less than 18 inches long will be left from 3 to 12 inches long after pruning. In general, the longer

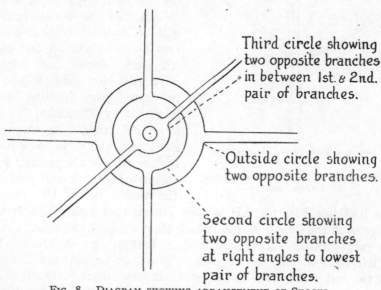

Third circle showing two opposite branches in between 1st. & 2nd. pair of branches.

Outside circle showing two opposite branches.

Second circle showing two opposite branches at right angles to lowest pair of branches.

FIG. 8.—DIAGRAM SHOWING ARRANGEMENT OF SHOOTS.

shoots are to begin with, the longer they should be left after pruning. The exception to this rule is when one shoot is much longer than its corresponding opposite one. In such cases the longer of the two shoots should be pruned more severely and left shorter than the weaker one.

As a rule, the more erect growing side shoots should be completely removed, but there are occasions when one or more will be retained, for instance, when there are only erect ones to select from. This often happens in the case of the two-year-old "cut-back," that is a tree that has had its centre stem cut back at the end of its first growing season with a view to forming an ordinary open centre. These erect shoots will only form satisfactory branches provided that future extension shoots from them take a more outward direction. To effect this a suitable outward-facing bud on each erect shoot will be chosen, but the actual pruning will be done at a point one or two buds higher up the stem. All buds above the selected outward-facing ones should be prevented from forming strong growths by "nicking." This is an old trick, long known to gardeners, and consists of pressing the edge of the pruning knife through the bark and well into the wood, below the base of

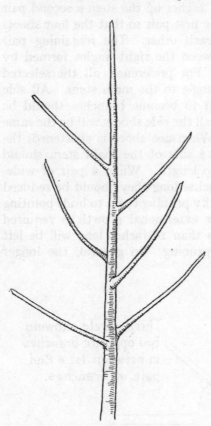

FIG. 9.—TWO-YEAR TREE AFTER PRUNING.

Three pairs of opposite shoots 12–17 inches long.

the bud (see Fig. 10). It is well known that young shoots tend to grow in the direction from which they receive most light. When an erect-growing shoot is pruned so that an outward-facing bud is left right at the top, it usually grows in an outward direction for the first inch or two, but after this it grows more vertically. The whole shoot would grow in an outward direction provided it derived most of its daylight from the side rather than from above. When the pruning is done so that one or two buds are left above an outward-facing bud, overhead shade is provided sufficient to ensure that an outward direction is taken as the young shoot grows. Although the buds above the selected outward-facing bud will not make strong growth because nicking has been done, they usually form enough leaf and shoot to provide further shade, thereby helping to ensure that growth in the outward direction is maintained.

Poorly developed two-year-old trees with no side shoots, or with only one, or with several, all on the same side, should be treated as described for maiden trees, but in addition the side shoots should be completely removed.

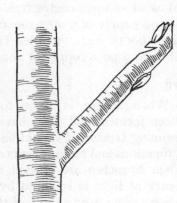

Edge of knife pressed beneath top of bud "NICKING" to prevent extensional growth.

Bud required to make extensional growth in a more outward direction.

FIG. 10. NICKING.

(b) *Treatment of Centre Stem.*—The centre stem should be from 9 to 12 inches taller than the tallest side shoot after pruning. Normally, as a result of the pruning, three or four young shoots may be expected from buds directly below the point of pruning. If side shoots are wanted from buds lower down than this, notching, as suggested for maiden trees, should be practised (see Fig. 3). Some growers will prefer to have a tall centre stem over which the branches are formed, whereas others will prefer a short one. If a tall centre stem is favoured, bud number one, at the top, will be left to continue its extension growth, and bud number two from the top will be removed as in the case of the maiden tree.

The same treatment will be applied whether a tree be two, three, four, or five years old, depending on how tall a centre stem is required.

Supposing no further extension of the centre stem is wanted, the top-most bud should be prevented from making vigorous growth by nicking just below the bud (see Fig. 10).

This treatment is advised so that most of the young growth will be made by lower buds in an outward direction, thus forming an open-centre head.

YOUNG TREES OVER TWO YEARS OLD

A well-grown D.O.C. tree will consist of a centre stem with a number of newly formed wide-angle branches. The lower branches will be two or more years old, and these may have divided to produce further branches and young shoots. The topmost branches may be wide-angled maiden shoots selected because they do not lie directly above neighbouring branches. There will be no further extension of the centre stem, and all vigorous erect central shoots will have been removed as in an open-centre tree. Strong-growing trees will have made a good supply of young shoots, both principal, i.e., "leaders," and side shoots, i.e., "maiden laterals," whereas weak-growing trees will have a poor supply of young shoots.

PRUNING TREATMENT

General Treatment.—When a tree is three to five years old, young branches have been formed, and these have on them young shoots and spurs. A pruning treatment should be given that takes into account the varied functions and requirements of these branches, shoots and spurs. When branches are shaded they are usually unproductive, since plenty of light is required by the spur leaves for blossom bud formation. The main object of the pruning treatment is, therefore, to provide every branch with plenty of space and light in order to ensure blossom bud formation, and sufficient room for the production of young side shoots.

In practice, when one branch or shoot trespasses over another, so that rubbing or extreme shading occurs, one of them should be shortened or completely removed. Blossom buds are readily formed on young shoots when they are left unpruned, provided they are well supplied with light (see Figs. 11 to 13). One of the main points to remember is that *reliance for the supply of blossom bud should be placed upon side shoots that are left unpruned*. In view of this it is evident that the branches should be well spaced, first, to provide enough room for side shoots, and secondly, that these side shoots should be well supplied with light. Not only is it necessary to space branches to make it possible to leave side shoots unpruned; it is also necessary to have them well spaced so that there is room for the actual production of new side shoots. Young shoots are readily formed when severe pruning is practised. It is well known that when existing shoots are severely pruned back during winter, the tree reacts by sending out more side shoots. It is not enough to shorten side shoots with the idea of making more room so that two branches may remain near together, since

84

this would lead to even more crowding the next season ; the correct treatment would be to remove one of the branches. The general principle underlying the treatment of side shoots or "maiden laterals" is to ensure ample space and light to each of them by restricting their number on any one main branch. Once this has been done, some will be shortened so that a further supply of young shoots is ensured for the next season, and the remainder will be left unpruned so that blossom buds can form on them. The detailed treatment of side shoots is dealt with later (see Treatment of Maiden Laterals). For strong-growing trees of the apple varieties *Bramley's Seedling, Blenheim Orange, Newton Wonder, Worcester Pearmain,* and others like them that are normally slow to yield much bossom bud, no further pruning is required once the branches and young shoots are well spaced, and all tall erect-growing shoots near to the main stem have been removed. Trees that have made very little growth usually produce blossom buds in large numbers, and the pruning of such trees should consist mainly of removing blossom buds in the hope that better growth will result. It is doubtful, with trees so young, whether pruning alone will succeed ; improvements in manuring, cultivation, or drainage may be necessary first.

TREATMENT FOR BRANCH FORMATION

In varieties such as *Cox's Orange Pippin* and *Fertility* pear, which produce whippy growth, leading shoots that are wanted for the extension of branches, or "leaders" as they are called,

FIG. 11.—BRANCHES THAT ARE TOO TALL SHOULD BE SHORTENED TO A SUITABLE SIDE SHOOT.

FIG. 12.—BRANCHES THAT CROSS OVER OR RUB AGAINST OTHERS SHOULD BE SHORTENED OR REMOVED.

FIG. 13.—ALSO THOSE THAT LIE NEAR PARALLEL WITH OTHER BRANCHES.

should be shortened every year. The pruning cuts should be made at positions where future new growth is wanted, and this usually involves removing from one-third to one-half of their " maiden " growth. Once the branches are long enough, i.e., when no further extension growth is required from them, the pruning or " tipping " of leaders at their extreme ends should cease. As trees increase in size, and the branches are pulled lower by crops, occasional erect-growing side shoots may be selected to take on the rôle of leaders (see Fig. 14).

These new leaders should be shortened as suggested above, so that

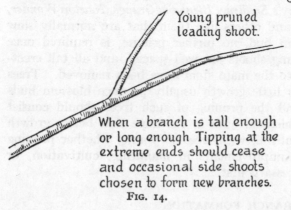

Young pruned leading shoot.

When a branch is tall enough or long enough Tipping at the extreme ends should cease and occasional side shoots chosen to form new branches.

FIG. 14.

new branches are formed from the original branches. Thus although the pruning of leaders at the extreme end of branches that are sufficiently long ceases at this stage, it continues to be done where new branches are being formed. Care should be taken not to introduce too many branches at this stage of a tree's development ; this will be avoided if, when pruning, care is taken to ensure that the tips of the leaders are at least 12 inches apart. By the time the trees are five years old, it is wise to increase this distance to 18 inches. It is important that leading shoots should be evenly dispersed around a tree, and they should be so pruned that a balanced branch formation results. Stated another way, there should be as many leaders on one side of a tree as on the other, and although some will be taller than others, both taller and shorter ones should be evenly divided between both sides. Sometimes there are tall vigorous shoots close to the leading shoots ; all such shoots should be completely removed.

TREATMENT OF MAIDEN LATERALS

Young laterals that are left unpruned can be looked to for an early supply of blossom buds ; when they are shortened they can be looked to for a further supply of maiden laterals. Hence for apples and for pears (excepting vigorous-growing trees of those varieties, like *Bramley* and *Worcester*, which are slow to yield much

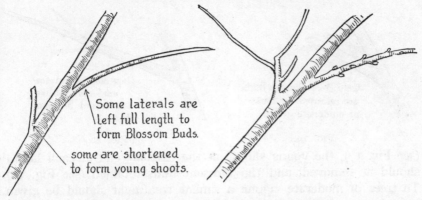

Some laterals are left full length to form Blossom Buds.

some are shortened to form young shoots.

FIG. 15.   FIG. 16.

blossom bud) some maiden laterals should be left unpruned, and the remainder shortened to leave them 2 to 3 inches long (see Figs. 15 and 16). Before this is done it will be necessary to remove some laterals altogether. These will consist of the erect vigorous ones that are not required as leaders, particularly those close to leading shoots, and those that trespass over branches or other shoots, thereby causing rubbing or extreme shading. Although it is usual to remove shoots of the latter category, they may be shortened provided there is reasonable expectation that subsequent shoot growth from them will not give rise to a similar fault. When trees are making a lot of growth, more laterals should be left un-pruned than for trees of moderate vigour. In the former case two should be left unpruned for every one that is shortened, and in the latter case every alternate lateral should be shortened, and the intermediate ones should be left unpruned.

TREATMENT OF OLDER LATERALS

In the case of strong-growing trees, supposing blossom buds and young shoots are formed on laterals that have been left unpruned

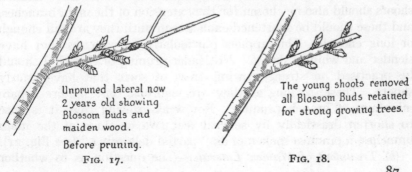

Unpruned lateral now 2 years old showing Blossom Buds and maiden wood.

Before pruning.

FIG. 17.

The young shoots removed all Blossom Buds retained for strong growing trees.

FIG. 18.

87

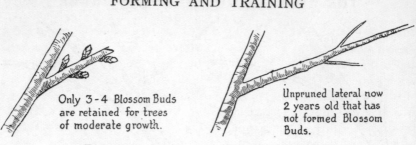

Only 3 - 4 Blossom Buds
are retained for trees
of moderate growth.

Unpruned lateral now
2 years old that has
not formed Blossom
Buds.

FIG. 19.   FIG. 20.

(see Fig. 17), the young shoots at the extreme end of each lateral should be removed, and the blossom buds retained (see Fig. 18). To trees of moderate vigour a similar treatment should be given, retaining a smaller number of blossom buds, say not more than three or four. All blossom buds in excess of this number will be pruned away with the young shoots (see Fig. 19).

MATURE TREES

Having established the principal branches, the main concern of the pruning technique is to obtain productive crops regularly. In order to do this branches should be suitably separated from neighbouring branches so that no one branch is unduly shaded. Furthermore, it is necessary to have an annual succession of blossom buds, and to make this possible a regular supply of young shoots is needed each season.

(a) *Treatment of Branches.*—Each branch should have a definite position on a tree, and because of this individual branches should be removed or shortened when they cross over, rub, or lie near, and parallel (i.e., within 1 foot) to other branches (see Figs. 11 to 13). Branches that are too low should be removed, and those that are too tall shortened to a suitable side branch. Once a branch begins to bend outwards, it is usually wise to select an upward growing side shoot and shorten it so that a new branch is being formed in readiness to take the place of the older one. Maiden shoots should also be chosen for the extension of the main branches, and these should be shortened each season until they are tall enough or long enough. This applies particularly to varieties that have slender and whippy shoots. No leader pruning of this kind should be practised on strong-growing trees of sorts that have sturdy shoots. These, so long as they are vigorous, only require a bare minimum of branch pruning. For weak-growing trees it is wise to shorten drastically by several feet two or three of the main branches, a practice spoken of as " partial dehorning " (see Fig. 21).

(b) *Treatment of Maiden Laterals.*—The question as to whether some of the side shoots should be shortened or not depends on vigour and variety. For most varieties it is necessary to provide for a regular seasonal supply of young shoots, and to ensure this a certain number of maiden laterals should be cut back every winter to within 2 or 3 inches of their base. Strong-growing trees of varieties that are normally slow to yield blossom, and that produce a sturdy type of young shoot, such as *Bramley's Seedling* apple, produce enough laterals of their own accord, and on them no cutting back of maiden laterals is necessary. Strong-growing trees of most varieties, and weaker-growing trees of varieties such as Bramley, should have one-third of their maiden laterals cut back. Most trees of medium and poor vigour should have one-half of the maiden laterals shortened. For trees in this category the treatment of the spur systems (see page 90) is more important since there is invariably a shortage of laterals. On early cooking apples

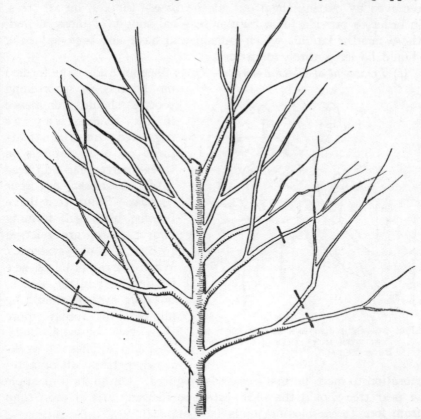

FIG. 21.—FOR WEAK-GROWING TREES IT IS WISE TO SHORTEN DRASTICALLY BY SEVERAL FEET TWO OR THREE OF THE MAIN BRANCHES.

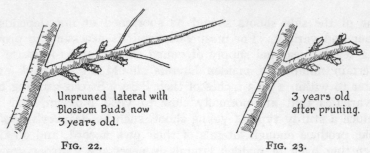

Unpruned lateral with Blossom Buds now 3 years old.

3 years old after pruning.

FIG. 22.

FIG. 23.

such as *Early Victoria* (*Emneth Early*), from which very large fruits are wanted early in the summer, making it necessary to keep the vigorous state of growth, at least two-thirds of the maiden laterals should be cut back. On all trees strong maiden laterals close to the selected leader, and erect-growing shoots near the main stem, commonly called " water shoots," should be completely removed by cutting them out at the base. Finally, on all trees, in order to provide for a regular seasonal supply of blossom bud, those maiden laterals which remain and have not been cut back should be left entirely unpruned.

(c) *Treatment of Older Laterals.*—Once blossom buds have formed on laterals, a shortening process should commence in the same way as suggested for the treatment of older laterals on three- to five-year-old trees.

(d) *Treatment of Spur Systems.*—Spurs that have become branched, forming two or more, are referred to as " spur systems." When large fruits are wanted early in the season, no spur system should be allowed to retain more than two blossom buds. This also applies to weak-growing trees when a restoration to more normal vigour is required. On no kind of apple or pear tree should the spur system be allowed to retain more than from four to six blossom buds (see Fig. 24).

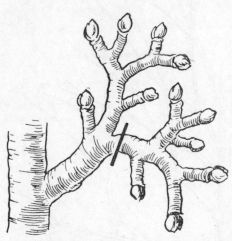

FIG. 24.—SPUR SYSTEMS SHOULD NOT BE LEFT WITH MORE THAN 4-6 BLOSSOM BUDS ON EACH.

NOTE.—For a full description of his modern pruning methods the reader should consult " Modern Apple Tree Pruning " by C. R. Thompson, published by Headley Bros., price 2s.

CHAPTER VIII

PLANNING AND PLANTING

PLANNING

MANURIAL REQUIREMENTS OF DIFFERENT FRUITS

In planning the lay-out of a new piece of ground, whether for fruit-garden, plantation or orchard, consideration should be given in the first place to the broad distinction in the manurial requirements of different fruits to which attention has already been drawn in Chapter III.

The stone fruits and black currants, which are going to require a lot of nitrogenous manure and relatively small dressings of potash, should be planted in one part of the garden or orchard. Cooking apples, pears, strawberries, raspberries, loganberries, blackberries, red currants, gooseberries and cobnuts, all of which require regular dressings of both potash and nitrogen, should be planted in another part, whilst dessert apples, which will require heavy regular dressings of potash and very little nitrogen in the early years, ought to be planted by themselves in a place where, if necessary, grass can be sown to reduce the supply of nitrogen available to the tree roots.

SPRAYING REQUIREMENTS OF DIFFERENT FRUITS

Consideration should next be given to the spraying requirements of the fruit. Apart from the general importance of having an adequate supply of water for spraying in the immediate neighbourhood, there are particular factors to be considered in this connection.

Tar-oil Sprays.—One of the worst insect pests of apples, pears, plums and cherries, is the aphis or green fly, and the most economical way of dealing with this pest is to spray the trees in winter with a tar-oil wash in order to kill the eggs which are then on the trees. Other bad pests such as the apple sucker, and the winter moth, can all be controlled to a greater or less degree by the application of tar-oil sprays in winter.

It should be pointed out, however, at this stage that tar-oil sprays will burn the foliage of tender herbaceous plants, and if it comes into contact with such vegetables as cabbages and lettuces it will impart an unpleasant flavour to them. This means, for instance, that if cordon fruit trees are planted to form the background for a herbaceous border or are interplanted with tender-leaved vegetables, they cannot be sprayed in the winter without injuring the under crop. Tar-oil wash discolours grass also for a time, but does no lasting injury to it.

Another point in connection with the use of tar-oil sprays is that there are a few fruits, such as the cherry-plum (Myrobolan), the strawberry, the cobnut and the filbert, which are susceptible to damage by these sprays when used at the strengths usually recommended for other fruits. This means that these fruits should be planted by themselves whenever possible.

Lime-sulphur.—This spray plays a very important part in protecting the trees and bushes from certain fungus diseases and insect pests, and although less injurious to tender-leaved plants than tar-oil, it does burn the foliage of flowers and vegetables to a certain extent. So far as possible, therefore, when planning the fruit lay-out, provision should be made for the use of these two sprays under conditions which will not cause damage to other plants.

As in the case of tar-oils, there are certain varieties of fruits, as for instance, *Stirling Castle* apple and *Davison's Eight* black currant, the leaves of which are specially susceptible to damage when sprayed with lime-sulphur, and care should be taken to plant " sulphur-shy " varieties of this kind in situations where they can receive special spray treatment.

One other consideration should be noted in connection with the use of lime-sulphur. When gooseberries are to be picked in the young tender stage for market, they should not be grown between tree fruits which are to be sprayed with lime-sulphur, because the deposit of lime-sulphur remains on the fruits and, although perfectly harmless, is likely to spoil their appearance. For this reason gooseberries, also, are best grown by themselves.

It is hardly necessary at this point to enlarge on the particular diseases and pests which require spray treatment with tar-oil and lime-sulphur, because the subject is fully dealt with in the chapters devoted to the separate fruits. It cannot be repeated too often, however, that under present-day conditions the spraying programme must inevitably occupy a key position in fruit culture, and that everyone who wants to grow fruit really well must become to a certain extent " spray-minded." Fortunately, with the rapid advances in knowledge that are now being made, and with recent improvements in spray machinery, this is not such a difficult matter as it used to be.

POLLINATION

When planning the lay-out, it must be remembered that the flowers of certain varieties of certain fruits are self-sterile and require the presence in the near neighbourhood of other varieties of the same fruit which flower at the same time, from which the pollen may be easily carried by insects to cross-pollinate the sterile flowers. Notable examples of self-sterility in this sense are the *Doyenné du Comice* pear, the *Cox's Orange Pippin* apple, the *Coe's Golden Drop* plum and *Early Rivers* cherry. Moreover, many varieties, including these four, appear to set better with the pollen of some varieties than with that of others.

Thus *Glou Morceau* in this country and *Nouveau Poiteau* in Holland and Sweden are supposed to be good pollinators for *Doyenné du Comice* pear, *Worcester Pearmain* and *James Grieve* for *Cox's Orange Pippin* apple, *Oullins Golden Gage* and *Comte d'Althan's Gage* for *Coe's Golden Drop*, and *Governor Wood* and *Bigarreau Frogmore* for *Early Rivers* cherry. It so happens that many of the varieties of fruits which people most want to grow are either self-sterile or inter-sterile with many other sorts, so that when a single tree of any such kind is planted in a garden which does not happen to contain a pollinating variety, disappointment is too often the result. Such trees may flower profusely and yet fail to set more than a few fruits.

Obviously, such difficulties are best prevented by careful planning in the first place, but when the problem turns up in established trees it can best be got over by top-grafting one or two trees with a pollinating variety, or more locally still, by grafting one or two branches of each self-sterile tree with scions from a pollinator variety, by one of the methods described in Chapter IV.

TIME OF BLOSSOMING

In choosing pollinator varieties, time of flowering is important. It does not follow, because a certain variety flowers early, that, therefore, it is an early maturing fruit. The *Monarch* plum, for instance, the *Turkey Heart* cherry and the *Baldwin* black currant are all early flowerers, but late season fruits. Generally speaking, most varieties overlap each other in their flowering periods, so that it is only in the case of very early flowerers planted with very late ones that difficulties of this kind are likely to arise.

It is, however, important when planning the layout to remember that cross-pollination has a two-fold aspect ; the flowering period of the pollinator must overlap, and its pollen must be of a sort which will successfully cross-pollinate the self-sterile variety.

CHOICE OF ROOTSTOCK

Since the war of 1914–18, experiments in the research stations and demonstration centres of the country have given much information on the subject of rootstocks, with the result that fruit trees on known rootstocks are obtainable from all the best nurserymen. The question of which stocks are the best for different purposes will be dealt with later in the sections dealing with each fruit, but it should be emphasized here that when planning the fruit-garden or orchard, the question of distance of planting must be considered in close relationship to the rootstocks on which the trees are to be grown.

DIFFERENT SYSTEMS OF PLANTING

A " Quincunx " Plant for an Orchard of Cherries and Plums.— A popular plant for a mixed orchard of standard cherries and plums is to set the cherries " square " at so many feet as " permanents," with a plum in the middle of each square. This is known as a " Quincunx " plant, and the idea is to treat the plums as " filler " trees to give a temporary crop while the cherry trees are gradually developing and filling up the space they will ultimately require as the " permanents."

Figure below shows the plan of such an orchard.

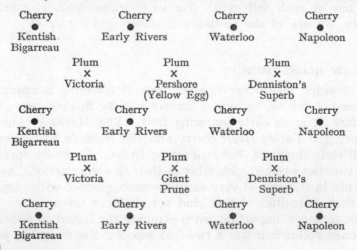

A " QUINCUNX " PLANT OF CHERRIES AND PLUMS

Cherry ● Kentish Bigarreau	Cherry ● Early Rivers	Cherry ● Waterloo	Cherry ● Napoleon
	Plum × Victoria	Plum × Pershore (Yellow Egg)	Plum × Denniston's Superb
Cherry ● Kentish Bigarreau	Cherry ● Early Rivers	Cherry ● Waterloo	Cherry ● Napoleon
	Plum × Victoria	Plum × Giant Prune	Plum × Denniston's Superb
Cherry ● Kentish Bigarreau	Cherry ● Early Rivers	Cherry ● Waterloo	Cherry ● Napoleon

A TRIANGULAR PLANT

These four varieties of cherries selected are suitable for cross-pollination, and not difficult from the ladder-moving point of view when picking, the order of ripening being *Early Rivers*, *Kentish Bigarreau*, *Waterloo* and *Napoleon*. The first and third named are so-called " black " cherries, and the second and fourth are so-called " white " cherries.

Of the plums, *Pershore* makes excellent jam and bottles well, *Victoria* and *Denniston's Superb Gage* are excellent mid-season croppers with quite a good flavour, and *Giant Prune* is a very large late plum worth growing if only for its size.

A TRIANGULAR PLANT OF APPLES

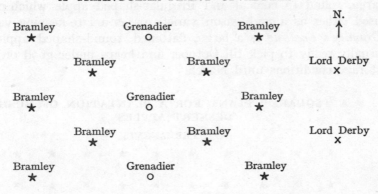

A " Triangular " Plant for an Apple Orchard.—The *Bramley's Seedling*, a late cooking apple, comes next to the sweet cherries in the matter of size of tree, and where a grass orchard of apples is required it is probably the best variety to plant. It is not easy to choose the ideal pollinator for *Bramley*. Being what is known genetically as a " triploid," it is itself a bad pollinator for the majority of apples which are " diploids." This means that if the pollinating variety is to be expected to crop, it must in its turn be given a pollinator. From the manurial point of view, we have seen the desirability of keeping cooking apples together, so that we have to find at least three varieties of cooking apples whose blossoming periods overlap.

The *Bramley* grown as a standard tree will be worked on a very vigorous stock, so that on a strong-growing soil the trees will have to be at least 30 feet apart.

In order to illustrate what is known as the " triangular " plant, we will assume that *Bramley's Seedling* is to be planted with

Grenadier and *Lord Derby* as pollinators at 32 feet " triangular " with a view to making a permanent grass orchard of standard cooking apples, as in the diagram on page 95.

This plant gives a total of 49 trees to the acre, whereas a square plant at 32 feet would give 42 trees to the acre.

It is not likely that at this distance of planting the orchard would become overcrowded, but if it did the second row of *Bramleys* running north and south could be taken out without interfering with the pollinators.

Of the three varieties of apples in this plant, *Grenadier*, a large, flattened, round to conical-shaped apple, can be picked at the end of July and is a non-keeping variety. *Lord Derby* is a very large, round to conical and irregular-shaped apple which can be used either as a mid-season variety or as a late-keeping variety. *Bramley's Seedling* is a large, flattened, round-shaped apple, not usually ready to pick till October and keeps under good ordinary storage conditions until March.

A " SQUARE " PLANT FOR A PLANTATION OF BUSH DESSERT APPLES

ALL PERMANENTS

```
 *   *   *   *   *   *   *   *   *   *

 *   ×   *   ×   *   ×   *   ×   *   ×

 *   *   *   *   *   *   *   *   *   *

 *   *   *   *   *   *   *   *   *   *

 *   ×   *   ×   *   ×   *   ×   *   ×

 *   *   *   *   *   *   *   *   *   *

 *   *   *   *   *   *   *   *   *   *

 *   ×   *   ×   *   ×   *   ×   *   ×

 *   *   *   *   *   *   *   *   *   *

 *   *   *   *   *   *   *   *   *   *
```

85 trees   ★ = *Cox's Orange Pippin.*
15 trees   × = *Worcester Pearmain or other Pollinator.*

GRAPES—*Muscat of Alexandria* and *Black Hamburgh*

A SQUARE PLANT

In this plant about one-seventh of the total plant consists of a pollinator variety.

If desired the second row of pollinators might consist of another variety such as *Lord Lambourne, James Grieve, Laxton's Superb, Ellison's Orange,* or *Fortune.*

Lord Lambourne is a medium-sized, round to conical dessert apple for use from October to December. *James Grieve* is a medium-sized, round to conical dessert apple for use in September and October. *Laxton's Superb* is a large to medium-sized, round to conical and flattened dessert apple, which keeps well and may be used from November to March. *Ellison's Orange* is a fairly large-sized, round to conical dessert apple which is ready for use in September and October. *Fortune* is a medium round to conical dessert apple for use in October and November.

ANOTHER "SQUARE" PLANT FOR BUSH APPLES—EITHER DESSERT OR COOKING
PERMANENTS AND FILLERS

```
★   ×   ★   ×   ★   ×   ★   ×   ★   ×

×   ○   ×   ○   ×   ○   ×   ○   ×   ○

★   ×   ★   ×   ★   ×   ★   ×   ★   ×

×   ○   ×   ○   ×   ○   ×   ○   ×   ○

★   ×   ★   ×   ★   ×   ★   ×   ★   ×

×   ○   ×   ○   ×   ○   ×   ○   ×   ○

★   ×   ★   ×   ★   ×   ★   ×   ★   ×

×   ○   ×   ○   ×   ○   ×   ○   ×   ○

★   ×   ★   ×   ★   ×   ★   ×   ★   ×

×   ○   ×   ○   ×   ○   ×   ○   ×   ○
```

	Dessert	Cooking
25 trees ★ =	*Cox's Orange Pippin*	or *Bramley's Seedling*
25 trees ○ =	*Worcester Pearmain*	or *Lord Derby*
50 trees × =	*Laxton's Superb*	or *Grenadier*

In this plant, if the trees had to be thinned at any time, it would be possible to remove all those marked with a ×, leaving the other two varieties intact for the purposes of cross-pollination.

PLANTING

MARKING OUT THE GROUND

To mark out on the ground the position which the trees are to occupy a long wire is often used on which pieces of string or coloured wool are tied tightly at intervals corresponding to the distances at which the trees are to be planted in the rows. A base line AB, is first set out at one end of the field from which to square off the rest (see diagram). At each end of the base line a right angle is found by the most convenient method and the two side lines, AC and BD, are marked off. Supposing the distance between the tree rows to

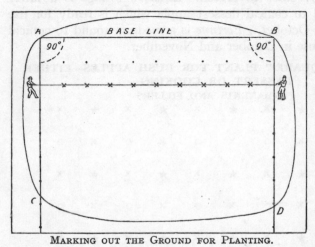

MARKING OUT THE GROUND FOR PLANTING.

be 15 feet, short pegs are stuck into the ground 15 feet apart all down each of the side lines AC and BD. The wire then comes into play. One man takes hold of each end, and starting at A and B respectively, they walk down the side lines AC and BD. Stopping at the first peg, each one fastens down his end of the wire beside the peg. Then all they have to do is to follow the wire across the field, sticking a straight stick about 18 inches long into the ground at each point indicated by the pieces of string tied on to the wire. In this way the whole field can quickly be marked out.

TIME TO PLANT

Fruit trees and bushes are planted some time in the dormant season between leaf fall in the autumn and bud burst in the spring. As to which is the best month it is impossible to generalize, but on the whole the conditions in October and early November are likely to be the most favourable.

The physical condition of the soil is of vital importance in deciding the best time for planting. If the ground is cold and wet and sticks

98

in lumps, planting should not be contemplated. Should the trees arrive from the nursery at such a time, they must be heeled in by the roots in a sheltered position well secured from rabbits and other vermin, until the weather is suitable for planting. Should trees arrive for planting during frosty weather when the ground is too hard to dig, they should be kept in a frost-proof shed covered with several thicknesses of sacking. When the trees are taken out to be planted in their permanent quarters, the roots should be covered with old sacks to prevent drying out.

NUMBER OF TREES PER FULL ACRE AT DIFFERENT DISTANCES APART

Distance in Feet	No. of Trees in Square Plant	No. of Trees in Triangular Plant
10	435	502
12	302	348
14	222	256
15	193	222
16	170	196
18	134	154
20	109	125
25	69	79
30	48	55
40	27	31

Note : 1. The numbers given above make no allowance for the fact that headland space of at least half the planting distance should be allowed for all round the sides of each orchard or plantation. The best way to find out the number of trees that will be required for planting any given field is to draw the field to scale on squared paper and mark out the positions to be occupied by each tree.

2. To find the number of trees or bushes per full acre at any given distance, multiply the distance between the rows by the distance between the trees or bushes in the row, and divide that into the number of square feet in an acre, namely 43,560. For instance, raspberry canes at 6 feet by 2 feet—6 × 2 = 12. 43,560 ÷ 12 = 3,630 canes will be required to plant a full acre of raspberries. In the case of strawberries planted 18 inches apart in rows 2½ feet between the rows, 11,616 plants would be required to plant a full acre.

DIGGING THE TREE HOLE

This operation is best done immediately before planting. The size of the hole will vary with the size of the root-system to be planted. The hole should not be made so small that the roots have to be trimmed up drastically or twisted round to make the tree fit the hole ; on the other hand, the hole should not be more

99

than a few inches wider than the diameter of the root-system at its widest point, because much of the success of the planting operation depends on consolidating the soil round the roots, and if the hole is too large, this will be more difficult to do. Nor must the hole be too deep, or scion-rooting may take place as a result of planting the tree with the union between stock and scion below ground level. When planting in heavy clay soils, the tree holes should be made very shallow and the soil slightly mounded up in order to ensure surface drainage and aeration for the tree roots.

PLANTING THE TREE

Before planting a tree, the roots are trimmed up, a long sloping cut being made with a sharp knife on the underside of each root with a view to stimulating rapid callousing and the growth of new adventitious roots from the cut surface. The tree is then held upright in the hole by one man, who lifts it gently up and down while a second man throws a few spadefuls of the finer soil over the roots. This soil is then stamped firmly down round the roots and more soil is thrown in. It is most necessary to make the soil really firm at each stage of the planting by treading and ramming in order to make sure that the soil particles are in close contact with the roots. In planting a tree against a wall, the roots should be as far from the wall as possible with the stem sloping slightly towards it.

A PLANTING-BOARD TO SAVE SIGHTING WHEN PLANTING

When there are a large number of trees to be planted, it is a good plan to use a " Planting-Board." This is a plain wooden board about 5 feet long by 4 or 5 inches wide by ¾ inch thick, with a V-shaped notch cut in the centre and at each end as in the diagram. The central notch should be about 1¼ inches wide at the wide end.

When digging the holes in which to plant the trees, the planting-board is placed with the central V-shaped notch round the stick which marks the first position. Two thin, straight sticks, such as those that have been used for marking out, are then stuck in the

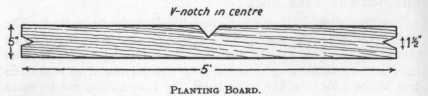

V-notch in centre

5″

↕1½″

←———————————— 5′ ————————————→

PLANTING BOARD.

ground in the two notches, one at each end of the planting-board (see diagram). The planting-board is then taken away, the stick marking the site is removed, and the tree hole dug out to the required dimensions, care being taken to leave intact the two end sticks. When it comes to planting the tree, the planting-board is put across the hole with the central notch facing the same way as before, and the two end notches round the two end sticks. The man with the tree to be planted holds it with its stem in the central notch, which automatically keeps it in its right position as originally marked out. This saves having to look along the row and sight the tree to find its true position.

TRANSPLANTING

It is possible to transplant fruit trees even when they are quite large, but the operation is expensive and on the whole rather risky. Some experts advise dehorning the tree (see page 56) in the winter preceding that in which it is to be transplanted. This reduces the size of the tree in preparation for the corresponding reduction in the size of the root-system, which is inevitable when the tree is dug up. This is done the following winter, keeping as much of the root-system intact as can be conveniently carried to the new position. An extra large tree hole should be dug, *the soil must be rammed thoroughly after planting*, and a good mulch spread round the tree to keep the soil moist. For bush trees a 7-foot spile driven in at an angle, heading into the prevailing wind, and fastened to one of the main central branches, forms the best support. No pruning is usually done until the end of the first season after transplanting.

PROTECTION OF THE STEM

When fruit trees are planted where stock of any kind is likely to be grazing, some form of guard will be necessary to protect the stem of the tree from being eaten. Every fruit district has its own form of tree guard, and it is a good thing to consult the county horticultural officer in regard to the best type to suit local conditions.

Young trees planted in poultry runs will require a special form of protection, in that hens are fond of scratching the loose soil away from round the roots of newly-planted trees. This exposes the roots, which then tend to dry out. One way to deal with this problem is to make two wire-netting guards on frames for each tree, which are laid flat on the ground as in the diagram on page 24 to prevent the birds from scratching the soil away from the roots.

Rabbits and hares are some of the worst pests of fruit trees. The best way to keep them out is to erect good wire netting, 4 feet high from ground level, mesh $1\frac{1}{4}$ inch to $1\frac{1}{2}$ inch, and gauge 18 or 19, all round the orchard or plantation, let well into the ground and laid outwards, in the furrow, with a line of strong hedging or barbed wire strung along about 6 inches above the top of the fence to which the wire netting is attached at intervals with thin wire as shown in the diagram.

Another method of protecting the trunks of trees from being eaten is to paint them with one or other of the proprietary mixtures which are sold for this purpose as deterrents. These should be painted on the trees before the autumn frosts begin. They should be slightly warmed before being applied and should be painted on fairly thinly. There are several mixtures containing such substances as linseed

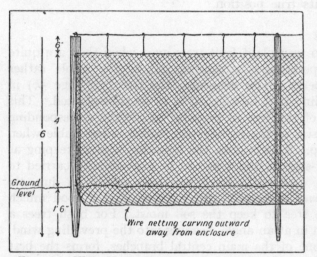

Ground level

1' 6"

Wire netting curving outward away from enclosure

ERECTING WIRE NETTING TO KEEP OUT RABBITS AND HARES.

oil, sulphur and resin, which can be made at home and which will act as deterrents, but it should be noted that any mixtures containing paraffin oil are likely to damage the stems of young trees and should not be used.

TREE STAKES

It is worth going to a good deal of trouble with staking at time of planting. For standard and half-standard trees one really strong Spanish chestnut, oak, or ash stake, driven well in close beside the tree, cut off just below the crotch (the point on the main stem from which the branches spring) and well pared over, will generally give sufficient support, provided the bottom two feet have been well treated under pressure with a good wood preservative, and that the tree has been fastened securely.

If stakes are plentiful, some people like to drive in two, one on either side of the tree, screwing on a crosspiece between the two stakes to which the tree is fastened. If the crosspiece works loose, the tree wobbles about between the two stakes and is held less firmly than if it were fastened securely to a single stake, so that care must be taken to screw the crosspiece firmly on and not to trust to nails.

For low-headed bush trees, stakes from 3 to 4 feet long are generally used, driven well into the ground either vertically beside the stem, or obliquely as in the lower diagram, in which case they should point in the direction of the prevailing wind.

For small trees on very dwarfing stocks, whose branches are likely to need supporting when loaded with fruit, a dual-purpose stake has been devised, which supports the stem in early years and to which the fruiting branches can be attached by wires in later years. The stake consists of a round iron bar 8 to 9 feet long, ¾ of an inch thick, pointed at one end

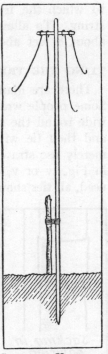

STAKING: VERTICAL.

and with a short tee-piece braised on at the top end. It is driven 18 inches into the ground about 6 to 8 inches away from the tree, sloping slightly into the prevailing wind. The tree stem is firmly fastened to the stake just above the union and again just below where the lowest branch is to be. When the tree comes into cropping and needs shoring up, long pieces of strong wire are twisted round the tee-piece and bent half-way round t h e branches. Alternatively, the branches can be temporarily supported by pieces of h o p string or coir yarn fastened to the tee-piece. A more elaborate extension of this system is to stretch permanent wires in two directions along and across the whole row of stakes at the top,

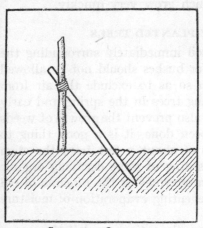

STAKING: OBLIQUE.

to which the fruiting branches can be secured by wires or hop string. To allow for implements to pass, these wires must be about 8 feet above the ground.

TYING THE TREE TO THE STAKE

There are many different ways of tying the tree to the stake. Some people wrap sacking or old cloth in a band about 6 inches wide round the stem of the tree, as in Fig. I, to prevent chafing, and then tie with rope or string as in Figs. II and III. Others merely use straw rope or strips of rubber tyres, fastened either as in Fig. IV or V, but without any sacking. Whichever method is used, all ties should be taken off yearly just before winter spraying,

Sacking in position — Rope looped round sacking and stake — Tie completed

TYING THE TREE TO THE STAKE.

Fig. I.   Fig. II.   Fig. III.

and renewed afterwards. If the old ties are left on, they harbour insects and may constrict the growth of the stem, especially in the case of young plum trees, which grow very quickly.

HOEING AND MULCHING NEWLY-PLANTED TREES

It is very important that the soil immediately surrounding the roots of newly-planted fruit trees or bushes should not be allowed to remain lumpy or to pan down so as to exclude the air from the roots. Hoeing round the young trees in the spring and early summer will prevent this and will also prevent the growth of weeds or grass. After the hoeing has been done, it is a good thing to cover the ground within a radius of about 3 feet from the stem with some form of mulching, consisting of some decaying organic material, such as spent hops, lawn mowings or the remains of old compost beds, with the idea of preventing evaporation of moisture from the soil.

This can seldom be done in large plantations, and if the young plant is vigorous and the soil conditions are normal, the stirring of the soil with cultivators and hoes throughout the first few seasons is usually enough to keep the plant growing sufficiently vigorously. But in gardens or where mulching material is

Straw rope tie   Tube tie

TYING THE TREE TO THE STAKE.
Figs. IV and V.

readily available, mulching is a very wise precaution to take against an abnormally dry season, in clay soils, which are likely to crack, or in sandy soils, which are liable to drought.

PROTECTION FROM FROST, WIND, BIRDS AND WASPS

Provided fruit trees are not too much exposed to the full force of east winds in the spring or to south-west gales in the late summer and autumn, no extra precautions should be necessary. The wisdom of planting shelter belts for protection from the wind is a subject about which there is some controversy at the present time. A walled or fenced garden gives the best shelter of all, but should never be made in a low-lying situation for fear of damage from frost.

Wall trees may be partially protected from frost by hanging double thicknesses of fish-netting in front of the trees. If the situation is known to be a frost pocket, orchard heaters may be used with advantage. (See also page 276.)

One of the most satisfactory methods of protecting the buds

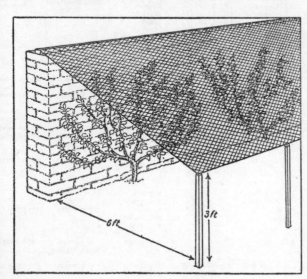

6 ft   3 ft

PROTECTION OF WALL FRUIT FROM HAIL.   (Page 276.)

105

of fruit trees from the attacks of birds in winter and spring is to wind black cotton round the trees or bushes by means of bobbins specially devised for the purpose. The only certain way to protect bush fruits from birds or squirrels is to enclose the bushes in a fruit cage. The cage should be at least 6 feet high, the sides being made of strong half-inch mesh galvanized wire netting nailed to posts let into the ground. The roof may be a permanent one of the same wire netting, or a temporary roof of fish-netting may be stretched across the cage as soon as the first fruits begin to ripen. In either case a door of wire netting will be necessary.

Protection from wasps can be secured only by enclosing each entire fruit in a muslin or strong transparent paper bag, just before it begins to ripen.

PLANTING DISTANCES

Form	Distance apart to Plant		Most Suitable Stock	Best Age to Plant	Years to come into Bearing	Useful Life of Tree
	Between Rows	Between Trees or Bushes in the Row				
APPLE						
Standard . . .	30 ft.–40 ft.	30 ft.–40 ft.	Very Vigorous XII, XVI or Selected Free Stock	2 years	5–10 years	80–100 years
Half-standard . .	30 ft.–40 ft.	30 ft.–40 ft.		2 years	5–10 years	80–100 years
Pyramid . . .	15 ft.–20 ft.	15 ft.–20 ft.	IX, I, or II	1–3 years		
Dwarf Pyramid (Fuseau) . . .	6 ft.–8 ft.	3 ft.–6 ft.	IX, I, or II	1–3 years	2–6 years according to treatment and stock	30–50 years according to treatment
Espalier . . .	6 ft.–8 ft.	15 ft.–20 ft.	IX, I, or II	1–3 years		
Bush	12 ft.–30 ft.	12 ft.–30 ft.	IX, I, or II	Maiden		
Cordon . . .	6 ft.–8 ft.	2 ft.–3 ft.	IX, I, or II	Maiden		
Double Vertical .	6 ft.–8 ft.	5 ft.–6 ft.	IX, I, or II	Maiden		
APRICOT						
Fan	6 ft.–8 ft.	12 ft.–18 ft.	Brompton or Common Mussel	1–4 years	5–6 years from Maiden	15–20 years
BLACKBERRY AND HYBRIDS . . .	6 ft.–8 ft.	12 ft.–16 ft.		1 year	2 years	10–15 years
BULLACE . . .	15 ft.–20 ft.	15 ft.–20 ft.	Myrobolan B or Own Roots	1–2 years	5–6 years	20–30 years
CHERRY						
Standard . . .	30 ft.–40 ft.	30 ft.–40 ft.	Selected Mazzard	1–2 years	6–8 years	40–50 years
Fan	6 ft.–8 ft.	18 ft.–20 ft.	Selected Mazzard	1–2 years	6–8 years from Maiden	40–50 years
COBNUT	15 ft.–18 ft.	15 ft.–18 ft.		2–3 years	10–12 years	60–80 years
CURRANTS (RED AND WHITE)						
Bush	5 ft.–6 ft.	5 ft.–6 ft.		2 years		
Espalier . . .	5 ft.–6 ft.	5 ft.–6 ft.		2–4 years		
Cordon. Single .	5 ft.–6 ft.	1 ft.		2 years	2–3 years	15 years
Cordon. Double .	5 ft.–6 ft.	3 ft.		2–3 years		
Cordon. Triple .	5 ft.–6 ft.	4 ft.		2–3 years		
(BLACK)						
Bush	5 ft.–8 ft.	4 ft. 6 in.–6 ft.		1–2 years	2–3 years from Maiden	5–8 years
DAMSON						
Standard . . .	15 ft.–18 ft.	15 ft.–18 ft.	Myrobolan B	2 years	5–6 years	30–50 years
Half-standard . .	15 ft.–18 ft.	15 ft.–18 ft.	Myrobolan B	2 years	5–6 years	30–50 years
Bush. . . .	15 ft.–18 ft.	15 ft.–18 ft.	Myrobolan B	1–2 years	5–6 years	30–50 years
For Shelter Belt .	6 ft.–8 ft.	6 ft.–8 ft.	Myrobolan B	1–2 years	—	30–50 years

FILBERT. See COBNUT.

PLANTING DISTANCES—*continued*

Form	Distance apart to Plant		Most Suitable Stock	Best Age to Plant	Years to come into Bearing	Useful Life of Tree
	Between Rows	Between Trees or Bushes in the Row				
GOOSEBERRY *						
Bush . . .	5 ft.–6 ft.	5 ft.–6 ft.				
Espalier . .	5 ft.–6 ft.	5 ft.–6 ft.				
Fan . . .	5 ft.–6 ft.	5 ft.–6 ft.		⎫		
Cordon. Single .	5 ft.–6 ft.	1 ft.–2 ft.		⎬ 2 years	2–3 years	10–15 years
Cordon. Double .	5 ft.–6 ft.	3 ft.				
Cordon. Treble .	5 ft.–6 ft.	4 ft.		⎭		
LOGANBERRY . .	6 ft.–7 ft.	8 ft.–12 ft.	Rooted Tips	2 years	2 years	10–15 years
MEDLAR	10 ft.–20 ft.	10 ft.–20 ft.	Pear	2 years	1–2 years	40–50 years
MULBERRY . .	25 ft.–30 ft.	25 ft.–30 ft.	White Mulberry	2–3 years	6–8 years	60–100 years
NECTARINE. See PEACH.						
PEACH						
Fans	6 ft.–8 ft.	15 ft.–18 ft.	Brompton Pershore or Common Mussel	1–4 years according to circumstances	5–6 years from Maiden	15–20 years
PEARS						
Standard . . .	18 ft.–25 ft.	18 ft.–25 ft.	Pear Stock	2 years	6–8 years	50–60 years
Half-standard . .	18 ft.–25 ft.	18 ft.–25 ft.	Pear Stock	2 years		
Dwarf Pyramid (Fuseau) . .	6 ft.–8 ft.	3 ft.–6 ft.	Quince A or C	Maiden		
Bush	12 ft.–15 ft.	12 ft.–15 ft.	Quince A or C	Maiden	⎫	
Espalier . . .	5 ft.–6 ft.	15 ft.–20 ft.	Quince A or Pear Stocks	4–5 years	⎬ 4–5 years	50–60 years
Grid-iron, Wall or Wire Trained .	5 ft.–6 ft.	6 ft.–8 ft.	Selected	4–5 years		
Cordon. Single .	6 ft.–8 ft.	2 ft.–3 ft.	Quince A or C	Maiden		
Cordon. Double .	6 ft.–8 ft.	5 ft.–6 ft.	Quince A or C	2–3 years	⎭	
PLUMS						
Standard (Strong) .	20 ft.–30 ft.	20 ft.–30 ft.	Myrobolan B	2–3 years	⎫	
Standard (Moderate Growth) . .	15 ft.–20 ft.	15 ft.–20 ft.	Myrobolan B	2–3 years		
Half-standard . .	15 ft.–20 ft.	15 ft.–20 ft.	Myrobolan B	Maiden ⎰ Form head when and where desired	⎬ 5–6 years	30–50 years
Bush	15 ft.–18 ft.	15 ft.–18 ft.	Myrobolan B	Maiden		
Fan	6 ft.–8 ft.	15 ft.–20 ft.	Myrobolan B	4–5 years (already trained to shape)	⎭	
QUINCE	12 ft.–18 ft.	12 ft.–18 ft.	Own Roots	2–3 years	6–8 years	30–50 years
RASPBERRY . .	6 ft.–8 ft.	2 ft.–3 ft.		1 year	2 years	5–10 years according to circumstances
STRAWBERRY . .	2 ft. 6 in.–3 ft.	12 in.–18 in.		1 year runners	2 years	5–10 years according to circumstances
(Alpine)	1 ft.	1 ft.		1 year runners	2 years	
VEITCHBERRY. See LOGANBERRY.						
WALNUT . . .	40 ft.–50 ft.	40 ft.–50 ft.	*Juglans regia* or *J. nigra*	2–3 years	10 years	80–100 years

CHAPTER IX

GATHERING AND STORING FRUIT

GATHERING FRUIT

The period of fruit gathering may be said to extend roughly from June until early November; the time at which it should be picked varies with the conditions prevailing locally, that is to say, it is affected by the weather, the soil, the situation, and the species and variety of fruit grown.

In addition to all these, there is the consideration as to whether the fruit is to be gathered *fully ripe*, for immediate use, or whether it must be gathered earlier for storing purposes or for travelling to market.

MATURITY OF FRUIT

No fruit should be gathered for storing before it has arrived at maturity, or it will shrivel up when stored, and lose its flavour. By maturity, however, we are not to understand its full flavour and ripeness, but merely the completion of its growth and size; and as all fruit, even upon the same tree, does not come to maturity at the same period, it will frequently be found the safest and most economical plan to make the gathering at two or three different times.

It is very easy to ascertain when any particular fruit is ready; for mature fruit always leaves the tree upon a gentle touch —the fruit-stalk parts easily from the twig on which it grows if the fruit is gently raised to the horizontal position. Were it not mature it would require a pull to detach it from the tree.

WINDFALLS

In a general way, with both apples and pears, several of the most forward will have fallen before the general crop is in a fit state to be gathered, and this fallen and bruised fruit should never be mixed with that which is intended to be stored; all unsound fruit which may be found upon the trees at the time of gathering should also be rejected. Every care should be taken not to bruise the fruit when gathering, as *bruised fruit will not keep*.

GATHERING FRUIT

WHEN TO GATHER

Fruit which ripens in summer and autumn should invariably be gathered just a shade before it is absolutely ripe ; thus gathered, it is better in quality and higher flavoured than when picked absolutely ripe. But this must not be carried too far. A single day before they are perfectly ripe suffices with peaches and similar delicate stone fruit, a week for apples and pears ; but cherries are gathered only when completely ripe. Apples and pears which arrive at complete maturity in winter, are best gathered at the moment when the leaves begin to fall. Late-keeping fruit should be left on the trees as long as possible, so that it may increase in weight and improve in flavour. To keep well, fruit must be picked at just the right time, and it must, therefore, be carefully watched. It is better to lose a few apples through falling from the trees than to gather late-keeping varieties too soon. In the latter case they will shrivel and lose their flavour when stored. Fruit that has been damaged by insects or

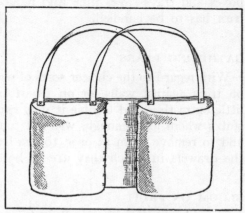

HOME-MADE FRUIT-PICKING BAG.

fungus will drop a considerable time before other fruit and this must not be taken as an indication that the sound fruit is ripe. Fallen immature fruit is best gathered up and burnt. Windfalls, the first fully-mature fruits, which drop, are usable if gathered immediately, but if left lying on the ground, the bruises sustained in falling quickly develop and the fruit soon begins to decay.

PICKING UTENSILS

There are so many patent kinds of picking bags, buckets and baskets on the market that it is difficult to know which to recommend. The main requirements are adequate padding to protect bruising and easy accessibility. For picking long-keeping apples and pears from high trees on ladders, some form of picking bag that can be worn like a coat with large pockets behind, leaving both hands free to pick, is as good as anything, and can be made out of two clean sacks and some straps or webbing (see diagram).

For picking long-keeping cooking apples and pears from low trees the " orchard box " is to be recommended because it can also be used for storing the fruit. The orchard box is designed to hold one bushel (40 lbs.) of apples without being quite full, and is sufficiently well ventilated to allow one box to be stacked on top of another. The boxes, if well wired, will last a long time.

For picking dessert pears and apples the shallow trays now used for gas-storage are to be recommended. These have bevelled slats, are well ventilated, and will stack for storing. They will take either one or two layers of all but the largest apples, but pears should always go in single layers. Picking straight into orchard boxes and trays saves time and reduces the number of times the fruit has to be handled.

GATHERING PEARS

With regard to the choicer sorts of pears, especially those growing on trees against walls, or on dwarf trees, it will well repay the little extra time and trouble it may cause, to gather these by their stalks where long enough, without touching them with the hand, and to remove them at once to the fruit room on the trays or in the drawers in which they are to be stored.

BLOOM ON FRUIT

There is on the skin of all fruit a secretion, more or less pronounced, commonly known as bloom. This, though less conspicuous on apples and pears than on plums and peaches, is nevertheless present, and its use is to protect the skin of the fruit from the ill effects of excessive moisture. While this bloom can be preserved, the fruit will never require wiping and will retain its full flavour and freshness. Handling soon removes the bloom.

APPLIANCES FOR GATHERING

These are various in form, but the main object in all is the same, namely, to detach from the tree fruit which is out of reach without having recourse to ladders, and, at the same time, to catch it in some receptacle attached to the fruit gatherer, or to hold it fast by some contrivance so as to prevent it falling to the ground when detached which would only result in bruise and injury. It is manifest that the principle on which all gatherers are constructed involves the use of a long pole with a cap or receptacle of some sort at the end of it. The simplest way of gathering fruit otherwise out of reach is to take a long stick with a hook at the end of it, and to pull the branches down to such an extent that the fruit may be easily picked, but this is not always practical, and great care must be used in the operation to prevent injury to the branches. The next step forward is a rod with a cup at one end, from the edge of which project sharp tongues of metal. The cup is thrust upward until the fruit rests in it, and a slight twist or pull is sufficient to detach the fruit, the stalk being caught between the sharp metal tongues attached to the cup and broken or severed by the twist or pull. Another fruit gatherer consists of a pole with a basket attached to it, constructed on the same principle and acting in a similar manner, the projections above the basket affording the means of detaching the fruit.

Contrivances similar to the above in general construction and purpose have long been used in this country for gathering wall fruit, such as apricots, peaches, nectarines, and plums, with as little injury as possible to the bloom that is on them. For the fruits just mentioned, a tin funnel is used, and this may be held in a ring of metal at the end of a long rod. The funnel is placed under the fruit and the edge brought gently against the fruit in order to detach it. The fruit then drops gently into the funnel and remains there for removal. Another gatherer of a similar kind has the edge of the cone or funnel notched in order to provide a better means of detaching fruit with tougher stalks, such as pears. This fruit gatherer is also useful for gathering mulberries. The pole must either be in the same straight line with the axis of the funnel, or, in other words, must have the funnel fixed directly on its end, or must be slightly inclined to it. It is better, perhaps, to have the ring that holds the funnel as near the rim as possible, and to attach it by a flange to a cap on the end of the handle, so that it may be brought to any desired angle to the handle and retained in that position.

GATHERING FOR MARKET

The main thing to remember when gathering fruit, especially when it is intended for market, is to avoid damaging it by rough handling. The value of the crop at market depends largely on the care in picking. Careful picking is essential, for if the fruit is roughly handled here, its keeping qualities will be injured, and all the care in the world in packing cannot remedy the initial damage. A valuable crop of fruit can be rendered valueless by careless handling. Good pickers know exactly which fruits to pick, and which to leave (unripe fruit must not be mixed with ripe) and how to grade as they pick. Fruit must never be gathered wet and the earlier it is gathered in the morning, the better.

See also the instructions devoted to the culture of particular fruits Chapter XIII.

STORING FRUIT

THE STORE ROOM

With most people the provision of a good fruit room is a difficult problem. A loft, a spare room in a gardener's cottage, or what is even more generally the case, a top attic in the dwelling-house, is often converted into a fruit room ; not because it is well adapted for the purpose, but because it is the only place that can be spared. As a matter of fact, all such places are definitely unsatisfactory storage rooms for fruit on account of the wooden floors, which make them too dry for storing most fruits.

A dark, well-aired, vault underground makes a good store room. Above ground, a room or substantial outhouse, preferably brick built, with a north aspect, is to be preferred, and if the room has a sloping roof this should slope towards the north. The roof and walls must be substantial and frost and rain proof, preferably of brick, and the floor, too, should be of brick, tiles, concrete, or earth. Though the fruit room should, for the most part, be kept dark, it is desirable that there should be one or two small windows in it, and some good and simple method of through ventilation, so that on dry days, and whenever necessary, the atmosphere may be completely changed. This is most important : for though it is not desirable to admit air unless needed, ventilation must never be neglected when the exhalations from the fruit have, in any way, tainted the air of the room.

Whenever there is a strong smell in the fruit room, we may be quite sure that something is wrong. The atmosphere should be moist *but never stagnant.* An even temperature of about 40° F. in winter and 45° F. in summer is most suitable for storing apples and pears. Ventilation during the first three weeks must be considerable, later it may be reduced. The store room should be fitted with a substantial broad dresser or bench running down the centre, with tiers of good, solid wood drawers underneath on one or both sides, according to its width. The top of this dresser should be provided with a deep ledge, about 2 inches deep on all sides, to prevent any fruit that may be laid on it from falling off. The depth of the drawers may vary according to requirements. Some may be deep for storing dry fruits that may be stacked one on top of the other and some shallow for storing fruits in single layers. The walls may be fitted up in similar manner with dressers all round with drawers underneath, or a series of tiers of drawers, ledges and shelves may be constructed according to individual requirements.

Any shelves should be fitted with ledges in the same manner as the dressers, to prevent fruit falling off. The store should be lined, the floor, sides and roof, with small-mesh wire-netting to keep out mice and rats.

Where long-keeping apples and pears are to be stored in orchard boxes or in " gas storage " trays, there is no need for any form of benching in the store. Where stacking is to take place, however, plenty of air-space should be allowed between the stacks.

Portable Hen-houses as Fruit Stores.—Small portable hen-houses make quite good stores for long-keeping apples, provided they are well ventilated, water-proof and vermin-proof, and the fruit is kept in orchard boxes or trays.

The advantage of this form of store is that it can be kept out of doors and can be opened up at night, to give ample ventilation, provided all openings are covered with fine-mesh wire. One word of warning is necessary, however. Hen-houses which have recently been creosoted should not be used for storing for fear of tainting the fruit.

HOW TO STORE FRUIT

APPLES AND PEARS

Unless properly stored, apples and pears will shrivel and deteriorate in flavour. They must be kept in an even temperature and should be looked over periodically (once a fortnight) so that any decaying ones may be removed ; if these are allowed to remain, they will contaminate the whole.

Pears, especially, need constant inspection, as once they become over-ripe, decay is rapid and quickly spreads to all surrounding fruit. It is not always easy to tell when pears are beginning to ripen. With several varieties, however, the skin becomes a golden yellow or the tinge of red, if present, will become brighter. This may be taken as an indication that most of the fruit of these varieties is ready for eating. Above all, do not try to store kinds that are only intended for immediate consumption, and never endeavour to make even " storing " fruit last much beyond its " season."

There is evidence to show that long-keeping apples will last better in store if they are first stacked out of doors in orchard boxes or single-layer trays covered with a tarpaulin at night or if raining, for a week or ten days, to undergo the process known as " sweating." They can then be looked over carefully and fruits showing rots or cracks can be taken out.

Oiled Wraps.—There is no doubt that the use of oiled wraps for storing apples is to be recommended. The wraps are made in different sizes of tissue paper which has been treated with a flavourless mineral oil. Each fruit is folded in one of these wraps and then placed in the orchard box, single-layer tray, on the shelves or in the drawers of the store.*

Another method is to store the fruit on the floor of the fruit room, spread out upon dried fern leaves, and covered with similar leaves. Straw is sometimes substituted for the fern leaves, but this is not to be recommended as straw sometimes imparts an unpleasant flavour to the fruit, whereas fern leaves form an ideal bed.

Apples and pears may also be stored as follows :—

1. In baskets or hampers, lined with fern leaves or straw, but without any material between the layers of fruit. If the fruit is dry when placed in the baskets or hampers, and the store room of an even temperature, the fruit keeps very well in this manner. Fern leaves are preferable to straw for the reason mentioned above.

2. In boxes or casks with sawdust, bran, wheat-chaff, or oat-flights. But all these substances have drawbacks, and although useful for packing fruit in when travelling, they are not to be particularly recommended for storing purposes.

3. In boxes with dry sand or powdered charcoal.

4. In deep drawers, one upon another without any substance between them, or with sheets of paper or dried fern leaves between the layers.

5. In heaps in dark, well-aired vaults. In this way both apples and pears, in large quantities, may be well and easily kept, and if the vaults are sufficiently beneath the surface to exclude frost, the fruit will require no further protection and give but little trouble. The heaps should not be more than about 2 feet 6 inches high.

* Ordinary newspaper wraps have given quite good results in storage trials and are to be recommended in preference to no wraps.

GRAPES

Cut the grapes, when quite ripe, so that the laterals remaining below the bunches are about 9 inches long. These should be inserted into wine-bottles almost filled with water containing a few lumps of charcoal to keep it sweet. The bottles are then placed in racks or secured to the wall at an angle of 40° so that the grapes will hang naturally as if still on the vine.

The room in which they are stored must be kept cool and dark, but well aired. Bunches so kept will last almost into the new year.

COBNUTS AND FILBERTS

Cobnuts and filberts, to be stored for winter use, should be left on the trees until fully ripe, and then gathered on a dry day. They must be cleared of their husks, and thoroughly dried. They may then be packed in glazed earthen jars, tied down with coarse brown paper, and kept in a cool but frost-proof and dry cellar. Cobnuts and filberts keep best in this manner without their husks : but if the husks are to be preserved, the fruit must be left to stand for a night in open baskets, and should be well shaken to get rid of earwigs.

Many growers shake a little salt over the last layer of nuts before the jars are tied down.

WALNUTS

These should be harvested from the ground as soon as they fall. After removing the green outer husk, the crevices of the shells must be freed from every trace of fibre, as it is here that moulds begin to grow. The fibre can be easily removed by scrubbing the nuts with a soft nail-brush in water. The nuts should be removed from the water after a few moments, and spread out in single layers to dry at room temperature. The walnuts may then be stored in earthenware crocks filled with alternate layers of a storage medium consisting of equal quantities of common salt and slightly damp coconut fibre.

The crocks should be kept in a cellar as recommended for cobs and filberts.

All drawers, shelves, boxes, or jars containing fruit should be labelled every year as soon as the fruit is stored, so that the different sorts may be easily and readily known.

COLD STORAGE AND GAS STORAGE OF FRUIT

In recent years intensive research has been carried out under the auspices of the Food Investigation Board of the Department of Scientific and Industrial Research in various methods of keeping hardy fruit in cold storage chambers and in refrigerated gas-stores. Dr. Franklin Kidd and Dr. Cyril West have been mainly responsible for the success of these experiments, which have been conducted at the Low Temperature Station at Cambridge, and at the Ditton Laboratory, East Malling, near Maidstone, Kent.

From time to time the reports of these workers on the results of their experiments have been published in leaflet form by the Food Investigation Board and are obtainable from the Department of Scientific and Industrial Research, 16 Old Queen Street, Westminster, S.W.1.

The application of this work to commercial practice is seen in the relatively large number of cold-storage chambers and in the increasing number of refrigerated gas-storage chambers which are being used at the present time by commercial fruit-growers in the main fruit-growing areas in this country.

Owing to the relatively high cost of building and running these stores, they are mainly of interest at the present time to large commercial growers. The time may come, however, when small refrigerated gas-chambers for certain varieties of apples and pears will be worth considering even for comparatively small units.

Refrigerated gas-storage merely means the preservation of fruit in a gas-tight chamber to which oxygen can be admitted from the outer air by controlling the ventilation through an adjustable porthole and in which the temperature can also be controlled. The living fruit in the store absorbs oxygen and gives off carbon dioxide, and by keeping the proportions of these two gases at certain known concentrations and the store at a known temperature for the variety, the ripening of the fruit in the store can be slowed down to about half the speed it would normally take to ripen in air at the same temperature.

A lucid account of the latest findings on this subject will be found in Food Investigation Leaflet No. 6, " The Refrigerated Gas Storage of Apples," by Drs. Kidd and West, obtainable from The Secretary, Department of Scientific and Industrial Research, 16 Old Queen Street, Westminster, S.W.1.

CHAPTER X

MARKETING FRUIT

MARKET PACKAGES

The principal market packages of to-day are divided into two classes: 1, Returnable, and 2, Non-returnable. The former are a survival of the older market baskets, which are gradually being displaced by the more satisfactory non-returnable.

RETURNABLE

Returnable packages are those which are usually forwarded by the salesman to the grower, to be returned full of fruit. This is quite the reverse of their early and original use when they were supplied by the grower and returned to him from the market. Returnables still in use include—

Half-barrel.—This is still used for large cooking apples, both as a returnable and as a non-returnable package.

Sieve or Bushel Basket.—This is the largest and strongest of the old returnable baskets, still in general use for cooking apples and pears.

Half-sieve or Half-bushel Basket.—This is one of the handiest of the old returnable baskets and is still frequently used for the better-class apples and pears, various stone fruits, and gooseberries.

Strike.—This is slightly over the quarter bushel, may be used for cherries, currants, damsons, gooseberries, and plums.

Flat.—The flat basket with a lid is useful for dessert apples and cobnuts, and a small-sized flat basket is frequently used for grapes.

Wicker-handle Basket.—These are used in several sizes, particularly for grapes.

Peach Box.—This is made in three depths and is used for sending up various kinds of specially choice fruits.

NON-RETURNABLE

Non-returnable packages are, in many ways, far more convenient than the old returnable baskets, particularly so in the case of the more delicate soft fruits, as the complete package can then be disposed of intact, and although there are certain disadvantages to their general use, they are gradually taking the place of returnables.

Chip Baskets.—These are now manufactured in all sizes to contain fruit up to 12 lb. in weight.

Chip Bonnets No. 1 *and No.* 2 (½ bushel and ¼ bushel).

Chip, Waxed Paper or Paper Pulp Punnets No. 1 *and No.* 2 (capacity 75 and 160 cubic inches).

Veneer Boxes No. 1 (bushel), *No.* 2 (24 lb.), *No.* 3 (12 lb.) *and No.* 4 (6 lb.).

Apple Box (2,277 cubic inches) ; ½ *Box* (1,174·5 cubic inches) ; *and* ¼ *Box* (612·5 cubic inches).

No. 1 *Tray* (single layer) (724·5 cubic inches).

No. 2 *Tray* (double or treble layer) (1,035 cubic inches).

Following the cultural details regarding each particular fruit will be found particulars as to which are the most suitable packages.

CHAPTER XI

EXHIBITING AT COMMERCIAL FRUIT SHOWS

In commercial fruit shows the schedule of points on the judges' score card for apples and pears usually allots from forty to fifty points for packing, as against from fifty to sixty points for the fruit itself. Hence, however good a crop of fruit one may have, it is not much use entering it for a commercial show without having previously visited one to see how the packing is done. If this is not possible, the next best thing is to get the county horticultural advisory officer to come and demonstrate the various packs, and to advise on the most suitable for the particular classes in which the entries are to be made.

Each show committee usually sends out a schedule of classes giving regulations and hints for packing, and these should be followed to the letter. Some show committees provide the empty packages in which the fruit is to be packed, but where this is not done, all packing materials such as sieves, half-sieves, barrels, the wood for boxes, half-boxes and trays, cleats, nails, lining paper, corrugated liners, woodwool and wraps can be bought from any good horticultural sundriesman to the specifications given in the show schedule. It is very important that the packages and packing material should comply in every detail with the particulars given in the schedule, and if there is any doubt on the point, it is wise to write to the show secretary about it well in advance of the packing time.

118

In the same way, all the material needed for packing should be got in at least a month before the show.

SELECTING THE FRUIT

Apples for showing should be allowed to hang on the tree as long as possible in order that the process of ripening shall continue under natural conditions to the last moment. Protection from south-west gales is important, and for this purpose " hop-lewing " made of coir yarn netting in 6-foot widths makes a very good temporary shelter for bush trees. All birds, especially jays, magpies, pigeons and pheasants should be kept away by fair means or foul.

If apples have to be picked some weeks before packing for the show, they should be stacked in orchard boxes or trays in the open or in an open shed, and covered at night with a tarpaulin, and protected from rats and mice.

For commercial shows it is as well to have from five to ten times as many fruits to choose from as will be ultimately required for packing.

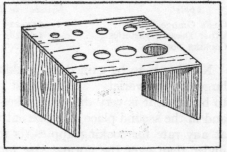

GRADING BOX FOR APPLES.

The least blemish will mean discarding the fruit, and even in the best regulated plantations the proportion of absolutely perfect fruits is usually very small indeed.

SIZE GRADING

There are now on the market a number of mechanical graders which will size the fruit according to diameter or weight. Where a comparatively small number of fruits have to be graded, the simplest method is to cut a number of circular holes out of a piece of three-ply wood, starting with a diameter of $2\frac{1}{4}$ inches and going up by quarter inches to $3\frac{1}{2}$ inches.

This board is then nailed on to two standard or half-standard box ends as in the diagram, and the apple to be graded is simply passed downwards from above through each hole in turn until it exactly fits.

When size-grading, all the apples should be passed through the grader facing in the same direction, either all eye-downwards or all eye-upwards.

Size-grading by eye only from a specimen fruit is even more simple, but unless this operation is done by the same person, there is likely to be a good deal of variation in the grade. In size-grading, the smaller the package to be filled the greater is the need for accuracy in size-grading. Thus for single-layer trays requiring from twelve to twenty-four fruits according to the variety, the sizing should be accurate to within less than a quarter of an inch, whereas with sieve baskets and the barrel it is usually safe to allow a variation of nearly half an inch in diameter between the smallest and largest apple in each package.

The best commercial sizes for apples are as follows :—

Apple	" Standard Box." Number in Box	" Standard Half-box." Number in Box	Half-sieves, Sieves and Barrels. Diameter
Cox's Orange Pippin . . .	113–225	72–112	2¼ in.–2¾ in.
Other Dessert Varieties . .	150–188	72–100	2½ in.–2¾ in.
Cooking Sorts	80–120	—	3½ in. or over

Nothing is to be gained by packing fruits which are abnormally large for the variety. In the first place, if several packages have to be filled, it is very difficult to keep the size uniform throughout, and in the second place, the present tendency at commercial shows, at any rate for cooking apples, is to pack a size which is slightly under than over the normal size for the variety. With *Bramley's Seedling*, for example, a diagonal 2–2 pack in four layers giving 112 apples to the box is one of the most popular packs for commercial shows. For sieve baskets and for barrels, the larger sizes, 3½ inches upwards, can be used with advantage.

For trays, twenty-four apples 2¾ inch in diameter usually make the best pack, while with pears the number will vary from twelve to eighteen according to variety.

GRADING FRUIT FOR UNIFORMITY OF COLOUR

Since most schedules award the same number of points for uniformity of colour as for uniformity of size, it is important to keep the fruit from different plantations separate before packing, since different manurial or cultural treatment may produce quite different colour and skin finish.

SKIN COLOUR AND FINISH

The fruit should be entirely free from blemishes. Russetting in apples is becoming rather unpopular with judges, with the exception of *Cox's Orange Pippin*, in which a certain amount of russetting is natural to the variety. The skin must not be greasy. Apples for commercial shows in this country are never polished, but varieties such as *Rival* which have a natural bloom should retain it in the show package.

It is not always easy to know the best colour for any one variety. With *Cox's Orange Pippin* the specimens should not be too dark in colour, a mixture of red and yellow, and a limited amount of russet being popular at the present time for that variety.

Cooking apples need not necessarily be green, since some markets prefer them red, but whatever colour is chosen should be typical of the variety, e.g. *Crimson Bramley* should not be shown in a *Bramley Seedling* class.

INTERNAL CONDITION

Two physiological troubles known as Bitter Pit and Water Core are apt to develop very quickly in some varieties of apple after they have been picked, especially after a season of climatic contrasts such as drought followed by very heavy rainfall or by excessive artificial watering (see page 173).

Apart from these particular troubles, the general condition of the apple or pear should be sound, not so immature as to be green where it should be coloured, nor so over-mature as to wrinkle when it is pressed with the fingers.

Pears are particularly treacherous in this respect, and should always be shown at an earlier stage in their development than would be advisable for apples.

PACKING POINTS

STANDARD BOXES

The packages are usually sent in the flat, each box consisting of two end pieces, two or four side pieces, two top pieces, two bottom pieces and four cleats. These constituent parts are in three different thicknesses, the ends being the strongest, then the sides, whilst the tops and bottoms are made of very thin wood which gives with the bulge of the pack and so forms a natural spring to keep the fruit in place. It is best to make a rough framework to hold the two ends upright while the sides are nailed on, touching each other in the centre. The bottom pieces are then nailed on, also touching in the centre, with two of the four cleats, the other two cleats being kept for nailing down the tops when the box has been packed. Show boxes are usually arranged so that the first layer to be packed ultimately becomes the top layer when the box is opened. The idea is that the weight of the remaining layers will keep the first layer firmly in position and it will, therefore, look the best when the box is judged.

Care must be taken to see that the packing material used is as per schedule. Usually a "liner" of corrugated paper is put first into the empty box, care being taken that the corrugated side is downwards, away from the fruit. The box is then lined with two strips of good quality white lining paper of a kind specially made for the purpose, the dimensions of which are 23 inches long by 18 inches wide. These two lining papers should slightly overlap at the bottom of the box, and should cover the whole of the two sides, the remainder being folded outwards until the box has been packed, when they are folded back again over the fruit. Two more pieces of lining paper, 18 inches long by 11 inches wide, are used in the same way to line the ends of the box. In most commercial shows some form of label giving the entry number must be nailed on inside the box before packing begins. The end of the box furthest from the packer is then raised slightly for ease of packing. For exhibition work the first layer to be packed is left unwrapped, all the remaining layers being wrapped. When the box is packed the last layer of apples to be put in will bulge out slightly over the top of the box, and in order to get the top on without injuring the apples some form of press will be necessary.

The lining papers are folded inwards over the fruit, a second "liner" of corrugated paper is laid on these, with the corrugations upwards, and the two top pieces are put in position. The box is then placed in the press, which grips the ends of the two pieces at either side while the cleats are nailed down. The box is next turned upside down and the word "TOP" is written or stencilled on what was originally the underside. Finally, a second label bearing the entry number and class number is tacked on to the end of the box.

Box packing is an exact process depending for its success on accurate size-grading and careful alignment of the fruit in the box. Full particulars of the various types of pack used for different sizes of apples are given in the special leaflets on the subject published by the Ministry of Agriculture and Fisheries.

Neat wrapping of the fruits in tissue-paper wraps of the correct size for the variety is an important item in box packing. A good deal of practice both in wrapping and packing is advisable before undertaking the packing for commercial shows.

STANDARD BOXES AND TRAYS

The most popular " packs " for dessert apples in standard boxes are those known as the 3–2 diagonal in five layers.

When sending boxes off to the show great care should be taken to see that they are stacked on their sides and are not allowed to rest on the thin, bulging boards which form the top and bottom of the boxes.

STANDARD HALF-BOXES

Whereas the standard box holds approximately 40 lb. net weight of fruit or one bushel, the standard half-box holds roughly 20 lb. or half a bushel. The standard box is used for cooking and for dessert apples and pears, but the half-box is used only for dessert apples and for small dessert pears. It is put together and pre-pared for packing in the same way as the box, but there is the big difference in packing which makes the half-box much easier to pack than the standard box. In the box there is an art in packing the apples, so that those in the centre of the box on the top layer project further from the top than those at the end, thus making what is known as an even " bulge " or curve to the surface of the pack. The object of the bulge is to ensure that the apples are held firmly in position and do not rattle about in the box during transit.

In the half-box, a bulge is not considered strictly necessary, provided the whole of the top layer projects from $\frac{1}{4}$ to $\frac{1}{2}$ an inch above the level of the box after packing. This is to ensure that the fruit will not sink below the level of the box during transit. Not only does this make the packing of the half-box much easier, but it means that the top pieces can be nailed down under cleats without the aid of a box-press.

In packing for show, in half-boxes, the first three layers of fruit are wrapped, the last layer to be packed is left unwrapped and remains the top layer. As soon as the two top pieces have been nailed on, the word " TOP " is clearly marked on them, and not on the underside as in the case of the box.

The most popular packs for the half-box are the 2–2 diagonal packs in four layers.

STANDARD No. 1 TRAYS

The tray is nailed together in the same way as described for boxes and half-boxes. There are several ways of preparing the tray for commercial show packing, one of the most popular methods being as follows :

First put a thin layer of fine-grade woodwool in the bottom of the tray and cover it with a piece of good white lining paper cut to the required size. Next make narrow pads about $\frac{3}{4}$ of an inch thick of rolls of corrugated paper or woodwool wrapped in pure white tissue paper or in good lining paper. The pads should be the same length as the ends and sides of the tray, and are placed all round the inside to protect the fruit. In packing trays for commercial shows the object is to fill the space with fruit without overcrowding. Particular attention should be paid to meticulous accuracy of size-grading and to the exact alignment of the fruit in their rows.

Another popular method of packing apples in trays is to put each apple in a small crinkly paper cup, and then to place the apples gently but firmly in straight lines across the tray. With *Cox's Orange Pippin*, a size-grade of $2\frac{3}{4}$ inches gives a good pack with six rows of apples, four apples in each row, making a total of 24 fruits in each tray.

Conical-shaped apples, such as *Worcester Pearmain*, are usually placed in the cups on their sides, coloured side uppermost, with the eye pointing forwards in the direction of the end of the tray. Round apples, like *Cox's Orange Pippin*, are either placed in the paper cups on their sides, coloured side uppermost, with eyes pointing sideways, towards one side of the tray, or on their stalk ends, with eyes pointing vertically upwards. A sheet of lining paper is then placed on the top of the apples, and a layer of woodwool or a liner of corrugated paper, corrugation upwards, is laid over the whole. The tray can then be lidded in the ordinary way with or without cleats according to the type of tray provided, using cement-coated nails when possible.

SIEVES AND HALF-SIEVES

To prepare the sieve or half-sieve for show packing, a circle of thick blue lining paper or of cardboard is put in the bottom of the basket, and a collar made of similar material is put round the whole of the inside. Three pieces of good white lining paper, cut to the right size to allow a fair overlap at top and bottom, are then folded neatly down to line the sides of the basket, leaving sufficient outside to cover the fruit when packed. The apples are then " ringed in " in layers, usually with the stalk pointing outwards, and the eye pointing inwards towards the centre of the basket. The skill in " ringing in " consists in finding the best size of apple to give not less than the minimum net weight required, and at the same time to fill the basket and give it the right amount of " crown."

For show work the baskets should be new and should be all of the same dimensions. When the basket is packed, the white lining papers are folded neatly back over the fruit, another circle of blue lining paper or of cardboard is laid over the top, and a good thick pad of woodwool is fastened on with two or more pointed hazel wands crossing each other diagonally and stuck through the wicker-work.

The fruit should be well up to the rim of the baskets, and the " crown " should be well marked, but not excessively high.

BARRELS

Barrels, or " half-barrels," as they are usually called, are sent ready made up and for show purposes should be new. They are prepared for packing in the same way as baskets, but as they are generally sent without lids, means must be found to fasten on the woodwool which covers the top layer of fruit when packed.

The method of doing this is to drill three pairs of holes 3 inches apart at equal distances round the circumference of the barrel, 2 or 3 inches below the rim. Now knot in three short loops of rope, each loop about 8 inches long, through the holes, knots on the inside of the barrel. Drill one more hole between two of the loops and knot in a yard length of rope. When the barrel has been packed and covered over with a really thick wad of woodwool, take the single piece of rope, pass it through the three loops, drawing them tight over the pad of woodwool, and fasten all together.

LABELLING

When packing for commercial shows, no matter what the package may be, particular attention should be given to the directions supplied for labelling the exhibits. In many cases a printed card or label bearing the class number and exhibit number has to be nailed into the box, tray, basket or barrel just below the inside top edge, and unless this is done before packing begins, it is often impossible to do it afterwards. As failure to do this might involve disqualification of the exhibit, it is worth taking special precautions to see that the rule is observed.

All packages for show have to be labelled externally, printed labels usually being supplied by the show committee.

Intending exhibitors for Commercial shows should consult the leaflets published by the Ministry of Agriculture and Fisheries giving particulars with regard to the method of wrapping and packing and the number of fruits comprising the various " diagonal " packs.

SOFT FRUITS FOR EXHIBITION

PACKING CHERRIES AND SOFT FRUITS FOR EXHIBITION

Commercial show committees usually supply standard chips or punnets, but great care should be taken to conform in every particular with the rules given in the show schedule on the subject of lining materials and net weight of fruit. Exhibits are frequently disqualified before the judges see them, through neglect of one of these rules.

The packages may be prepared and lined the night before the show. The fruit is best picked as early as possible on the morning of the show day, but must not be packed until it is dry. At least twice as much should be picked as will be needed to fill the packages. All the fruits in each package should be identical in size, shape, and colour, and completely free from blemish of any kind.

In commercial shows of these fruits there is generally a rule against any form of "fancy packing." By "fancy packing" is meant the placing of individual fruits in layers, with all the stalks facing the same way. Such packing is very attractive and, where the rules allow, it should always be practised. Red currants always look best when the trusses are all laid in the same way, and in these fruits length of truss and size of individual berry score heavily.

Brightness of colour in the fruit is important in currants, raspberries, loganberries, blackberries and strawberries. In all these fruits and also in gooseberries, size of fruits is important, but it must be remembered that uniformity of size and colour is almost equally important, because of its effect on the general appearance of the fruit in each package. The package should be filled, but not too full to travel safely to market, and should be fastened down and carefully labelled with the special labels issued by the schedule committee.

Fruit shown on plates, either singly or in collections, requires smaller quantities to choose from, but just because the number of fruits is limited, there is all the more need for deadly precision in sizing and in selecting fruits that are uniform in colour, skin quality, and freedom from blemish.

CHAPTER XII

THE CONTROL OF PESTS AND DISEASES

ORCHARD HYGIENE

There are certain measures of general orchard hygiene which, if attended to, will simplify the control of pests and diseases. On the other hand, neglect of these measures is bound to make spraying much more expensive and considerably less effective than it should be.

When planning the layout of a new plant of fruit, trees and bushes should be spaced wide enough apart to allow sun and air to reach them on all sides. Overcrowding of trees or branches leads to an unhealthy condition, predisposing the tree to attacks of pests and diseases. In old orchards, where the trees are so close that they cannot be properly sprayed, the first principle of orchard hygiene is to grub out some of the trees, remove dead and dying branches from others, trim up the hedges, and so let the sun and air into the orchard.

Mention has already been made (page 92) of the importance of planting different fruits separately. One of the chief reasons for this is the difficulty of spraying mixed plantings of fruit.

Thus, when strawberries, currants, or gooseberries are planted under pear trees or apple trees, the fruits on the undercrop may be spoilt in appearance by receiving the drip from the spray given to the top fruits. Again, apples and plums are a bad combination from the spraying point of view, the plums being in full bloom when the apples should be sprayed with fairly strong lime-sulphur.

The part played by manuring in preserving the growth-balance in a tree has already been referred to. Unsuitable manuring, in disturbing this balance, may make the tree more susceptible to attack by diseases or pests. In general it may be said that frequent and heavy applications of nitrogenous manures, without the right amount of potash to keep the balance, tend to promote sappy, rapid, and unripened growth. Such growth seems more readily to fall a prey to certain pests and diseases, and where this is the case, much good may often be achieved by withholding all forms of nitrogenous manures, and by applying potash to restore the balance of nutrition.

MECHANICAL METHODS OF PEST CONTROL

Trapping.—Trapping is one of the oldest methods of pest control, and for some pests it is very effective. For instance, the wingless females of the Winter Moths can be prevented from laying eggs on the twigs and branches by the application of a grease-band to the trunk of the tree. Similarly, the Clay-Coloured Weevil and other wingless weevils of similar type can be kept away from newly inserted grafts on which they like to feed, by putting a narrow band of a specially-prepared grease round the stem of the tree (see Apple, page 155). Hay or sacking bands have long been used for the trapping of the Codling Moth Caterpillar, and a more recent development of this type of trap is a band treated with special chemicals.

Pruning.—The removal of unwanted branches, and the cutting out of cankers on apple trees, or of dead wood bearing the silver-leaf fungus, are important mechanical measures of pest and disease control.

Poultry.—Poultry has often been recommended as a means of controlling certain pests that pass part of their life-cycle in the soil. Poultry certainly do eat large quantities of insects, but they can hardly be relied upon to exercise more than a partial control on any specific pest.

Natural Control.—Were it not for the combined influence of parasites, predacious insects, insectivorous animals and the vagaries of the weather, it is probable that man would never be able to hold his own in the struggle with insects. Owls, rooks and other birds eat insects, and among the predacious insects may be mentioned Ladybird beetles and their larvæ, feeding on greenfly, Wasps feeding almost entirely on flies and grubs, and a host of Ichneumon Flies, which are true parasites in the sense that they actually lay their eggs in the bodies of other insects. Attempts have often been made to breed certain types of parasites for the purpose of controlling particular pests by biological means, but in this country, with one or two exceptions, little success has attended such efforts. Some plants are by nature immune from, or highly resistant to, particular pests or diseases, and by careful selection the plant-breeder can sometimes succeed in combining disease-resistance with the good qualities of certain of the more susceptible varieties.

SPRAYING—TYPES OF SPRAY

Winter Washes.—Before the advent of tar-oils, winter washes were used largely as part of the orchard hygiene to remove moss and lichen. Tar-oils are now used almost exclusively to destroy

APPLE SAWFLY.

1. Adult Sawfly (inset, natural size).   2. Larva.   3. Apples scarred
by larva.   4. Attacked fruitlets.

From the Ministry of Agriculture and Fisheries Advisory Leaflet No. 13.

Knapsack spraying machine.   Four-gallon tank hand pump.

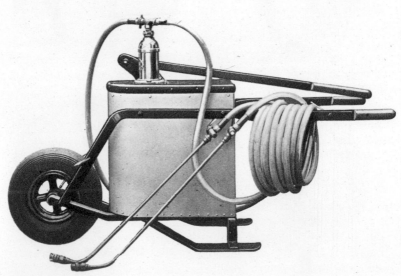

Photos by courtesy of]   [*W. Weeks & Son, Ltd.*

Small Wheel-barrow-type hand pump.

SPRAYING MACHINERY.

the overwintering eggs of Greenfly, Apple Sucker, Scale Insects, and other pests. They will also burn up moss and lichen, but have little or no effect on the eggs of Capsid Bugs or Red Spider. These can be killed with petroleum-oil sprays, which, however, are not harmful to the eggs of Greenfly or the Apple Sucker. In some cases, therefore, two winter washes may have to be administered in the same season. Winter washes should be applied as a drenching spray with sufficient force to ensure that every twig and bud is adequately covered.

Cover Washes.—Fungous diseases are carried about chiefly by spores which are wind- water- or insect-borne. When a spore falls on a leaf, it must first germinate, sending out a small, delicate, root-like extension before the leaf can be infected with the disease. If the leaf has been previously coated with a protective covering of a fungicide such as sulphur or copper, the spores that fall on it are killed as soon as they start to germinate. Again, if the leaf is covered with a stomach-poison insecticide, e.g., lead arsenate, insects with biting or chewing mouth-parts, such as caterpillars or beetles that eat pieces out of the leaf or the fruit, will die before they can do much damage. Cover washes provide these protective coatings of fungicide or of stomach-poison insecticide.

Contact Insecticides.—Many types of insect, for instance Capsids, Aphids, Scale Insects, Apple Sucker, and Red Spider, are unable to chew, but they are provided with mouth-parts specially adapted for piercing and sucking. These creatures bore through the surface layers of the leaf, and suck the sap from the inner tissues, so that they remain unaffected by cover washes such as lead arsenate. For this type of insect it is necessary to use a poison like nicotine, which kills when it comes into direct *contact* with the body. Contact washes of this kind, to be effective, must not only penetrate the hiding places of the insects, but must actually wet the skin of the insects themselves. To this end a drenching spray must be applied with plenty of pressure. Cover washes, on the other hand, should, in theory, be applied as a fine misty spray to ensure an even covering of the leaves. In practice, however, it is often necessary to effect a working compromise between these two extremes, and to combine stomach-poisons, contact insecticides, and fungicides in one so-called " omnibus " wash. Moreover, economy and rapidity of spraying is further increased by applying this type of mixed wash at high pressure as a driving spray, and modern developments in spraying machinery are largely directed towards this end.

I—F.G.

DUSTING

Dusting can be done much more quickly and easily than wet spraying, and there are times in the best-regulated plantations when a coating of dust, applied rapidly, will make all the difference between success and failure in controlling a sudden outbreak of pest or disease. Yet dusting cannot be relied upon as the chief means of applying insecticides and fungicides, except possibly in a small garden where it can be done very frequently. Dust is more easily washed off by rain than a wet spray, and can be applied only when there is little or no wind. It is apt to drift a long way in a breeze, and may get on to plants for which it is not intended, and damage them.

In spite of these objections, the possession of a dusting machine is a valuable form of insurance for all fruit-growers against some sudden outbreak of pest or disease.

SPRAYING MACHINERY

If fruit trees are to be kept healthy and in a well-balanced condition, the control of diseases and pests must be a routine operation in the garden or plantation, and spraying an essential part of that routine. Hence the selection of the very best spraying tackle is a matter deserving of serious consideration, and one that is not altogether as simple as might appear.

In choosing a spraying machine, the main points to look for are as follows :

Suitability of Type of Machine for the Purpose.—For gardens and for small areas of young trees or bushes up to 2 or 3 acres in extent, one of the many types of hand-operated machines should meet the requirements. Larger trees, to be sprayed effectively, will need a machine giving high pressure and a large output of spray, and this entails some form of power-driven machine. In selecting such a machine, the main choice to be made is between a centrally-placed stationary pumping plant and some form of portable or mobile spraying outfit. This is a matter that will require careful thought, consideration being given to the slope of the ground, the nature of the soil, the distance at which the trees are planted, and the whereabouts of the water-supply.

For instance, a mobile, motor-driven outfit, drawn by horse or tractor, the men following behind and spraying as the machine goes up and down the rows of trees, may be ideal in flat grass orchards, with trees widely spaced, and water close at hand. But for a cultivated plantation on sloping ground or in sticky clay, such a machine might prove quite unsuitable, because it would either skid out of control, going downhill, or stick fast in the mud. Again, where long rows of large trees have to be sprayed, far from the water-supply, a mobile spraying machine may have to spend too much time going back to the mixing station for refilling. In such cases a portable machine, operated at the headland in conjunction with overground steel mains, might be more economical.

Capacity of the Pump.—This means the output of spray-fluid in gallons per minute, or per hour. To be most effective, spraying should be done in the shortest possible time, and the period during which any area of fruit can be efficiently sprayed is mainly governed by the output of the machine. Increasing the number of men in the spray gang does not increase the output if the machine is already working to full capacity. It is always wise to allow for a certain amount of reserve capacity in the pump, so that more men can be put on if required, and so that provision is made for growing trees.

Power to Drive the Pump.—In choosing a hand-operated machine, the available manual labour should be taken into account, having in view the desirability of working the pump to full capacity without undue strain on those who do the pumping. Similarly, with a power outfit, it is unwise to get a machine which has a powerful set of pumps, with an engine incapable of sustaining the work over a long period.

Simplicity of Design.—A spraying machine of any kind needs constant attention and an occasional overhaul to maintain its efficiency. Accessibility of the various working parts is, therefore, an important point to be borne in mind, and rapid service in the replacement of spare parts should be guaranteed.

Pressure Gauge.—The machine should be fitted with a reliable pressure gauge, for this is the only readily available test of efficiency. When poor pressure is obtained at the nozzle although the gauge shows good pressure, the trouble must be looked for at some point between the pump and the nozzle. It is often due to a " bottle-neck," such as would be produced by a joint or tap with a bore too small for the rest of the system.

Suitability of Materials of Manufacture.—In these days when so many different chemicals are used for spraying, it is important that those parts of the machine that come into close contact with the spray should be made of materials that will withstand corrosion. The tank should be made of well-galvanized iron, or of wood.

TYPES OF SPRAYING MACHINE

Spraying machines vary in price according to size and design. The following brief notes should serve as a rough guide to intending purchasers of new machines.

HAND-OPERATED MACHINES

DOUBLE-ACTION SYRINGE TYPE

This is one of the most efficient forms of the syringe pump. A length of rubber piping is attached to the syringe, and is suspended in a bucket or tub containing the spray. The pump is operated by both hands and is of a double-action type, giving a continuous spray. The pump gives a pressure of about 60 lb. per square inch.

KNAPSACKS

(a) *Internal and External Pump Types.*—The usual tank capacity of this type of machine is about 3 gallons. No pressure gauges are fitted, but pressures up to about 70 lb. can be obtained.

(b) *Pneumatic Type.*—This type is cylindrical in shape, and fitted with an air pump for charging the container with compressed air. One of the chief advantages claimed for this type of machine is that pumping is done before spraying begins, thereby leaving both hands free for working. The most obvious disadvantage is that the pressure is relatively low. The most popular size holds about 4 gallons.

BUCKET PUMPS

The main advantage of this type over the knapsack is its larger tank-capacity of about 6 gallons, an advantage, however, which naturally detracts from its portability. The pumps vary a good deal, but only comparatively low pressures can be obtained. A double-action pump or a large air-chamber for single-action pumps seems to be desirable.

The types of spraying machines so far described can hardly be regarded as ideal for fruit-tree spraying, although they can be used quite satisfactorily for small pieces of bush fruit, or for espaliers, cordons, and low-headed bushes in very early stages of their growth. But for established fruit trees, the pressures obtainable on these types of spraying machine, and the capacity of the tanks, fall below the minimum requirements for really efficient spraying. For such trees a choice should be made from one of the more highly-priced and more powerful machines.

SPRAYING MACHINERY

BARREL PUMPS

In this class, the pump unit, including the agitator, can be clamped on to any spray-receptacle, barrel, tank, etc., thus saving the cost of a tank. The pump closely resembles those mounted on the wheeled types of spraying machine, and gives pressures of from 150–200 lb. Its advantage lies in its relative cheapness and portability.

HEADLAND PUMPS

In this class the pump is usually mounted on a platform with or without wheels for use in conjunction with rainwater tubs, galvanized tanks or other spray receptacles placed in suitable positions in the orchard. The mixed spray is poured into the receptacle, whence it is sucked up by the pump through a short length of hose, and delivered through a longer hose pipe to the lance. The twin pumps are usually designed to maintain an average pressure of from 150–200 lb., and are of the hand-lever type to be worked by one or two men.

WHEELED TYPE OF SPRAYING MACHINES

This class contains some of the most suitable types of hand-operated spraying machines for fruit-tree spraying, where larger trees are concerned. Tank capacity varies from 12 to 40 gallons. Pressures of from 150 lb. up to 300 lb. are claimed, and on most of them a pressure of 200 lb. can be obtained with an output of from 1 to 2 gallons per minute. It should be realized, however, that to keep up the maximum pressure on these machines throughout a day's spraying involves hard physical labour, and to carry out the spraying properly, there should be one man on the pump, and one on the lance. Most types of hand-operated machines have a pump-handle action. This has the obvious disadvantage that the natural tendency to work with a short instead of a full stroke will ultimately result in uneven cylinder wear. Purchasers should insist on having a pressure gauge, since it is impossible to spray efficiently unless a constant pressure is maintained.

PORTABLE POWER-SPRAYING MACHINES

For orchard trees of any size, or where fruit is grown for market on any scale, there is no doubt that power-sprayers are more efficient, and in the long run more economical than any type of hand-operated machine. Portable power-sprayers can be used as stationary units in conjunction with overground steel mains, coupled

133

together with flexible rubber joints, or they can be used as mobile units, to be drawn through the orchard.

(a) *Small Power Sprayers.*—The pumps on these small machines are operated by a 2- or a 3-h.p. engine, either air- or water-cooled, with two-throw high-pressure pump, giving pressures between 250 and 350 lb. for use with up to two nozzles. Their tank capacity varies from 50 to 100 gallons, and they can be drawn by horse or tractor.

(b) *Medium-sized Sprayers.*—These larger machines have a 4- or 5-h.p. engine with a three-throw high-pressure pump, giving 300 to 450 lb. pressure, and with an output of about 500 gallons an hour for use with up to six nozzles. Their tank capacity is 80 to 180 gallons, and they can be drawn by horse or by tractor.

(c) *Large Power Sprayers.*—These large machines usually have an 8- to 10-h.p. engine, giving up to 550 lb. pressure, and with an output of from 800 to 1,200 gallons an hour for use with up to twelve nozzles. Their tank capacity is from 100 to 250 gallons, and they are drawn by tractor.

STATIONARY ENGINES

For large acreages of fruit it may be economical to put in a central spraying plant. For this purpose four-throw pumps are used, driven by petrol, Diesel, or electric motor. Very high pressures up to 700 lb. are obtainable, with an output up to 3,000 gallons an hour, for use with up to sixteen leads. For these plants a system of underground pipes is necessary to take the spray-fluid from the mixing-tank at the central plant through the orchards. The cost of the pumps is proportional to those of the largest portable power-spraying machines, but allowance must be made, also, for the additional cost of laying down underground mains, and for a system of stand-pipes for hose attachment.

HOSES, LANCES, GUNS AND NOZZLES

Hoses.—Where tar-oils are to be used, it is advisable to buy rubber hoses guaranteed suitable for this purpose. The hoses get very muddy in wet weather, and this adds to their weight, so that, within reason, the shorter the hose, the easier the work.

Lances and Guns.—Lances are made in all shapes and sizes, and it is wise to consult the local advisory officers as to the type of lance that is likely to be most suitable for the purpose. For efficient spraying, the lance should be light and not too long, a good average length being about 4 feet 6 inches. Spray-guns are usually shorter

134

than this because they can be adjusted to project a narrow cone of spray to a considerable distance when required. Spray-guns have certain advantages for the high-pressure power-spraying of large trees with a narrow, driving jet of spray. When used with the larger hand-operated machines, they are not satisfactory because, to be effective, they must put out so much wash that it is practically impossible for the man pumping to keep up the required pressure.

Nozzles.—Nozzles vary a great deal, and are constantly being improved upon. Here, again, the expert should be consulted. The chief requirement is a nozzle that can easily be stripped for cleaning, since a blocked nozzle is one of the bugbears of spraying. Moreover, the nozzle should have the minimum of adjustable components. Nozzle discs can generally be bought in three groups of sizes for giving a fine and soft, a medium, or a very driving spray, according to the nature of the wash to be used and the job to be done. The use of two or more nozzles on one lance has now become popular. These " multiple " nozzles, when properly used, are found to save labour and speed up spraying without increasing the consumption of wash. When ordering spray accessories, spare discs and washers should not be forgotten.

TYPES OF DUSTING MACHINE

There are many types of dust-blowers, from the small hand-bellows to the large motor-driven outfit. The main points to look for are convenience of manipulation and uniform distribution of the dust.

KNAPSACKS

These machines are carried on the back, and are worked by a handle at the side in the ordinary way, the outlet pipe being held in the other hand. A double-action bellows is a useful refinement, ensuring more even distribution of dust. A double-outlet lance can be fitted.

SMALL HAND-OPERATED ROTARY BLOWERS

These are specially useful for strawberries and low bushes, but are fatiguing and cumbersome when used for large bushes and trees. They are carried in front of the body, one hand turning a handle at the side, while the other hand guides the delivery tube. In this way a man can dust strawberries quite efficiently while walking at an ordinary pace. A uniform distribution of dust is secured

135

by a fan-operated dust feed. A Y-piece can be fitted on the delivery tube for dusting two rows at once.

HAND-OPERATED ROTARY BLOWERS ON WHEELS

This is the same kind of machine as the small rotary blower just described, but with a larger capacity. Being on wheels, it can be moved about by one man while another turns the handle.

GEARED-DRIVE DUSTING OUTFITS

(a) *Horse-drawn.*—In these machines the fan is geared to the road-wheels, and blows the dust through flexible delivery tubes, each of which can be arranged to point in any direction. The dust " hopper " holds about 1 cwt. of dust. The road wheels are usually adjustable for width, and the machine is drawn by a horse or pony. Some makes are fitted with a freewheel clutch. The main criticism of this type of duster is that it cannot be geared sufficiently high. The price varies with size and type.

(b) *Motor-driven.*—These machines are capable of dusting large acreages very rapidly, but their purchase involves considerable capital outlay in addition to what is being spent on wet-spraying machinery. They can be recommended only for large farms where special circumstances, such as scarcity of water, would seem to indicate a real need for such an outfit.

SOME SPRAYING HINTS

Before the winter washing season begins in December, all spraying tackle should be thoroughly overhauled. The machine should be stripped to see whether any repairs are needed, and the hoses, lances and nozzles should be cleaned, repaired or renewed. A day or two before spraying begins, the tank should be partly filled with water, and the machine given a trial run to see that the engine, pump and agitator are all in working order. Washers may have to be renewed, or there may be some leaks to be mended in the rubber hoses. The strainer is one of the most important parts of the spraying machine, and since imperfect straining means repeated blocking of the nozzles, the strainer must be kept in good repair.

At the end of each day's spraying it is a wise plan to empty the tank and pump clean water through to wash out the pipes.

At the end of the winter spraying season the tank should be scrubbed out with weak caustic soda in readiness for the spring spraying.

SPRAY MATERIALS

The " owner-sprayer " should provide himself with a strong boiler-suit for spraying, and should always carry with him, when spraying, a supply of tools and spare washers. When there is any spraying to be done, it should be started in good time on account of the number of unforeseen hitches that usually occur. If a mixed spray has to be left standing in the tank for any length of time during the day, the pump should be worked for a few minutes before spraying begins again, to allow the agitator to mix up the spray. The liquid already in the hoses should be sprayed on to the ground.

In frosty weather, spraying should not be begun very early in the morning, or carried on very late in the day, in case the spray should freeze on the trees while still wet. In cold weather, drums containing spray fluid should be kept under cover, or be protected from frost.

When buying spray-materials, the " owner-sprayer " will find it much cheaper to buy in large rather than in small quantities, the price for small amounts being relatively high. If tar-oils or lime-sulphur are kept over from one season to the next, care should be taken to see that the container is rendered perfectly airtight.

CHIEF SPRAY MATERIALS EMPLOYED

TAR-OIL WASHES

These are emulsions (usually of the " miscible " type) containing certain selected grades and fractions of tar-distillate as the chief ingredients. They are used, normally, at 5 per cent. dilution, during the dormant season only. They are toxic to eggs of the Apple Sucker, Aphides, and, at higher concentrations, to those of the Winter Moth. They will remove Scale and Lichen and help to control Blossom Wilt.

PETROLEUM-OIL WASHES

Sometimes known as mineral-oil washes, these are emulsions of selected grades of petroleum-oils of the light lubricating type. They are used at 5 per cent. to 8 per cent. dilution at bud-break or even later to kill the winter eggs of Capsid Bugs and Red Spider.

Both the " miscible " oil and the " stock " or " mayonnaise " type of emulsion are obtainable. The former mixes more readily with water and is somewhat more convenient to use. Emulsions of special grades of highly-refined " water-white " oil are sometimes used at 1 per cent. dilution as summer sprays for Red Spider.

TAR-PETROLEUM MIXTURES

These are emulsions containing tar-distillate and petroleum oils, and are intended to do the work of both a tar-oil and a petroleum-oil wash in one operation. They are not recommended except for bush fruit, e.g., black currants.

D.N.C. WASHES

Sometimes referred to as D.N.O.C. washes, these are petroleum-oil emulsions incorporating a small amount of a nitro-cresol, usually a dinitro-ortho-cresol, the function of which is to kill the eggs of Apple Sucker and Aphis. They can be used as dual-purpose washes, replacing both petroleum- and tar-oil winter washes, and applied any time up to bud-break. Their wetting power is often indifferent and this must be borne in mind when using them.

THIOCYANATE-OIL WASHES

Like the D.N.C., these are dual-purpose washes and have the same uses. They are more expensive, but can be used later with safety.

LEAD ARSENATE (Poison)

This is obtainable as a powder, as a paste, and in a semi-liquid (so-called " colloidal ") form. The paste should contain at least 15 per cent., and the powder at least 30 per cent. of arsenic in the form of arsenic pentoxide. The paste is generally used at a dilution of 4 lb. and the powder, which is the most popular and convenient form, at 2 lb. per 100 gallons. It may be used alone or in combination with any spray-material other than soap or soap-containing preparations. Being heavy, it needs to be constantly agitated.

NICOTINE (Poison)

This is an alkaloid manufactured from tobacco. Sold with a guaranteed purity of 95 to 98 per cent. Used as a contact insecticide at the rate of 8 oz. per 100 gallons of spray (6 oz. when used against Greenfly only) for Capsid Bugs, small Caterpillars, Apple Sawfly eggs, Apple Sucker, and all kinds of Greenfly. It can be mixed with any other spray-material.

In the form of nicotine sulphate, it is employed as the active ingredient in many proprietary powder insecticides.

DERRIS PREPARATIONS

These are insecticides composed of finely-ground Derris root, or containing the powdered root or an extract of it as the active

138

ingredient. Derris is a tropical plant, the roots of which contain various chemical substances (such as rotenone) toxic to insects but non-injurious to warm-blooded animals. Purchasers of Derris insecticides should either ask for a declaration of the rotenone content or obtain only brands of guaranteed insecticidal efficiency.* Toxic to many classes of insects, e.g., Aphides, Capsids, Caterpillar, Derris is of especial value where a non-poisonous insecticide is required. The pure root may be mixed with any other spray.

LIME-SULPHUR

Lime-sulphur is a clear, amber-coloured solution, manufactured by boiling lime and sulphur together. It is most conveniently purchased ready-made in concentrated form. Such a concentrate should have a specific gravity of 1·3, be free from sludge and contain not less than 24 per cent. (weight in volume) of sulphur in the form of polysulphides. It is used as a fungicide for Scab, Mildew, etc., and as a contact insecticide for Red Spider and Big-Bud Mite. Lime-sulphur is compatible with any of the commonly-used insecticides but not with soap.

" COLLOIDAL " SULPHUR

This is a suspension of sulphur of very fine particle-size. It usually contains approximately 40–50 per cent. elementary sulphur. Sometimes it is used as an alternative to lime-sulphur, because, at the dilutions recommended, it is generally non-injurious to fruit trees and bushes, and leaves no visible deposit on fruits. It is not as fungicidally powerful as lime-sulphur at normal dilutions.

" COLLOIDAL " COPPER

This is similar in type to colloidal sulphur but has copper as the fungicidally-active ingredient. It is not as generally " safe " on fruit as the sulphur form, but is increasingly popular because easier to prepare than Bordeaux Mixture.

BORDEAUX MIXTURE

Bordeaux Mixture is a fungicide prepared by pouring a solution of copper sulphate (" bluestone ") into milk of lime. Milk of lime is obtained when already-hydrated lime powder is stirred up with water. When the lime has been diluted with the bulk of water,

* For small Caterpillars etc., the diluted spray should contain about 0·004 per cent. rotenone ; for Greenfly 0·002 per cent. is sufficient.

the bluestone, dissolved in a little water, is added slowly, the mixture being stirred during the process. The proportions generally used in fruit-tree spraying are : 1 part bluestone to 1½ parts hydrated lime, e.g., 4 lb. bluestone, 6 lb. hydrated lime to 100 gallons water.* In making Bordeaux Mixture, the use of galvanized-iron vessels should be avoided when the bluestone is being dissolved. Wooden buckets or tubs are best. Any commonly-used spray-material, other than soap, can safely be added to Bordeaux Mixture.

SOFT SOAP

This is purchased in drums or in wooden tubs. It must be dissolved in hot water before use. The most convenient way is to boil it in water, diluting the resulting concentrate when required for spraying. It has a slight insecticidal value when used alone, especially against Greenfly, but is used largely as a spray auxiliary. It is the best wetting agent known for fruit trees. Used with an insecticide such as nicotine, it enables the insecticide to penetrate amongst the foliage, and thus to wet the surface of the insects it is desired to destroy. It should not be used with lime-sulphur, Bordeaux Mixture or lead arsenate, or shortly before or after such sprays, especially lead arsenate, are applied.

PROPRIETARY WETTING PREPARATIONS

There is a wide choice of these preparations, most of which can, unlike soft soap, be used with lime-sulphur, Bordeaux Mixture or lead arsenate, and which are intended to improve the wetting and spreading properties of the sprays with which they are used. Such preparations should be used according to the makers' instructions.

GROUND SULPHUR DUSTS

These yellow powders should contain 90 to 95 per cent. sulphur, the rest being a " carrier," often of the china-clay type. Fineness of particle-size is important. The use of these dusts is an excellent adjunct to wet spraying, especially for late-summer applications against Apple Scab ; their chief advantage lies in the ease and rapidity with which they can be applied. They are not safe on sulphur-shy varieties.

---

* It has recently been found that the addition of Cotton-seed oil at 6 pints per 100 gallons prevents much of the injury commonly associated with Bordeaux Mixture, but it makes the spray rather more expensive to use. The oil should be stirred into the dissolved copper sulphate before this is added to the milk of lime.

FLOWERS OF SULPHUR

A yellow powder, coarser than the ground sulphur dusts, and is therefore less desirable for application to fruit trees. It is generally used for Mildew-control on Hops and Strawberries. It should be practically pure sulphur. It is not safe on sulphur-shy varieties.

COPPER-LIME DUST

This is a form of copper sometimes used in dusting for Scab and other fungous diseases. Fineness of particle-size is important here also ; the finer the dust, the more effective will it be. It is risky to use on many varieties of apples.

MATERIALS LESS COMMONLY USED

Liver of Sulphur (potassium or sodium polysulphide).—This is a greenish, rock-like solid ; it should be dissolved in hot water ; formerly it was often used for Red Spider ; it can be used in conjunction with soft soap.

Quassia and Hellebore.—These are plant products hitherto used as non-poisonous insecticides, but now superseded.

Pyrethrum Preparations.—The active constituents of these are derived from the flower heads of *Chrysanthemum cineraræfolium*. They are occasionally used on fruit trees, but are more expensive and generally less satisfactory than Derris preparations.

Paris Green (Poison).—This is a form of arsenic now seldom used for pests of fruit, having been superseded by lead arsenate.

Ammonium polysulphide.—This is a deep red solution with an objectionable smell. It has been much recommended in the past as an alternative to lime-sulphur, largely for sulphur-shy varieties. It has been superseded by " colloidal " sulphurs.

Ammonium Copper Carbonate.—This is a copper-containing spray, which has sometimes been used instead of Bordeaux Mixture.

Burgundy Mixture.—This resembles Bordeaux Mixture, but is made with bluestone and washing-soda (sodium carbonate). It is liable to cause severe injury and is not recommended for fruit.

D.D.T. Preparations.—Dichloro-diphenyl-trichlorethane, commonly referred to as D.D.T., is an insecticide with a very wide range of usefulness. It will not be available for fruit-spraying purposes till after the war, but by then much experimental evidence will have been obtained. For many pests it may largely replace derris, pyrethrum, lead arsenate and, to some extent, nicotine. It is non-poisonous, safe and pleasant to use, and unlikely to cause spray damage.

A GUIDE TO SPRAYING

See footnote, page 144.

APPLE

Time of Application	Treatment	To Control
October	Apply grease bands	Caterpillar
December–February	**Tar-oil emulsion at 5 per cent.**	Greenfly, Apple Sucker, Scale Insects
February–March	D.N.C. wash at 8 per cent. may be used in place of both tar and petroleum oil sprays	Greenfly, Apple Sucker, Scale Insects, Capsid Bugs, Red Spider, Winter Moth
February–Early April	Petroleum-oil emulsion at 8 per cent. (6½ per cent. if put on late March or early April)	Capsid Bugs, Red Spider, Winter Moth
April (at " green-cluster " stage)	**Lime-sulphur at 2½ per cent.** Lead arsenate powder at 2 lb. per 100 gallons	Scab Caterpillars
Late April–Early May (at " pink-bud " stage)	**Lime-sulphur at 2 per cent.** Lead arsenate at 2 lb. per 100 gallons **Nicotine at 8 oz. per 100 gallons**	Scab Caterpillars Capsid Bugs, Greenfly
Late May (at " petal-fall " stage)	**Lime-sulphur at 1 per cent.** **Nicotine at 8 oz. per 100 gallons**	Scab and Red Spider Sawfly, Capsid Bugs, Greenfly
Early June	Apply sackbands	Apple Blossom Weevil (see page 157)
Mid-June (at " fruitlet " stage)	**Lime-sulphur at 1 per cent.**	Scab and Red Spider
Late June	Lead arsenate at 2 lb. per 100 gallons	Codling Moth

Note.—Leave *Stirling Castle, Beauty of Bath,* and *Lane's Prince Albert* unsprayed with fungicide after blossoming.

For *Newton Wonder,* apply lime-sulphur ¾ per cent. after blossoming. This dilution, or alternatively colloidal or other appropriate sulphur preparation, should be used at " fruitlet " stage for other varieties where experience shows 1 per cent. lime-sulphur to be unsafe.

BLACKBERRY

Time of Application	Treatment	To Control
Early and Mid-July	Derris at 2 lb. per 100 gallons	Raspberry Beetle

COBNUT AND FILBERT

Time of Application	Treatment	To Control
April–May	Lead arsenate at 2 lb. per 100 gallons	Caterpillar, Nut Weevil
June	Lead arsenate at 2 lb. per 100 gallons	Nut Weevil

CURRANT, RED

Same programme as for Blackcurrant (page 143), but omitting lime-sulphur and Bordeaux Mixture.

A GUIDE TO SPRAYING—*continued*

BLACKCURRANT

Time of Application	Treatment	To Control
December–February	**Tar-oil emulsion at 5 per cent.**	Greenfly and Winter Moth [Moth
February–March	Petroleum-oil emulsion at 8 per cent.	Capsid Bugs and Winter
February	D.N.C. at 8 per cent. or a tar-petroleum-oil emulsion at a concentration recommended by the makers may be used in place of above two sprays	Capsid, Winter Moth, Greenfly
April (just before flowers open)	**Lime-sulphur at 2–8 per cent. (To this add lead arsenate, 2 lb., or derris 2 lb., per 100 gallons if caterpillars present)**	Big-Bud Mite
June–July [picked]	Roguing	Reversion
July (after crop is	Bordeaux Mixture 4–6–100	Leaf Spot and Rust

CHERRY

Time of Application	Treatment	To Control
October	**Apply grease bands**	Caterpillar
December–January	Tar-oil emulsion at 5 per cent. Spray very thoroughly and as late as possible if Blossom Wilt is bad	Blackfly and Blossom Wilt
April–May (not during blossoming)	Lead arsenate at 4 lb. per 100 gallons Bordeaux Mixture 6–9–100 pre-blossom and 4–6–100 post-blossom	Caterpillar Bacterial Canker

DAMSON (See Plum)

GOOSEBERRY

Time of Application	Treatment	To Control
December–February	**Tar-oil emulsion at 5 per cent.**	Greenfly, Red Spider
February–March	Petroleum-oil emulsion at 8 per cent.	Capsid Bugs, Winter Moth, Red Spider
April (before flowering)	**Lime-sulphur at 2½ per cent.**	Mildew, Red Spider
April (after flowering)	Lime-sulphur at 1 per cent. (omitting "sulphur-shy" varieties)	Mildew, Red Spider
April–May (as required)	Derris at 2 lb. per 100 gallons Note : May be added to lime-sulphur	Sawfly, Caterpillar

LOGANBERRY

Time of Application	Treatment	To Control
May	Bordeaux Mixture 4–6–100	Cane Spot
Mid-June	Derris at 2 lb. per 100 gallons Colloidal Copper at makers' recommendations	Raspberry Beetle Cane Spot
Late June	Derris at 2 lb. per 100 gallons	Raspberry Beetle

A GUIDE TO SPRAYING—*continued*

PEACH AND NECTARINE

Time of Application	Treatment	To Control
December **February–March (at bud- burst)**	Tar-oil emulsion at 5 per cent. **Lime-sulphur at 3 per cent.**	Greenfly Leaf Curl and Red Spider

PEAR

Time of Application	Treatment	To Control
October December–January **Early April (at " green- cluster " stage)** **April (at " white-bud " stage)** **Mid-May (at " petal- fall " stage)** ⎫ **June** ⎭ July	Apply grease bands Tar-oil emulsion at 5 per cent. Lime-sulphur at 2½ per cent. Lead arsenate at 2 lb. per 100 gallons Lime-sulphur at 2 per cent. Lead arsenate at 2 lb. per 100 gallons Bordeaux Mixture at 4–6–100 or a col- loidal-copper wash used at makers' directions Lead arsenate at 2 lb. per 100 gallons Derris or Nicotine (dust or spray)	Caterpillars Greenfly Scab and Blister Mite Caterpillars Scab and Blister Mite Caterpillars Scab Codling and Slugworm Slugworm

PLUM (INCLUDING DAMSON, QUETSCHE AND BULLACE)

Time of Application	Treatment	To Control
October **December–January** February Early April May May **Before Mid-July**	Apply grease bands **Tar-oil emulsion at 5 per cent.** Petroleum-oil emulsion at 4 per cent. Lead arsenate at 2 lb. per 100 gallons Derris at 2 lb. per 100 gallons Lime-sulphur at 1 per cent. **Cut out and burn all dead and dying branches and shoots**	Caterpillars Greenfly Red Spider Caterpillars Sawfly and Red Spider Red Spider Silver Leaf

RASPBERRY

Time of Application	Treatment	To Control
Mid-March **Late June**	Lime-sulphur at 5 per cent. or Bordeaux Mixture at 10–15–100 **Derris at 2 lb. per 100 gallons**	Cane Spot Raspberry Beetle

STRAWBERRY (see page 352)

Note.—In the above tables, the operations shown in heavy type are those which should always be carried out. The particulars given here are purposely brief, but further information is given in the sections dealing with the diseases and pests of each fruit. The nature of the actual sprays and dusts, and the precautions to be taken in using them, are dealt with in the early part of this section.

THINNING FRUIT.
Apple "Lane's Prince Albert," above, unthinned and below, thinned to
6-8 inches apart.

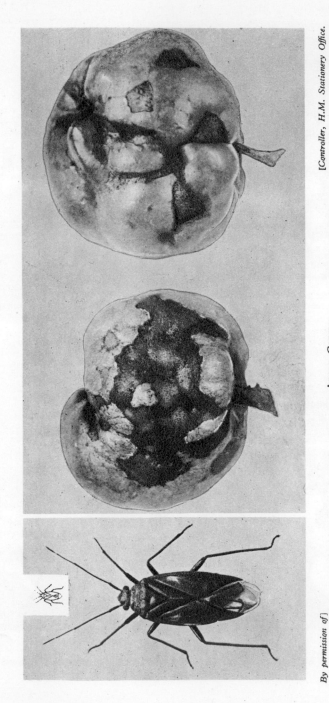

APPLE CAPSID.

1. The Apple Capsid (*Plesiocaris rugicollis*) (inset, actual size). 2. Apples attacked by Apple Capsids.

From the Ministry of Agriculture and Fisheries Advisory Leaflet No. 154.

CHAPTER XIII

THE CULTURE OF PARTICULAR FRUITS

THE APPLE *(Pyrus Malus)*

ORIGIN AND HISTORY

Apples appear to have been grown in England from the earliest times. For centuries they were used mainly for the making of cider, but with the introduction from the Continent of new varieties under the patronage of the Church, the Crown and the nobility, the apple gradually came to be regarded as a garden and orchard tree, until to-day it is more widely grown in England than any other fruit.

SOIL, SITUATION AND ASPECT

Apple trees can be grown successfully on a wide range of soil series. Those that are badly drained and liable to waterlogging at any depth down to three or four feet should be avoided, as also should those which are excessively drained and liable to dry out in a hot summer. Soils with a high nitrogen content such as are to be found in old hop gardens or in heavily-manured kitchen gardens, should not be used for planting apples until means has been found to reduce the amount of nitrogen that is available to the young trees.

If apples must be planted under high nitrogen conditions, cooking apples should be selected in preference to dessert varieties.

Sandy soils are usually deficient in potassium, and apple trees planted under these conditions will always need generous manuring with sulphate of potash. Shelter from the south-west and from the east winds and protection from spring frosts are necessary for successful apple culture. Although the apple can be grown under conditions of moderately high rainfall and low sunshine, these are by no means ideal conditions. It would appear that good dessert apples are grown most economically in districts with a yearly rainfall of from 20 to 25 inches, and with a correspondingly high rate of sunshine, these being conditions which impose a natural check on excessive growth, and ensure good skin colour and texture in the fruit. This does not mean that good dessert apples cannot be grown under conditions of medium to high rainfall, but that greater skill is required to produce the same results.

In districts of more than 40 inches of rainfall in the year, dessert apples must be regarded as difficult to grow successfully, and preference should be given to cooking apples.

FORM OF TREE

The form of tree to be adopted must be considered in relation to the type of apple culture required.

Grass Orchards.—For grass orchards where stock is grazing, the standard, three-quarter-standard and half-standard forms may be used according to the height above the ground at which it is necessary to keep the branches out of reach of grazing stock. Where there is no grazing stock, the bush form may be used in a grass orchard quite as well as the standards, and is to be preferred because it is more economical to prune, spray, thin and pick. It does not necessarily follow that a fruit tree grown in the form of a bush must necessarily be of small or medium size, since it is not the form of a tree but the rootstock, the variety and the subsequent management which ultimately determine its size. In actual fact, the standard forms are usually larger than others because the trees are on the most vigorous rootstocks, but it is possible to produce bush trees of any size according to the purpose for which they are required.

Commercial Plantations.—For commercial plantations the bush form is the most popular and is used in all sizes from the very large " permanent " to the very small " filler."

The oblique cordon form has been largely used for intensive apple culture, and in more recent years, the double cordon, the dwarf pyramid or dwarf fuseau forms have all been planted.*

The Fruit Garden.—For the fruit garden there are several forms of apple tree to suit the space available. Where there is very little headroom and hardly any lateral space in more than two directions, the horizontal cordon may be used, the trees being planted at intervals of from 10 to 12 feet for subsequent inarch grafting of one into the other. Where there is headroom but only limited lateral space in more than two directions, the vertical cordon, either single or double, the oblique cordon, and the espalier forms all have their peculiar merits. Where both headroom and lateral space in all directions are limited, the dwarf pyramid and bush forms may be useful, and where there are no restrictions of space, the large bush and even the half-standard may be used with advantage.

* For further particulars, see Ministry of Agriculture and Fisheries Bulletin No. 49.

ROOTSTOCKS FOR APPLES

Apple trees are raised by budding or grafting the scion variety (see pages 41–52) on to a rootstock raised either vegetatively by stooling and layering or from seed (see pages 37–40). The advantage of using vegetatively-raised rootstocks for fruit trees lies in the fact that the stocks from any one stool or layer can be depended upon to produce the same type of tree, and the same type of fruit in the scion variety. This uniformity makes it easier to control the behaviour of the individual trees than it would be if they were worked on different seedling rootstocks. For Vegetative Propagation by Layering, see Rootstocks, page 39.

SELECTION OF ROOTSTOCKS

Before grafting or budding a tree, or when ordering trees ready-worked, careful consideration should be given to the selection of the most suitable rootstock. Research has shown that the size of the tree when fully grown and, to a certain extent, the quality of the fruit are influenced by the rootstock. Local conditions, particularly the nature of the soil, should also be borne in mind when selecting the rootstock. For instance, if the conditions are conducive to excessive growth, the stock chosen should be of a more dwarfing nature than would normally be required for the purpose, and vice versa. In the light of present knowledge the most useful standardized apple rootstocks for different sizes of tree are as follows :—

Rootstocks for Dwarf Trees

Jaune de Metz (also called Malling Number Nine).—Under favourable growth conditions this stock makes a small but healthy tree which begins to come into bearing in from two to three years' time, and which throughout its life remains smaller than on any other commercial rootstock. Number Nine has recently fallen into disfavour with some commercial fruit-growers, partly because its roots are brittle and the trees are, therefore, liable to be blown over in a storm unless carefully staked, and partly because, unless the trees are planted under favourable growth conditions and carefully nursed when young, they are apt to make rather poor trees.

On the other hand, the early cropping of trees on this stock, combined with the high colour and large size of fruit which it tends to produce in trees worked upon it, make Number Nine the ideal rootstock for all varieties of apples grown under garden conditions. Here the natural shelter and the artificial support afforded by wall, fence, or wire can be relied upon to prevent the trees from being blown over.

Rootstocks for Trees of Medium Size

Doucin (Malling Number Two) and *Broadleaf* (Malling Number One).—At the present time the stock which appears to be most widely used by English nurserymen for bush trees, and which is also being used for cordons in many commercial plantations, is the Doucin (called Malling Number Two). In early years this is a semi-dwarfing stock with all varieties, but with *Cox's Orange Pippin* and some other sorts it becomes more vigorous as the trees grow older. The Broadleaf (also called Malling Number One) is a stock which appears to be more vigorous with some varieties than with others. *Cox's Orange Pippin* on Number One starts off fairly strongly and then settles down into a semi-dwarf tree, whereas with *Worcester Pearmain* and *Bramley's Seedling* there appears to be little to choose in size in later years between trees on Numbers One and Two. At East Malling Research Station, Number One has given a rather brighter colour to dessert apples such as *Worcester Pearmain* than Number Two. From the experimental point of view, it is not yet possible to say which of these two rootstocks is the better for commercial cordon plantations. Number Nine is the most suitable stock for *Cox's Orange Pippin* Cordons.

Rootstocks for Very Large Trees

Malling Number Twelve and Number Sixteen.—Of the standardized rootstocks for very large trees, whether standard, three-quarter-standard, half-standard or bush, Malling Numbers Twelve and Sixteen are to be recommended, trees on Number Twelve taking rather longer to come into bearing than those on Number Sixteen. Failing this, the trees should be on selected free or crab stocks, such as Malling Crab C., or one of the Long Ashton selections.

PRUNING OF APPLES

The general principles of pruning have been dealt with in Chapter V (Pruning), where it was pointed out that winter and summer pruning are two very different operations and affect the tree in different ways. In theory true " winter " pruning should be done only when the tree is in its most dormant stage, i.e., when there is the minimum flow of sap upwards or downwards. In practice there appears to be a fairly wide margin of time on either side of this stage when winter pruning may safely be carried out, without making any appreciable difference to the results. On very large fruit farms winter pruning often starts before leaf-fall in the autumn, and if bad weather intervenes, it may not be finished until just before bud-break. Probably the second half of November and December form the optimum period for winter pruning, and whenever possible, it should be completed before winter washing begins, if only to economize in the amount of spray required.

Very strong-growing varieties of apple, such as *Bramley's Seedling*, need little winter pruning after the first few years, the main object in such cases being to keep the centre of the tree fairly open, by spurring back ingrowing laterals, and cutting out interlacing branches.

One of the main difficulties with such varieties on vigorous stocks is to get the tree to come into bearing, and since hard winter pruning is one of the chief factors in delaying cropping, it follows that the less pruning such trees receive in early years the more quickly they will crop. Nothing is more fatal to quick cropping than the old-fashioned method of pruning the leading shoots and all laterals hard back every winter before the tree has come into bearing. If the leaders are only lightly tipped or even left entirely unpruned after, say, the third or fourth year from planting, and all the laterals of medium growth on the outside of the tree are left full length for one or two seasons, the trees will come into bearing reasonably quickly. If this is not done, strong growers like *Bramley's Seedling* and varieties like *Allington Pippin* and *Cox's Orange*, which make much lateral growth, may go on growing vigorously without cropping for years after they should have come into bearing.

Another varietal habit which is important in determining the degree of winter pruning for apples is the way in which the tree naturally carries its fruit-buds. Some varieties, such as *Worcester Pearmain, Bismarck, Gladstone, Grenadier, Irish Peach, Barnack Beauty, Cornish Gillyflower, St. Edmund's Russet*, and to a certain extent *Bramley's Seedling*, are what are known as " tip-bearers," carrying their fruit-buds, especially in early years, at the end of rather thin, twiggy lateral shoots. If these laterals are cut hard back in winter to within a few inches of the base, the fruit-buds are all cut away and the trees cannot be expected to bear fruit. To be fruitful such laterals must be left full length and allowed rather an untidy appearance in early years. (See Illustration facing page 65.)

Other varieties, such as *James Grieve, Cox's Orange Pippin, Early Victoria, Egremont Russet, Ribston Pippin, Lord Derby, Edward VII, Miller's Seedling* and *Duchess Favourite*, carry a large proportion of their fruit-buds on naturally-formed fruit-spurs or on artificial spurs made by shortening back the lateral shoots. Such varieties are naturally much easier to spur-prune than tip-bearers, and can be made to look tidy without ruining their prospect of cropping, provided always the leaders are not pruned too hard during the critical period in which the trees are coming into bearing. (See Illustration facing page 65.)

The more artificial the form of the tree, the more difficult it is to lay down hard and fast rules for successful pruning. With the standard and the bush forms the vegetative vigour of the tree can be distributed in lateral shoots over a large number of main branches, but when it comes to limiting the main branches to one, two, three or even to ten main branches as in cordons, pyramids, fuseaux and espaliers, there will always be the problem of how to deal with the dense crop of closely-growing new laterals which in the more natural forms of tree have room to spread themselves without overcrowding. With such trees the first essential is to leave the leaders as long as possible in order to counteract the tendency to throw out strong new shoots immediately behind them. Late spring pruning of the leader, when about one inch of new growth has already been made, will prove an additional check to this unwanted vegetative vigour, but probably the most certain method for all these artificial forms of tree is to adopt one or other of the summer pruning treatments already described in Chapter V.

Apples of Upright Habit of Growth.	*Apples of Spreading Habit of Growth.*	*Varieties that Need to be Pruned lightly.*
Adam's Pearmain	Belle de Boskoop	Blenheim Orange
Annie Elizabeth	Blenheim Orange	Bramley's Seedling
Christmas Pearmain	Bramley's Seedling	Belle de Boskoop
Edward VII	Gladstone	
Egremont Russet	Lane's Prince Albert	
Heusgen's Golden Reinette	Langley Pippin	
John Standish	Stirling Castle	
King of the Pippins		
Lord Derby		
Orleans Reinette		
Worcester Pearmain		

There is a certain amount of empirical evidence to show that when summer pruning shoots in a semi-woody condition back to about 5 or 6 inches, if the shoots are merely broken or " brutted," and allowed to hang down without being severed, there is less likelihood of secondary growth taking place than if the shoots were cut cleanly through with a knife or secateurs. " Brutting " is a common practice in the summer pruning of Kentish cobnuts, and although it gives the tree an untidy appearance, it may help to check the tendency to excessive lateral growth in cordons, espaliers and other artificial forms.

Whether summer pruned or not, new lateral shoots (with the exception of tip-bearers) are usually pruned or "spurred" back at the end of the first season's growth to 3, 4 or 5 inches from the base according to their strength (page 57). The stronger the lateral within limits,* the more lightly it should be pruned. During the following season it is quite likely that one or more woodbuds on this spurred lateral may send out shoots of varying length, and that one or even two buds toward the base will swell out and begin to look as if they might be fruit-buds. It is advisable not to cut hard back to these buds the following winter, but to cut back the new laterals on the old spur to within from ½ inch to 2 inches of their base according to their vigour.

It has been found by experiment that better results are obtained by allowing fruit-buds to form gradually on these artificial spurs rather than by stimulating them into growth by cutting hard back to them the first year. When there is no longer any doubt that fruit-buds are present at the base of the spur, the lateral shoots above them can be safely cut back to the fruit-spur.

For an account of "Delayed Open-Centre" Pruning, see Chapter VII.

MANURING OF APPLES

Potassium.—In Chapter III attention was drawn to the fact that in this country potassium is the most important fertilizer for apples.

Symptoms of Potassium Deficiency.—The chief symptoms of potash deficiency in the apple, as in other fruit trees and bushes, is a marginal browning of the leaf known as "leaf-scorch." This is not invariably a sign of lack of potash, there being other causes such as severe drought, or spray-damage which may cause scorching of the leaf. When, however, there is reason to suspect a deficiency of potassium available to the tree and "scorch" is prevalent on the margins of the leaf, the "immediate action" is to apply potash. Experiments have shown that sulphate of potash is the most satisfactory form in which to apply potassium to the soil for apple trees, in amounts varying from 2 to 4 cwt. per acre (1 to 2 oz. per square yard). In cases of acute potassium deficiency as much as 8 cwt. per acre (equal to ½ lb. per square yard) has been applied.

---

* Laterals which are so strong as to be positively gross are called by the French "gourmands"; these are best cut clean out at the base.

Nitrogen.—Young apple trees are usually better without nitrogenous manures. For trees in bearing the quantity required depends on the kind, variety and growth-conditions of the tree. For instance, cooking apples will take more nitrogen than dessert apples, and among dessert apples *Cox's Orange Pippin* will take more than *Worcester Pearmain*.

Symptoms of Excess Nitrogen.—Much vigorous shoot growth, very large, dark green leaves, badly-coloured fruit of greasy texture and poor keeping quality, and susceptibility to attack by the canker fungus, all these are symptoms of excess nitrogen in the apple tree. Trees showing such symptoms should receive no nitrogenous manures, and cultivations should be stopped altogether or limited to the first half of the growing season. Other alternatives are to leave the trees entirely unpruned, and in extreme cases to ring-bark or even to root-prune.

Symptoms of Nitrogen Deficiency.—Small weak shoots, small pale green leaves, small, sweet, highly-coloured fruit of good texture and good keeping quality, these are the symptoms of nitrogen shortage in the apple tree. The high colour of the fruit and the good keeping quality are both desirable conditions in dessert apples, and where these are required the less nitrogen the trees get the better, so long as the leaf does not get too small and yellow and provided the trees are not allowed to stop growing altogether. When this happens, it is often better, before applying nitrogen, to try the effect of one or more of the other growth-promoting measures, such as thorough cultivations or hard pruning. Trees on weak stocks may be invigorated by planting one or more vigorous rootstocks close beside the tree and inarching them into the stem below the bottom branches. Trees which are deficient both in nitrogen and in potassium will require heavy feeding with potash before they can benefit from applications of nitrogenous manures.

Forms and Amounts of Nitrogen for Apple Trees.—Of the organic forms of manure, farmyard dung, high-grade shoddy, and meat and bonemeal are most widely used by commercial growers for supplying nitrogen to apple trees. The organic forms are generally used on light soils to keep the moisture in the ground during the summer months.

Of the inorganic forms of nitrogenous fertilizer, sulphate of ammonia, nitrate of soda, and nitro-chalk are the most popular and are given usually in two half-dressings, say in February and May. Strong-growing varieties of cooking apples, such as *Bramley's Seedling* when in full bearing, may require up to 5 cwt. per acre, or even more, to give healthy foliage and large-sized fruits, provided the potash applications are being well-maintained. Dessert apples like *Cox's Orange Pippin*, on the other hand, even when in full bearing, should not require more than half this amount. In the light of present knowledge it is not possible to prescribe the exact amounts of nitrogen and potassium to apply. The trees themselves are the most reliable indicators of their own needs, and the wise fruit-grower will look to them for guidance.

Phosphorus.—Field experiments have so far failed to show exactly in what way, if any, phosphorus is necessary for an apple tree in this country. At the same time, many successful fruit-growers emphasize the importance of this element, and until experiments prove it to be unnecessary, experts are agreed in recommending the application of some form of phosphatic manure to apple trees. Steamed bone flour, is, perhaps, the most popular of the organic forms, and superphosphates and basic slag are both used as inorganic forms. Rates of application vary, 5 cwt. per acre being about the average dressing, applied in winter or very early spring.

Magnesium.—See page 35.

GUIDE TO THE MANURING OF APPLE TREES

The following table indicates the conditions under which the requirements of the trees for Potassium (K) and Nitrogen (N) are likely to be either more or less than normal.

	Subsoil Sandy, Gravelly or Badly-drained	Hard Pruned	Light Pruned	Cooking Apple	Dessert Apple	Uncultivated (Grass or Weeds)	Cultivated (No weeds or grass)
Potassium (K) ...	More	More	Less	Less	More	Less	More
Nitrogen (N) ...	More	Less	More	More	Less	More	Less

INDICATIONS OF MANURIAL REQUIREMENTS

Symptoms	Probable Cause
Leaves, marginal browning, " Leaf-scorch "	Potash deficiency
Leaves, large and dark green, vigorous shoot growth; badly-coloured fruit of greasy texture and poor keeping quality	Excess of Nitrogen
Leaves, small and pale green, weak shoots; small, highly-coloured, sweet fruit of good texture and good keeping quality	Nitrogen deficiency

THE APPLE

FRUIT THINNING

The three main objects in fruit thinning are to increase the ultimate size of the fruits which remain, to give a uniform sample, and to induce regular bearing in the tree. There is no doubt that with the codling types of apple, such as *Lord Suffield, Lord Grosvenor, Keswick Codling* and *Early Victoria* (*Emneth Early*), thinning the fruits to 8 or 10 inches apart when they are the size of walnuts is much the best way to get large fruit. The same is true of varieties like *Miller's Seedling, Duchess Favourite,* and *John Standish,* which normally produce rather small-sized apples.

It is becoming a widespread practice among commercial fruit-growers to thin dessert apples such as *Worcester Pearmain* and *Cox's Orange Pippin,* leaving not more than two, and often only one fruit to a truss, with a view to getting uniformity of size in the fruit. When thinning, the centre fruit of each truss, the " King " apple, is removed, because it is usually an abnormal fruit, which is often misshapen, and does not always keep well in store.

The best way to thin apples is to take the stalk between the first and second fingers of the right hand and to push the apple gently but firmly off its stalk with the thumb of the same hand.

GATHERING OF FRUIT

Different varieties of apples ripen in different months. Early ripening varieties should be picked over more than once, and cannot be kept for more than a few weeks except in low-temperature stores. Keeping varieties of apple develop more slowly, and late colouring varieties, if they are to be really well coloured, ought to be left on the tree as long as possible. It is generally considered that one of the best tests of whether an apple is ready for picking is to lift it gently on its stalk. If the apple comes away without an effort, the fruit is usually sufficiently ripe to finish the rest of the ripening process off the tree. If it is picked at a stage when the stalk has to be torn off, there is a likelihood that the apple may not keep well in ordinary storage. It should be emphasized, however, that for low-temperature storage of any kind, the fruit is best picked rather sooner than it would be for ordinary storage.

For selections of *Early, Mid-season* and *Late* varieties, see page 192.

Weather for Gathering.—Apples should be gathered when they are quite dry and should not be exposed unnecessarily to the sun after being picked.

For *Storing, Marketing* and *Exhibiting,* see pages 108–118.

154

INSECT PESTS OF THE APPLE

Apples are liable to attack by more pests than any other fruit crop, and this accounts for the large Spray Schedule for apples given on page 142.

WINTER MOTHS

In the spring the opening buds are attacked by caterpillars of the Winter Moth. These are at first very small and dark coloured, but eventually become an inch or more in length, green in colour, and may always be recognized by their characteristic "looping" method of walking. When small they feed in the buds and blossom trusses, but when foliage becomes more plentiful, they feed on the leaves, and often destroy small fruits also. In very large numbers they can defoliate the trees, with serious consequences. In June they drop to the ground and turn to pupæ (chrysalids) in the soil. Here they remain till winter comes, when the moths emerge and make their way to the branches and twigs. There they lay their small, oval, at first green but later reddish-brown eggs from which the destructive caterpillars ultimately develop.

The March Moth is the latest of the several species of winter moth to emerge in the spring. It differs from the others in its habit of laying its full complement of eggs not singly but in a band around a twig.

Control.—Although the male moths can fly readily, the females have no proper wings, and are therefore obliged to crawl up the trunks of the trees. Attack by caterpillars of this type of moth can therefore be prevented by applying grease-bands to the tree trunks in October, and by ensuring that the "tackiness" of the grease is maintained till the spring. If grease-banding is not practised, the trees should be sprayed with lead arsenate when the caterpillars start to appear in April and May.

TORTRIX MOTHS

Tortrix caterpillars can always be recognized by their habit of wriggling backwards when disturbed, and by the way in which they spin the leaves together. Several closely-related species occur, some of which hibernate as tiny caterpillars encased in cocoons of silk and rubbish, which they construct in crevices and under loose bark. From these hiding places they emerge when the buds break and quickly eat their way into the buds, which then wilt or shrivel

155

and turn brown. At this time the caterpillars are still very small, little more than one-tenth of an inch long, and are brown or green or yellowish-green in colour. Later, they feed on the leaves, which they spin together for protection, and, in May or June, turn to pupæ or chrysalids which shortly produce moths. These lay minute, pale green, almost colourless eggs on the leaves, either singly or in clusters. About the middle of July more caterpillars hatch out and feed on the leaves and frequently on the fruit too. Small portions of the skin of the apple are eaten but the damage often passes unnoticed when the fruit is picked. Consequently the caterpillars may be introduced into the fruit store, where they continue their feeding. Rotting follows and soon spreads to neighbouring sound apples.

Control.—No one remedy as yet seems adequate for the control of these destructive caterpillars. They can be kept within reasonable limits by the various spray mixtures used for other pests in the normal routine spray schedule (see page 142). Tar-oil winter washes destroy the more accessible of the hibernating larvæ, and the lead arsenate applied before, and in some cases after, blossoming destroys many of them whilst they are feeding. Lead arsenate cannot, of course, be safely applied in mid-July; for the fruit-eating generation, therefore, mid-July sprays of non-poisonous materials such as Derris Root should be used.

GREENFLY

Several species of aphides (green- or blackfly) occur on apple trees, and when plentiful can cause severe injury in the form of crippled growth or loss of crop. The two commonest species, the Permanent Green Apple Aphis (*Aphis pomi*) and the Rosy Aphis or Blue Bug (*Anuraphis roseus*), both spend the winter on the trees as small, black, shiny eggs. The eggs of the former are laid thickly clustered together on the young sappy shoots, whilst those of the Rosy Aphis are laid singly, mainly on the spurs.

The *Green Aphis* hatches in April, when the buds are breaking, but does little damage until June, when it becomes abundant on the younger growths. These become stunted and malformed and often die back from the tip.

The *Rosy Aphis* is a larger insect than the Green Aphis and may be distinguished by its bluish or purple colour and by its mealy appearance. It causes more damage than any other apple aphis, feeding not only on the leaves and shoots, but on the newly-formed fruits also. Badly-affected fruits may drop off altogether; those remaining on the tree become stunted and deformed, especially at the eye end, which becomes "knobbly." In July this insect migrates to certain weeds, such as plantain, but returns to the apple in the autumn.

Owing to their habit of curling the leaves on which they feed, aphides are not always completely destroyed by spring or summer spraying with nicotine. The eggs are easily destroyed by winter tar-oil washes.

WOOLLY APHIS OR AMERICAN BLIGHT (*Eriosoma lanigerum*)

This is a severe pest in the nursery and is often troublesome, though of less economic importance, on established trees. The insect itself is reddish in colour, but produces masses of white wax, the "wool," which in bad cases often hangs in festoons from the branches. A few aphides spend the winter on the trunk or main branches, in the shelter of cracks or crevices, and further protected by their covering of wool. In the spring they produce living young, which reproduce rapidly and so give rise to the heavy infestations often experienced in early summer. The insects are spread from tree to tree by the wind, or partly by the wind and partly by crawling over the ground.

The feeding of Woolly Aphis causes gall-like swellings on the twigs and branches. Badly-attacked twigs often die ; in any case the galls enlarge and split and become cankerous or provide a ready entrance for the troublesome fungus disease " Apple Canker."

There has been a great deal of controversy as to whether this pest feeds on the roots of apple trees, and it now seems certain that it does not do this to any extent, in this country at any rate.

Control.—If Woolly Aphis is present when the trees are lifted from the nursery they should be dipped in a 10 per cent. solution of tar-oil wash. In the nursery the pest can be kept within bounds by painting the larger colonies with methylated spirit, and by spraying thoroughly with nicotine and soap. Larger trees should, if necessary, also be sprayed with nicotine. This is best applied with the petal-fall scab spray. Winter application of tar-oil wash also helps to keep Woolly Aphis in check. Should it become troublesome in summer it can be dealt with by means of nicotine, used in conjunction with plenty of soap or with a summer-oil emulsion.

APPLE BLOSSOM WEEVIL (*Anthonomus pomorum*)

Very soon after the Winter Moth and Tortrix caterpillars start their damage, the Apple Blossom Weevil emerges from the litter, loose bark or other rubbish in which it has sheltered during the winter, and begins to feed on the buds. This insect is about an eighth of an inch or more in length, grey or black in colour, with a silvery V-shaped mark on its back. It is more or less oval in shape and possesses a long, slightly curved snout or rostrum, the apex of which is furnished with small, powerful jaws. It feeds on the sides of the buds, making small, round holes in the still folded leaves. The chief damage, however, is caused by the grub, which hatches in April from an egg laid within the flower-bud. On hatching it feeds on the stamens and style, sticking the petals down to form a kind of tent above it. Affected blossoms never open but remain " capped " until the petals turn brown and drop off. Such blossoms cannot be pollinated and so are usually unable to set fruit. The grub, which is white and legless and has a black head, develops into a yellow chrysalis and, subsequently, into an adult beetle. In this form it leaves the capped blossom and, after feeding for a while on the leaves and fruits, seeks out suitable sleeping quarters in which to remain till the following spring.

Control.—Sprays have proved of very little use against this pest, but some good can be done by trapping the beetles in sacking or corrugated cardboard bands. These should be placed around the tree trunk in June and removed and burnt in the winter.

APPLE SUCKER (*Psylla mali*)

This was formerly one of the most destructive apple pests. Since the advent of tar-oil winter washes, however, it has practically disappeared and is now found chiefly in gardens and neglected plantations. The damage is caused largely by the young insects (nymphs), which hatch out as soon as the buds break, from the very small, yellow, cigar-shaped eggs, which are laid on the spurs and smaller branches in the autumn. The nymph somewhat resembles greenfly, to which it is closely related, but may be distinguished by its flatter shape and more prominent eyes. It is at first minute and yellow, later becoming pale green. The young suckers, which may occur in large numbers, creep into the opening buds and suck the sap. Badly-attacked buds turn brown and fail to grow out, or the blossom may appear and then shrivel and drop off. Sucker damage has often been attributed to frost, but can always be recognized from the drops of white, sticky wax which exude from the suckers. The adult insect is rather more than a tenth of an inch long and possesses transparent wings, which are held roof-like over its back when not in use.

Control.—Sucker eggs can be easily destroyed in winter by means of a tar-oil wash. If this is not done and Sucker appears in the spring, recourse must be had to nicotine, which may be added to one of the pre-blossom scab sprays. (See Guide to Spraying, page 142.)

APPLE CAPSID BUG *(Plesiocoris rugicollis)*

When the leaves of the blossom trusses have unfolded, and the green flower buds are visible, the young of the Apple Capsid begin to hatch out. They are very small and green and somewhat resemble greenfly in appearance. Unlike these insects, however, they are very active and at the least alarm run rapidly and hide under a leaf or at the base of the flower-stalks. Capsid bugs feed on both leaves and fruits, first piercing the tissue with their needle-like stylets, and then pumping in salivary juices to enable them to suck up partially-digested sap. Certain toxic materials contained in the salivary juices cause the death of the punctured cells and surrounding tissue.

The first signs of Capsid damage are small black marks, later becoming brown and eventually turning into holes, on the young leaves. Soon after the fruits are set, the bugs feed upon them, the ultimate result frequently being small, deformed fruits disfigured with corky scars. As the Capsid bugs grow in size, they gradually acquire wing pads, fully-developed wings appearing only at the final moult. The winged, adult insects fly from tree to tree, laying their small, elongated eggs beneath the rind of the twigs and branches. Some damage is done by these adult bugs, which feed on the succulent new shoots, producing corky scars and sometimes distorting or even killing the shoots.

Control.—It is essential to destroy the bugs before they begin their attack on the fruits, as they are more easily killed when they are very small. Thorough spraying with nicotine just before the blossom opens will be found effective, especially if spraying is carried out in hot weather. As an alternative, good results can be obtained by using petroleum-oil sprays during the winter or at any time up to bud-break. The type that contains dinitrocresol obviates the need for prior spraying with tar-oil wash and will deal with the eggs of Sucker and Greenfly as well as those of Capsid.

APPLE SAWFLY *(Hoplocampa testudinea)*

This insect makes its appearance when the trees are in bloom, and feeds on the flower pollen prior to laying its eggs. The adult sawfly is rather more than a quarter of an inch in length, with transparent wings, a conspicuous head bearing a large compound eye on each side, and a pair of short, thick antennæ. The underside of the abdomen is yellow, but the upper surface is black. The female drills a hole just below the sepals with her saw-like ovipositor, and deposits an egg in the calyx tissue at the base of the stamens. The " sting " mark below the calyx can readily be detected as a minute brown spot, and after practice the egg also can easily be found. After a week or more a small, white, black-headed larva or caterpillar hatches from the egg and enters the side of the fruitlet. It does not enter directly but first tunnels just below the skin. It ultimately reaches and eats out the centre of the young apple. The latter drops from the tree, but not before the larva has deserted it and entered a sound fruit, this time by boring a round hole in the side. Such fruits may be detected by the hole in the side from which a wet mass of black frass and, very often, yellowish fluid exudes. These attacked fruits fall off during June and early July. Occasionally, a newly-hatched larva tunnels beneath the skin of a fruitlet, but for some reason fails to effect an entry. Such a fruit does not fall, but develops normally. The skin, however, splits along the line of the tunnel and a wide, ribbon-like, corky scar is the ultimate result. This is of relatively minor importance, however, for the chief damage is the loss of crop, often very considerable, caused by the dropping of infested fruit.

When fully fed, the larva drops to the ground and spins a tough, brown, parchment-like cocoon an inch or two below the surface of the soil. Here it remains till the spring, when it pupates, finally turning to an adult and emerging from the soil when the apples are in bloom.

Control.—The egg can be killed by an application of nicotine at petal-fall. Care should be taken to drench the trees so that the spray reaches the eye of the fruitlets within a few days of the fall of the petals. If this spray is neglected, all that can be done is to apply a Derris dust when migration and the secondary attack by the young larvæ begin (late in May), in the hope of arresting much of this secondary attack.

CODLING MOTH (*Cydia pomonella*)

This insect, like the Apple Sawfly, is responsible for maggoty apples, but its damage may easily be distinguished from that of Sawfly. In the first place, the damage occurs much later—sawfly larvæ having left the trees and most of the damaged fruits having

APPLE CAPSID.

1. Foliage attacked by immature Apple Capsid.
2. Attacked fruitlets (early stage).

*From the Ministry of Agriculture and Fisheries Advisory
Leaflet No. 154.*

By courtesy of]
1. Apple blossom wilt : infected trusses of blossom.

[Dr. H. Wormald.
2. A dead spur and canker which has half girdled a branch, taken in winter and showing spore-pustules on spur.

dropped by the end of June, when the first small Codling larvæ begin to attack the fruits. Moreover, Codling-damaged apples, if they drop at all, do not do so until shortly before picking time. If an apple is picked for eating and found to be maggoty, it is almost certainly attacked by Codling and not by Sawfly.

The moth itself does not appear until after petal-fall. It is grey in colour, with dark markings towards the apex of the wings, which have an expanse of about half an inch. It is a very shy creature and is seldom seen, since it flies chiefly at dusk and at sunrise and then only when the air is calm. The eggs are no bigger than a pin's head and are laid on the skin of the fruit or on the leaves. They are inconspicuous and almost transparent.

After hatching, the little white caterpillar eats its way into the fruit either at the eye or through the side, and feeds in the neighbourhood of the core. Often it reveals its presence by the heap of brown excrement which it pushes out of the entrance hole. When fully fed, it leaves the fruit and spins a cocoon in any convenient crevice on the tree. It is usually a pale pink colour by this time and spends the autumn and winter as a larva in the cocoon, turning to a chrysalis in the spring or early summer.

In some seasons, however, a few manage to pupate almost immediately, and a second generation of moths is the result. These give rise to more maggoty apples in September and October.

Control.—Codling is more difficult to contend with than Sawfly. Lead arsenate should be added to the petal-fall spray, which, although applied long before Codling larvæ appear, enables a poisonous deposit to be put into the calyx cup ready for those larvæ which choose to enter the apple at that spot. Then a further application—and this is the important one—should be made late in June to form the first meal of the larvæ which then begin to go in at the side of the apple. As the egg-laying period is a long one, extending well into July, further applications may have to be made. For all but late-picked varieties these later sprayings should be of Derris and not of lead arsenate. A useful adjunct to spraying is the use of sacking or corrugated paper bands treated with beta-naphthol. After scraping off the loose bark from the tree trunk, the band is affixed before the end of July. Larvæ that enter these bands are killed by the chemical.

RED SPIDER *(Oligonychus ulmi)*

This pest has increased since the advent of tar-oil washes which destroy some of the enemies of the Red Spider, but which are ineffective against the pest itself. The small, round, red winter eggs are laid in the autumn on the older twigs. These hatch out when the trees are in bloom, and the young spiders, or " mites," feed on the undersides of the leaves till they are fully grown. Summer eggs are laid throughout the summer from petal-fall onwards and vast numbers of the mites are sometimes produced, which by their feeding turn the leaves a brownish colour and absorb sap which would normally go into growth or fruit production.

Control.—The lime-sulphur sprays applied for Apple Scab (particularly at petal-fall) are valuable in destroying the active stages of this pest. Sulphur-shy varieties, such as *Lane's Prince Albert*, cannot receive this treatment and for them Derris or a special summer petroleum-oil emulsion is recommended. The most satisfactory control, however, is obtained by the use of a winter petroleum spray in February or March, and this will control Capsid too.

It is necessary to add a word of warning. It sometimes happens that the mites migrate, given suitable weather conditions, and drift through the air. From these migrants late summer attacks can arise, in spite of all previous spray treatment, and require further spraying with lime-sulphur or summer oil.

MINOR PESTS

The foregoing are the most widely occurring and most important insect pests of the apple. There are many others which can be very troublesome at times, such as the Fruit Rhynchites (*Rhynchites æquatus*), which drills holes in the sides of the fruit, the Twig Cutter (*Rhynchites cæruleus*), which cuts off the growing shoots in June, and the Apple Fruit Miner (*Argyresthia conjugella*), which makes holes in the side, and tunnels in the flesh of the fruit.

Mention should also be made of the Clay-coloured Weevil (*Otiorhynchus picipes*), which destroys grafts, and of the Pith Moth (*Blastodacna hellerella*), the larvæ of which destroy the opening buds.

Other minor pests are the Wood Leopard, the Goat Moth, Clearwing Moth, Lackey Moth, Case-bearers, Shothole Beetles, Scale Insects, and Chafer Beetle Grubs.

DISEASES OF THE APPLE

SCAB (*Venturia inæqualis*)

Often known as Black Spot, this is by far the most prevalent and most destructive disease of apples in this country. It attacks the leaves and fruits of all susceptible varieties and the bud-scales

162

and shoots of some, particularly the shoots of *Cox's Orange Pippin*, *Lord Suffield* and *Worcester Pearmain*. On these it forms blister-like pads (" pustules ") of fungous tissue that are exposed in spring when the bark covering them splits, and the spores formed on the surface of the pustule are dispersed, probably by wind-blown rain. On the leaves and fruits the disease appears as more or less circular, olive-green spots. These are velvety in texture at first because they are rapidly producing spores, but later they become rather dry and corky in the centre, when they more nearly resemble " scabs." Scab-infection is also responsible for indirect adverse effects. The pustules on the young shoots are a source of entry for the canker fungus, while fruits that are infected early and subsequently crack are victims of fruit-rotting organisms, such as brown rots and moulds, in storage. The crop can be greatly reduced by an early infection of the tiny fruitlets which causes them to drop.

Infection occurs in spring (primary) and throughout the summer months (secondary). As the host-tissues get older they become less susceptible to attack. Infection may arise from spores dispersed from (*a*) dead, over-wintered leaves on the ground, (*b*) pustules on the one-year-old shoots of susceptible varieties, (*c*) pustules on the bud-scales of susceptible varieties, e.g., *Worcester Pearmain*.

The prevalence of the disease greatly depends on the weather conditions in April and May. If, in general, this period is wet and cool, infection is encouraged, for these conditions are very suitable for the growth of the fungus and they tend also to hold the trees for a long period in a very susceptible condition. The converse is equally true. The soil, cultivation, manurial programme and the rootstock can each influence the susceptibility of the host-variety. Excessive nitrogenous manuring, which delays the ripening or " hardening " of the growth, and promotes luxuriant foliage that keeps the tree moist after rain, tends to increase susceptibility to Scab, while potash manuring tends to correct this, although the manurial problem is certainly not as simple as would appear from this generalization.

Control.—There are two chief methods : (*a*) general sanitation which includes collecting and burning, or burying fallen leaves in autumn, and pruning that opens up the head of the tree to light and air, and removes scabbed shoots ; (*b*) spraying to protect all new growth as it develops.

Lime-sulphur should be used at the following periods :

(1) *Green-cluster* or *green-bud*, when the short-stalked flower-buds

163

are still tightly clustered, the sepals are mostly covering the petals, and the truss is surrounded by a rosette of half-expanded leaves. Use 2½ per cent.

(2) *Pink-bud*, immediately pre-blossom, when individual flower-buds are well separated, the " cap " of petals not covered by the sepals and showing bold pink, and the truss is surrounded by fully-expanded leaves. Use 2 per cent.

(3) *Petal-fall*. When about three-quarters of the petals have fallen. Use 1 per cent. This spray can cause leaf-burn, leaf-drop, and fruit-drop on certain varieties, which should therefore be omitted from post-blossom applications of lime-sulphur. The chief are *Stirling Castle, Lane's Prince Albert, St. Cecilia*, and *Belle de Boskoop*, none of which are very susceptible under most conditions. It is probably wisest to omit *Stirling Castle* even before blossom, for this variety is excessively sensitive to the proximity of sulphur. In dry, warm summers, *Cox's Orange Pippin, Newton Wonder, Rival, Beauty of Bath, Duchess's Favourite*, and some others, are liable to show leaf- and fruit-drop from this spray. Where previous experience has shown this to be so, the strength may be reduced to ¾ per cent. or even to ⅔ per cent., or alternatively, a colloidal or other sulphur preparation, used at maker's directions, can be tried, though poor control of Red Spider must then be expected. A mixture of weak lime-sulphur with one of these other sulphur preparations may also be used.

(4) *Fruitlet*, two weeks after petal-fall. Repeat petal-fall spray. These four sprayings should suffice, but later ones can be given if necessary. It is always best to spray before infection occurs so that the fungicide can act protectively. Lead arsenate may be mixed with lime-sulphur *before* blossom for the control of cater-pillars ; indeed, the combined spray is more effective against Scab than lime-sulphur alone. Lead arsenate must not, however, be used with weak lime-sulphur of 1 per cent. or less because of the risk of arsenical spray damage, but there is no such risk in using it with colloidal or similar sulphur preparations. Dusting, either with ground sulphur or with copper-lime dust, is a useful adjunct to spraying, for application can be rapidly made. It should be borne in mind, however, that dust can drift over a wide area, and with sulphur, interplanted sulphur-shy varieties are liable to be adversely affected, while with copper-lime dust, the onset of prolonged, showery weather after application is likely to lead to copper injury on the fruits. This is usually seen as small, purplish-brown, circular, " peppering " of the skin, and its effects can be as

severe as those of Scab itself. Copper sprays and dusts are not generally safe on apples, and they are not widely recommended.

The type of soil, the weather conditions, the rootstock, and the manurial treatment each and all influence the trees' susceptibility not only to Scab but also to spray damage. Differing experiences in this connection are thus commonly met with, and no hard and fast ruling is possible.

In general, *Charles Ross, Stirling Castle, Egremont Russet, Belle de Boskoop*, and *King Edward VII* are highly resistant to Scab ; *Beauty of Bath, Gladstone, Lord Derby, Early Victoria, Grenadier, Rival, Lane's Prince Albert, John Standish*, and *Duchess's Favourite* are not very susceptible ; *Cox's Orange Pippin, Worcester Pearmain, Allington Pippin, Newton Wonder, Bramley's Seedling, Annie Elizabeth, Bismarck, James Grieve, Laxton's Superb*, and *Wellington* are usually very susceptible.

Scab sometimes develops on stored apples, but inadequate spraying early in the season is usually to blame. Spores from older infections are washed over the skin of the fruit in splashing rain just before picking and they give rise to Scab in the store, particularly when the fruit is stored in a moist condition.

CANKER *(Nectria galligena)*

This disease is very prevalent in some places, and is commonly said to be associated with poor drainage. At the same time it must be admitted that severe Canker is occasionally found on soils that are well drained though lacking perhaps some other desirable character, and in several instances heavy nitrogenous manuring has been suspect. Infection is most commonly centred around buds or fruit spurs, and not usually in wounds made by pruning until these have healed, when the fungus may become established on the calloused surface. Cankers can also occur where Woolly Aphis or Apple Scab has first attacked the shoots. The cankers often develop elliptically around the centre of infection, making more progress along the length of an affected branch than across the breadth. The cankered area is usually concentrically sunken and discoloured, and fringed, particularly in persistent wet weather, with a ridge of disintegrating stem tissue from which the covering bark flakes irregularly. Sometimes the canker girdles an affected branch, resulting in its death above the canker.

This fungus bears two kinds of fruit-body, each of which occurs on cankered areas : (*a*) Small, whitish pustules burst through the bark, often in rings around the centre of infection. They produce spores plentifully in spring and autumn and following wet periods in summer, and these are capable of causing fresh infections through wounds. (*b*) Crimson, spherical bodies densely clustered together in groups. Superficially, these resemble the eggs of the Fruit Tree Red Spider, but the latter are a brighter red, and are found on healthy as well as on diseased areas. These fruit-bodies produce spores in large quantities in winter and early spring, and are a very real source of danger in the plantation. Apple Canker can also cause an " Eye Rot " of the fruits, but there is a similar disease, " Dry Eye Rot," caused by another fungus, *Botrytis cinerea*, with which it can easily be confused.

Control.—The best method is to cut out the cankers as soon as they are seen, and before the fruit-bodies have been produced. A sharp gouge, or hollow-ground chisel, is very useful for this work with older cankers where the wood is affected. All diseased tissue, and dead or dying branches, should be removed and burnt. Though it is commonly held that the wounds should be dressed with a white-lead paint to prevent reinfection, experience shows that if the cankers are thoroughly cleaned out painting is unnecessary, except on varieties prone to Silver Leaf infection (see page 170). The normal programme of sprays for Scab control has little direct effect on the incidence of Canker, but the control of Scab and Woolly Aphis is indirectly helpful. Badly-drained soil should be aerated by some system of drainage.

Many commercial and garden varieties are susceptible, notably : *Worcester Pearmain, James Grieve, Laxton's Superb, Ellison's Orange, Warner's King, Beauty of Bath,* and *Cox's Orange Pippin.* This last is more susceptible on No. XII and No. XVI than on most other stocks in the Malling series. *Bramley's Seedling, Grenadier, Early Victoria, Gladstone,* and *Newton Wonder* are among the most resistant.

BROWN ROTS. (See also Plum, page 314.)

Blossom Wilt and Spur Canker (Sclerotinia laxa, forma mali).

The flowers become infected by spores from pustules on dead twigs and withered flowers infected during the previous year. Sometimes the whole flower-truss withers and dies when the fungus grows down the flower-stalks and into the spur, forming a canker there which sometimes extends into the branch and kills it. The variety *Lord Derby* is very susceptible, trees being sometimes so badly infected that the branch system is almost completely destroyed by the disease.

Control.—Cankered branches and spurs should be promptly cut out and burnt, for *grey-coloured* pustules of spores arise on them in the following spring, and these can, in their turn, infect the flower-trusses and so continue the disease-cycle. Spraying late in the dormant period with 5 per cent. tar-distillate wash, very thoroughly applied, burns up the fungus pustules on any dead spurs that may have been overlooked in the cutting out. It is thought that this fungus is distinct from that which causes Blossom Wilt of plums and cherries, hence, that apples are not likely to be infected from plums and cherries.

Brown Rot (*Sclerotinia fructigena*).

This disease causes heavy loss of picked fruits every year, The fungus produces a brown, soft rot of the fruits on the tree, usually within a few weeks of picking-time, and also after they are picked and stored. Spore-pustules are very readily produced on an infected fruit (often in concentric rings around the point of infection). Under certain storage conditions, however, a fruit may turn black and may bear few or no pustules.

The fungus gains entry through a blemish where the skin has been pierced ; this may happen in many ways—bird pecks, insect punctures, cracking following Scab or spray-injury, hail or spur damage, rough handling during picking operations, etc. A diseased fruit is capable of infecting a healthy one by persistent contact on the tree or in the orchard box. It is wise, therefore, to discard blemished apples at picking-time and during the preliminary sorting before the fruits are graded.

A *spur-canker* similar to that caused by the Blossom-Wilt fungus sometimes occurs on soft-wooded varieties such as *Lord Derby* or *James Grieve*. This arises when the fungus grows along the fruit-stalk and into the spur.

Control.—Dead spurs, which early in the following summer bear relatively large, *buff-coloured* pustules of spores (by which this fungus can be distinguished from that causing Blossom Wilt and Spur Canker) should be cut out and burnt. If infected fruits are permitted to remain on the tree, they become mummified, and, in late spring and summer, are covered with the familiar buff-coloured spore-pustules. Mummied fruits should be removed and burnt where they persist for they are a common source of infection. The spores are light and powdery when dry, and are easily blown about in the wind. They are also carried by insects.

SOOTY BLOTCH (*Glœodes pomigena*)
(See Plum, page 316.)

APPLE DISEASES

APPLE MILDEW *(Podosphæra leucotricha)*

Affected shoots and leaves are white and mealy; flower-trusses present a similar appearance, and the flowers are small and distorted and often fail to open. The buds become infected in summer and remain all winter with the fungus spawn alive between the bud-scales. Such buds grow out into mildewed shoots in spring or they may be killed and fail to start into growth. The powdery spores produced on affected shoots and leaves carry infection to healthy tissues throughout the summer; the spores are mainly wind-borne. A winter stage in the form of tiny, black fruit-bodies, produced mainly on the shoots, is thought to have little influence in this country in the annual cycle of the fungus.

Occasionally the fruits are affected. *Lane's Prince Albert* is a susceptible variety to this form of attack. Affected fruits bear the whitish, mealy fungus-tissue on the surface of the skin.

Control.—Cut out and burn infected shoots and flower-trusses, and spray as for Apple Scab.

Among susceptible varieties are *Lane's Prince Albert, Cox's Orange Pippin, Bismarck, Bramley's Seedling, Allington Pippin. Worcester Pearmain* is resistant.

ARMILLARIA ROOT ROT (Honey Fungus—*Armillaria mellea*)

This fungus is commonly found in woodlands, and it frequently causes a serious disease of conifers and of broad-leaved trees. It spreads underground by means of strands of fungous tissue that look rather like black boot-laces; indeed, the disease is often said to be caused by the "Boot-lace Fungus." When these "boot-laces" come into contact with the roots of fruit trees, they are able to attack them, causing infection which spreads back along the infected roots to the collar of the tree. Eventually all the feeding roots may be affected and the tree dies. This may happen suddenly if the collar of the tree is soon girdled by the fungal strands. The fungus produces sporing fructifications, usually in autumn, on the dead stump and on the surface of the soil immediately surrounding it. These fructifications are like toadstools and are usually densely clustered together. The "umbrella" of each "toadstool" may be from 2 to 4 inches across; it is honey-coloured and, when young, often bears dark scales on its upper surface. The bark of a dead tree can readily be peeled off, and underneath, between it and the wood, fan-like layers of white fungous tissue, sometimes flecked with black lines, will be found. These layers have a distinct fungous odour.

The fungus attacks not only apples but pears, plums, cherries, gooseberries, and even strawberries. The leaves usually show the first symptoms; they are yellow, sickly, and may be wilting, often over the whole tree, but since there are other possible causes (see Waterlogging on next page) an accurate diagnosis must depend on the presence or absence of the fungus.

Control.—It is most important that trees dying from attack by Armillaria Root Rot should be promptly removed and burnt. The digging-out of broken roots must be thorough and the sites of affected trees should be kept cultivated and, if planted up at all, used for annual crops such as potatoes for several years before being replanted with fruit. Frequent stirring of the soil breaks up any " boot-laces " or bits of affected root that remain, helps to dry them out and prevents the fungus from becoming re-established on the roots of weeds, which help to keep it going. Close watch must be kept on adjoining trees for the first symptoms of attack, and any that show these should also be promptly removed and destroyed, for only in this way can an outbreak be checked. Cleared woodland is best put down to arable crops for at least three or four years before fruit is planted up, otherwise there is considerable risk of infection.

Since the fungus can also attack fencing poles, these should be well creosoted before setting up.

When thinning out overcrowded plantations, it is bad practice to leave tree-stumps in the ground, for the fungus can become established on them by means of spores dispersed from the toad-stools.

CROWN GALL *(Bacterium tumefaciens)*

This bacterium occurs in the soil and infects the roots of apple stocks and many other plants including raspberries, loganberries, and blackberries. Wounds are a common source of entry. The bacterium produces galls or tumours of up to several inches in diameter on the roots and on the stems near soil level. East Malling No. VII rootstock is particularly susceptible and the scion variety is said to influence the susceptibility of the stock.

The galls probably have little adverse effect on the tree in most cases.

Control.—Affected stocks should not be planted in nurseries and precautions should be taken to protect wounded surfaces from infection; e.g., by covering with grafting-wax, or by dipping the roots in a mercurial preparation.

SILVER LEAF

This disease is described under Plum, page 315. In apple the most susceptible variety is *Newton Wonder*, infection often being associated with a condition popularly known as " Papery Bark." The danger to *Newton* is in *top*-grafting it to another variety, when large wounds must be made on established trees. These wounds provide a ready place of entry for the fungus, and they are therefore best avoided by using one of the modern methods of framework grafting (see page 49).

FUNCTIONAL DISEASES

These are non-parasitic diseases due to some disorder in the life-processes of the plant. They are not caused by a fungus or by any other organism of that nature.

WATERLOGGING

The leaf symptoms are similar in some respects to those caused by Armillaria Root Rot in that the foliage wilts and looks sickly. Where Waterlogging, also popularly known as " The Death," is the cause, the wilting usually occurs fairly suddenly and within a few weeks after growth starts in the spring, and it may affect only certain branches or parts of them. An affected tree may have looked quite healthy during the previous year, whereas with Armillaria Root Rot the chronic stage is frequently preceded by symptoms of steady decline. The signs of fungus attack present with Armillaria—toadstools in autumn, " boot-laces " in the soil, a mat of fungus under the bark near the soil—are absent with Waterlogging, and the clue to the cause of the trouble will be found in the root-system. Some of the larger roots show internal, and possibly external, discoloration, and they often have an alcoholic smell when freshly cut. This is due to their having been asphyxiated in a soil where the air has been excluded by excessive moisture, especially in badly-drained soils or pockets of soil during very wet weather in autumn and winter. In severe cases the affected tree dies, though in mild cases only certain branches, or even flower-trusses here and there, may wilt and die. Another form of the disease is sometimes found when inefficiently staked trees that have been rocked by autumn gales and have then been subjected to heavy rains show a rotting and discoloration of the bark of the collar at ground level, even in an apparently well-drained soil. Here, the soil surrounding the collar has been " puddled " by

170

the intermittent pressure of the swaying trunk and by frequent rain, it becomes impervious, and the excess water collects in the crater so formed, eventually resulting in rotting at the collar and the death of the tree.

Symptoms superficially similar to those of a mild attack of Water-logging are caused by excessive spraying with tar- or petroleum-oil, but in this case, though the bark may be blackened, the roots usually show no sign of disease, and the buds either fail to break, or fail to develop leaves after starting into growth. Severe potash-deficiency occasionally results in the wilting and death in spring of flower-trusses on individual branches of trees, though here, as in Armillaria Root Rot, the appearance of sickliness is a gradual, and not a sudden, process. It can be identified in earlier stages by general debility and a scorching of the margins of the leaves in summer. (See Leaf-Scorch, below.)

Control.—Some system of drainage must be adopted for in-efficiently drained and very retentive soils. Shallower planting on such soils also is recommended. Very badly drained soils should not be planted with fruit. Efficient staking of trees, especially where they are exposed to gales, will do much to prevent the " collar-rot " form. As no organism is responsible for this disease, an affected tree is not a source of infection for its neighbours. Some form of this disorder has been found on almost every type of fruit grown in this country (e.g., see Root Rot in Strawberries).

LEAF-SCORCH

The symptoms are best seen in summer when the leaves (especially the older ones) of an affected tree have a reddish-brown margin, sometimes, in bad cases, $\frac{1}{2}$ inch deep. Towards the end of summer, these margins become dark-brown, dry and crisp, and the leaves are " hard " and usually up-curled. The fruits on such a tree are often smaller than normal, lack colour and flavour, and do not store well. Trees on certain rootstocks, e.g., East Malling No. II and No. V, are particularly susceptible, and *Cox's Orange Pippin* and *Bramley's Seedling* are susceptible varieties.

Control.—This form of Leaf-Scorch can be controlled by regular applications of a potassic manure (e.g., sulphate of potash at 3–4 cwt. per acre) to restore the nutritional balance.

The symptoms should not be confused with those of lime-sulphur injury, which are superficially similar but are seen usually within a week of a spray-application. Furthermore, the *young* leaves, as well as the older ones, are affected, the spray-burn being present in reddish patches, often, but not always, concentrated around the leaf-margins, which later turn dark brown and die.

A different form of Leaf-Scorch from that caused by shortage of available potash is sometimes found on apples, and it is due to a shortage of available magnesium in the soil. The chief symptom is a thin " feel " with discoloration between the veins, and later in the season these areas die and become brown, thus giving rise to the usual descriptive phrase " interveinal scorch," as opposed to the "marginal scorch" of potash deficiency. The fruits are poor and lack flavour in severe cases. Magnesium deficiency is most usually found on light soils deficient in lime, and is most pronounced in wet seasons. An interesting practical point is that symptoms of magnesium deficiency can be induced on some soils by the too liberal use of artificial potassic manure to correct potash deficiency.

Control.—Magnesian limestone should be substituted for ordinary lime in the normal process of liming acid soils. A top-dressing of dung to established trees would also be helpful. These deficiencies are not confined to apples among the fruits ; pears, gooseberries, currants, strawberries, raspberries, plums, and cherries are all liable to be affected.

CHLOROSIS

This disease can affect pears, plums, cherries, and soft fruits as well as apples, the typical symptoms being pronounced loss of green colour and consequent yellowing or even bleaching of the leaves, especially those on the young growths. It is caused by deficiency of available iron, which, though necessary for healthy plant growth in only very small quantities—it is a so-called " trace element "—is nevertheless essential to the proper functioning of the leaves. Without iron the leaves are unable to form the green colouring matter (chlorophyll) on which the nutrition of the plant depends.

Chlorosis is commonly associated with fruit trees growing in soils rich in lime, and is thus frequently referred to as " lime-induced " Chlorosis.*

Control.—Since Chlorosis is due more usually to lack of availability of iron than to its absence, the disease is not likely to be curable by the application of iron salts to the soil, especially where the Chlorosis is " lime-induced." Spraying the leaves with ferrous sulphate at 4 lb. per 100 gallons as a constituent of the 1 per cent.

* Chlorosis can in some stages be confused with nitrogen or other deficiency symptoms. (See " The Diagnosis of Mineral Deficiencies in Plants " by Dr. T. Wallace.)

post-blossom lime-sulphur spray for Scab is effective, or solid compounds of iron, such as ferric citrate or tartrate, can be injected into holes bored in the trunk or branches. Grassing-down, too, tends to cure Chlorosis.

BITTER PIT

Within a few weeks before picking-time, affected fruits show scattered, slightly sunken, circular areas, in the skin, often on only one side of the fruit. The spots vary in colour from dark green to brownish-green. If the skin covering an affected area of fruit be peeled off, the flesh immediately underneath each sunken area will be seen to be collapsed and brown in little pockets of up to a quarter of an inch in diameter. The pockets are not usually very deep-seated in the flesh, but are more often near, or at the surface. This disease is known as " tree pit." " Storage pit," another form with the same, or similar, underlying causes, occurs in apples after a period of storage, though the fruits may have seemed quite normal when picked. In storage pit, especially in the early stages, the skin is often not sunken but merely mottled, though when the flesh of the fruit is exposed, numerous, scattered pockets, pinkish-brown in colour, will be seen sometimes extending nearly to the core. These pockets tend to be smaller individually than those of tree-pit, and are often concentrated at the calyx end.

The cause of these troubles is very complex and rather obscure. Hard pruning ; hot, dry weather (particularly when accompanied by hot winds) ; and, with storage pit, too-early picking, are all said to predispose the fruit to the disorder. Bitter Pit is often met with on fruit from young trees just coming into bearing and on those from older trees with only a light crop. Heavy nitrogenous manuring also is suspect.

Control.—The grower is able to control some of these factors, and his general line of attack is to do all he can to promote steady, balanced growth throughout the season, to check biennial bearing as much as possible by judicious pruning and crop regulation, and to avoid any practice likely to cause violent fluctuations in the reaction of the trees. To some extent, however, he must be at the mercy of the weather. Bitter Pit has been observed in many varieties. Most of the better-known ones are liable to show symptoms under appropriate conditions, but among these, *Allington Pippin, Newton Wonder, Edward VII, Bramley's Seedling, Lane's Prince Albert,* and *Cox's Orange Pippin* are perhaps the worst offenders.

APPLE DISEASES

" GLASSINESS " OR WATER-CORE

Affected apples show yellowish areas, which appear to be water-soaked or " glassy," in the flesh and often around the core. Natural recovery sometimes occurs, but apples prone to Glassiness are liable eventually to develop Bitter Pit. In severe cases, affected fruits appear to have been badly bruised, and in advanced cases, an extensive, discoloured " crinkle " may appear on the surface.

The underlying causes are rather obscure but are known to be similar to those of tree pit. (See page 173.) The varieties *Rival*, *St. Everard*, and *Lord Lambourne* are prone to Glassiness.

LENTICEL SPOT

Certain varieties, *Allington Pippin* prominent among them, are specially prone to develop small, brown, often sunken spots centred around the lenticels or breathing pores of the fruit. Again, the main cause is functional, though soft fungal rots may eventually set in at some of the affected places. The trouble is much worse in some seasons than others and affected fruits store badly. Soil and weather conditions are thought to be largely responsible. Fruits that develop Lenticel Spot also frequently show symptoms of other functional disorders.

Control.—As with Bitter Pit and Glassiness, the grower can do little apart from striving to maintain steady growth conditions.

SUN SCALD

Following a period of very high temperature in summer, apples and other fruits may show signs of burning on the exposed sunny side. Such conditions occurred at the end of August, 1942, when Sun Scald was very prevalent on apples. Severely affected fruits showed circular, brown, flattened areas sometimes surrounded by a bright, reddish halo, while those only slightly affected showed roughly circular, pale areas or deeper flushes of colour, depending on the variety. Occasionally, and especially on *Allington*, the affected area resembled a bruise, and was arc-like and sunken, and of a deep red or purplish-red colour. The baked, brown area on severely affected fruits was commonly a source of entry for the Brown Rot fungus.

Control.—There is no means of control under commercial conditions where shading would clearly be impracticable, but in gardens it might be feasible to shade the fruits by some simple means in the hottest part of the day during heat-wave conditions. The malady is not of frequent occurrence in this country.

THE APPLE

DISEASES AND PESTS :
DIAGNOSIS TABLE

DAMAGE	PROBABLE CAUSE
Branches and Twigs	*Pests*
Patches of " woolly " white substance; gall-like swellings	American Blight (Woolly Aphis)
Branches tunnelled	Goat Moth or Wood Leopard Moth
	Diseases
Cankerous formations—patches of small, whitish pustules or crimson spherical bodies grouped together	Canker
Sheets of fungous tissue under bark at base of trunk. Long black strands like " boot-laces " on roots and in adjacent soil ; tree dies	Armillaria
Galls on roots	Crown Gall
Shoots and Foliage (including Blossom)	*Pests*
Leaves, opening buds and blossom attacked by small " looping," green caterpillars	Winter Moths
Leaves and buds eaten and spun together by small brown, green or yellowish caterpillars which wriggle quickly backwards when disturbed. Eaten buds wilt or shrivel and turn brown. Leaves again attacked in mid-July	Tortrix Moths
Leaves curled and attacked by masses of small, green or bluish-purple aphides. Young shoots twisted, stunted and deformed	Greenfly or Rosy Apple Aphis
Flower buds eaten from within in April by black-headed white grub ; blossoms remain capped, turn brown, and drop	Apple Blossom Weevil
Buds attacked by yellow to pale green, flattish, aphis-like creature ; buds turn brown and drop after opening. Drops of white, sticky wax proclaim nature of trouble	Apple Sucker
Small black marks turning brown and then into holes on young leaves—quickly moving aphis-like creatures. Young shoots distorted and with corky scars	Capsid Bug
Leaves turn brownish	Red Spider
Growing shoots cut off in June	Twig Cutter
	Diseases
Leaves and shoots white and mealy ; flowers small and distorted, may fail to open, trusses white and mealy	Apple Mildew
Blister-like " pustules " on shoots and possibly on bud scales in Spring. Circular, olive-green spots, turning corky and scab-like later	Scab
Silvery sheen foliage on affected branch—brown stain in wood	" Silver Leaf "
Flowers wither, turn brown and die ; subsequently spurs cankered with grey pustules	Brown Rot, Blossom Wilt
Apparently healthy tree wilts or fails to grow soon after bud burst ; blossom trusses and surrounding leaves only may be affected above ground	Waterlogging
Reddish-brown margins to leaves in summer, becoming dark-brown, " hard " and usually up-curled	Potash-deficiency. Leaf Scorch
Brownish, scorched areas between veins, leaves feel thin.	Magnesium - deficiency. Leaf Scorch
Leaves yellow or bleached particularly on young growths	Chlorosis
Fruit	*Pests*
Small fruits eaten by green, " looping " caterpillars	Winter Moths
Small patches of skin on developed fruit eaten by tiny larvæ	Tortrix Moths
Small deformed and disfigured fruits, corky scars	Apple Capsid Bug
Fruits drop off in June and July—hole in side with wet mass of black frass exuding ; long, corky lines on fruits may be present	Apple Sawfly

DISEASES AND PESTS : DIAGNOSIS TABLE—*continued*

DAMAGE	PROBABLE CAUSE
Fruit	*Pests*
Maggoty apples ; may drop just before picking-time	Codling Moth
Holes drilled in sides of fruits	Fruit Rhynchites
Holes drilled in sides of fruits and tunnels in flesh	Apple Fruit Miner
Brown, often sunken areas around lenticels	Lenticel Spot
Spherical discoloured areas on sunny side of fruit, may be pale, flushed, or brown	Sun Scald
	Diseases
Eye-rot of ripening fruit	Canker
Brown, soft rot of fruit on tree (usually within few weeks of picking), also while stored ; buff spore pustules often in rings. Stored fruit may turn black ; fruit left on tree becomes mummified	Brown Rot
Brownish, roughly circular, indefinite smudges on skin (usually near picking-time)	Sooty Blotch
Skin white and mealy	Apple Mildew
Circular olive-green spots, velvety at first, turning corky and scab-like in summer	Scab
Slightly sunken, small, dark green to brownish-green spots within a few weeks before picking ; brownish pockets in flesh after picking	Bitter Pit

Once the trouble has been diagnosed, the reader should refer to the paragraph dealing with the particular disease and pest, and also to the Guide to Spraying, see page 142.

VARIETIES OF APPLE

With all the knowledge that is now available on the subject of apple culture, it should be possible to grow any variety successfully provided its particular requirements in such matters as manuring and cross-pollination are known. By force of circumstance, however, most of this experimental data has been obtained from a comparatively small number of commercial varieties, and such information as is available about the so-called garden varieties is of an empirical nature, based on the observations of a large number of individuals working under varying conditions. This accounts for the wide differences of opinion so frequently expressed at horticultural club meetings and at shows concerning merits and demerits of any particular " garden " variety. It is a pity that the great work which is being done for commercial varieties of fruits by the Royal Horticultural Society in the National Fruit Trials at Wisley, cannot be repeated for garden varieties grown under garden conditions. Many varieties, both new and old, which would never survive the rigorous tests to which a commercial variety is submitted, might well assume a new importance when grown under the more congenial conditions of a garden ; other varieties which still figure in nurserymen's catalogues might, under official trial, be definitely relegated to the obscurity for which they have been long overdue, whilst yet a third class, once condemned for some fault of growth, cropping or disease, might yet yield to treatment under modern methods and so regain their lost popularity.

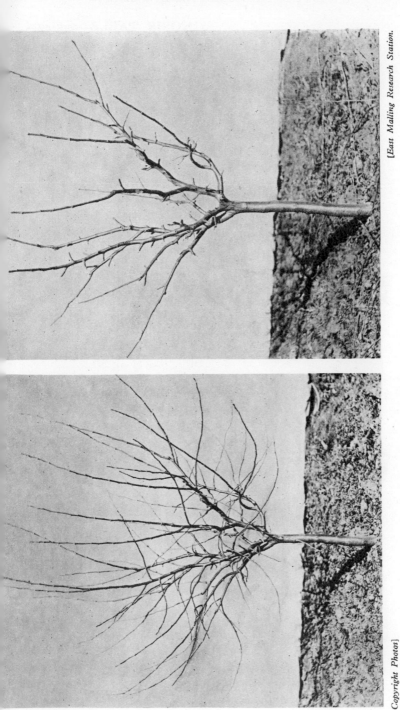

[East Malling Research Station.

WINTER PRUNING.

Bush Apple "Lane's Prince Albert" (six years old).

Before and——   ——after Pruning.

DESCRIPTIVE NOTES ON VARIETIES

DESSERT APPLES

Adam's Pearmain. A medium-sized conical apple, red and yellow with russet. Fine flavour. Season, December to March. Upright habit. Makes thin branches. An excellent late apple for the garden.

Advance. See Laxton's Advance.

Allington Pippin. A round, medium-sized apple, primrose-yellow with red. Season, October to January. A curious flavour not liked by all. Good cropper. Good when baked. Tree makes very twiggy growth and needs skilful pruning. Best grown as espalier. Susceptible to capsid bug. Liable to Lenticel spot in store.

American Mother. A medium-sized, conical-shaped fruit, rich yellow, flushed and striped deep red. Yellow flesh. Sweet and aromatic. Season, October. Uncertain cropper. Makes a good garden standard.

Barnack Beauty. A medium-sized conical apple, yellow and red with handsome open eye. Season, December to March. Crisp and acid flavour. A tip-bearer best grown as a bush. Somewhat shy cropper. Said to succeed on chalky subsoils.

Beauty of Bath. A small, round, flat apple, brilliant dappled scarlet widely grown for market as a first early. Season, early August. Strong growth, untidy habit and rather tip-bearing. Slow bearer. Very difficult to train in any artificial form. Fruit drops easily. Flavour fair and crisp but not first-rate.

Belle de Boskoop. Medium to large round apple, rather like a Blenheim Orange. Season, December to April. Very strong grower, useful for top-grafting on to standard trees. A very good flavour when ripe, but unattractive in appearance. Triploid variety, see page 191, and needs cross-pollinator diploid variety. (See colour plate facing page 193.)

Blenheim Orange. A medium to large-sized, flattish, round apple, rich golden-yellow, tinged and striped red and russeted. Fine flavour, firm yellow flesh. Season, November to January. Dessert or cooking. Good cropper when established but usually takes some years to come into full bearing. Stores well. Does well on medium loam and heavy soils, and in grass orchards. Forms strong and spreading standard or bush and needs maximum space. Does well as bush on East Malling No. IX. Prune hard to form tree and then lightly. Susceptible to scab and canker. Triploid variety, see page 191, and needs cross-pollinator diploid variety.

Brownlees Russet. A medium-sized, flattish and irregular-shaped apple, a reddish-brown and green russet. Excellent flavour, tender, greenish-white flesh, sharp but sweet and juicy. Season, January to April. A good cropper and stores well. A fine garden fruit, usually grown in bush form. Self-sterile.

Calville Blanche. A round medium-sized dessert apple, pale yellow. Season, January to April. Widely grown in France. Does well under glass.

Charles Ross. A large-sized, beautiful round apple, very similar in appearance to Peasgood Nonsuch, highly coloured, a greenish-yellow, streaked with red and patched with russet. Fair flavour, brisk, sweet and juicy. Season, September to November. A good cropper but does not store well and should therefore be used as soon as possible after picking. Thrives in chalky soils and in any locality. Best grown as pyramid or bush. The fruit is too large for cordon culture. Recommended for pot culture. A fine exhibition fruit and popular market variety, but not recommended for orchard culture. Self-sterile. Resistant to scab but susceptible to canker and capsid bug.

Christmas Pearmain. A medium-sized, round to conical apple, rosy cheek and russeted. Fine flavour, crisp flesh, slightly sub-acid. Season, December to January. Good bearer. Upright and neat in growth and recommended for inclusion in small private gardens in bush or cordon form. Said to be partially self-fertile.

Claygate Pearmain. A medium-sized, round to conical apple, somewhat similar to Ribston Pippin, dull green, flushed reddish-brown and russeted. Fine flavour, tender greenish-white flesh, luscious and aromatic. Season, December to February. A good cropper and stores well if gathered when perfectly ripe. Makes a big, spreading tree in standard form, but some growers recommend bush-form culture only. Recommended for garden culture. One of the best late dessert apples. Self-sterile.

Cornish Gillyflower. A medium-sized, oval and conical apple, ribbed at top, yellowish-green and red and thinly russeted. Excellent flavour, crisp yellowish-white flesh. Season, December to February. Of somewhat straggly growth. A good cropper in mild districts. Tip-bearer. Self-sterile.

Cox's Orange Pippin. A medium-sized, round to conical apple, a golden to orange and red russet skin. Delicious flavour, tender yellowish-white flesh, luscious and aromatic. A good cropper, storing well. Season, November to January. Does well only in well-, but not excessively-drained soils. In the colder districts the shelter of a wall should be provided. Medium vigour but twiggy in growth. It makes a fair orchard tree on loamy soil. Also grown as bush, espalier and cordon. Recommended for private garden culture. Also suitable for pot culture. Needs regular pruning and heavy potash supplies. Self-sterile, but cross-pollinates well with Worcester Pearmain and James Grieve. (See colour plate facing page 193.)

Crimson Cox's Orange Pippin. This is merely a coloured bud-sport of the above—a deep claret-coloured apple otherwise possessing all the characteristics of Cox's Orange Pippin.

D'Arcy Spice. A medium-sized, roundish, flattened and ribbed apple, a brownish russet over dull yellow. Excellent flavour, firm greenish flesh, sweet, juicy and aromatic. Season, March to May. A fair cropper but needs very careful handling and storing. Comes from Essex, where it is much prized but considered difficult to grow. Self-sterile.

Devonshire Quarrenden. A small, roundish, flattened apple, a deep crimson in colour. Good flavour, crisp greenish flesh, juicy and refreshing. Season, August to September. A good cropper but does not keep in store. Does well almost anywhere and in any kind of soil. Forms an upright standard, pyramid, bush or cordon. An old English favourite early dessert apple. *Extremely susceptible to scab.* Self-sterile. Fruit too small for modern markets.

Duchess's Favourite. A small, attractive-looking apple of distinctive appearance, bright " cricket-ball " crimson, with a markedly open eye. Once widely grown for market, but now considered too small. Season, September. Distinctly woody texture. Needs fruit thinning. Small tree.

Duke of Devonshire. A small to medium-sized, round apple, a dull yellow, tinged with russet. Excellent flavour, crisp flesh, juicy, sweet and aromatic. Season, March to April. A good cropper and storing well. Gather in October. Makes a good standard or may be grown as espalier, bush or cordon. Suitable for garden culture. One of the best of the late dessert apples. *Highly resistant to scab.* Said to be partially self-fertile.

Egremont Russet. A medium-sized, round and flattish apple, golden yellow and russeted. Very good flavour, firm greenish flesh, crisp and sweet. Season, October to November. A good cropper for immediate use. A good garden variety, forming a neat standard, pyramid or bush. One of the most attractive and best of the russets. Said to be partially self-fertile. Resistant to scab.

Ellison's Orange. A fairly large-sized, round to conical apple, said to be a cross between Cox and Calville Blanche, somewhat similar to Cox's Orange Pippin in shape and colour. Greenish-yellow, streaked with red. Of tender yellowish flesh, luscious and aromatic. Flavour not universally popular. Season, September to October. A good cropper for immediate use. Does well on almost any soil, thriving in the Midlands and Northern Counties. Forms an upright, neat standard or bush and is recommended for garden culture. Also grown as cordon. A popular market fruit. Said to be partially self-fertile. Good for top grafting.

Exquisite. See Laxton's Exquisite.

Fortune. See Laxton's Fortune.

Gladstone. See Mr. Gladstone.

Golden Reinette. See Heusgen's Golden Reinette.

Heusgen's Golden Reinette. A medium-sized, round and flattened apple, bright scarlet and russeted over. Good flavour, crisp yellowish flesh. Season, March. A good cropper and keeps well. Grown as standard, bush or espalier. Makes a small tree. Recommended for garden culture. One of the best of the late dessert apples. Self-sterile.

Irish Peach. A small-sized, roundish to conical and flattened apple, pale yellow, mottled and streaked red. Good flavour, tender greenish flesh, rich and aromatic. This is about the earliest of all dessert apples. Season, July to August. A fairly good cropper but does not keep and is best eaten as gathered. Does well in the Midlands and Northern districts. Apt to make a weak standard and is best grown in bush form. Prune lightly. A fine early dessert apple. Said to be partially self-fertile. *Very early flowerer.*

James Grieve. A medium-sized, round to conical apple, greenish-yellow, striped and tinged with red. Fine flavour, soft yellowish flesh, juicy and sweet. Season, September to October. Good cropper but does not keep in store. For market it should be picked in August and September while still hard and green, and to obtain large fruit, heavy thinning is necessary. Makes a compact neat bush excellent for private gardens or for growing in pots. Does well in the Midlands and the colder Northern counties. Susceptible to canker and brown rot. Said to be partly self-fertile.

John Standish. A small-sized, roundish and flattened apple, bright red in colour. Good flavour, firm white flesh, luscious and sweet. Season, December to March or April. A good cropper and keeping well. Grown as standard, bush, espalier or cordon. A useful late dessert. Self-sterile. Not of first-class flavour.

King of the Pippins. A medium-sized, roundish, oblong-shaped apple, a deep golden-yellow flushed reddish-brown. Fair flavour, crisp yellowish-white flesh, juicy and slightly sharp. Season, October to December. A prolific cropper and keeping well. Does best in the warmer districts and in light, well-drained soil. Makes a medium-sized, upright standard, bush, espalier or cordon. Said to be partially self-fertile.

King's Acre Pippin. A medium-sized, round to conical apple, somewhat similar in appearance to Ribston Pippin, dull yellowish-orange, warmly flushed and russeted. Excellent flavour, firm, yellowish flesh, juicy and highly flavoured. Season, January to March. A medium cropper and stores well. Forms a moderately robust standard, bush or trained tree. Suitable for garden culture. Needs a warm sunny situation to colour well. A good late dessert apple. Said to be partially self-fertile.

Lady Sudeley. A fairly large-sized round to conical and flat-shaped apple, a rich golden-yellow, with crimson stripes. Good flavour, tender, yellowish flesh, juicy and crisp. Season, August to September. A prolific cropper but will not keep and is best eaten as soon as possible after picking. Does well in all soils and situations, including colder localities, in standard, bush, espalier or cordon form. Recommended for garden and pot culture. Said to be partially self-fertile.

Langley Pippin. A small-sized, tall, conical-shaped apple, yellow with crimson blotches and streaks. Good flavour, soft, yellowish flesh, juicy and pleasant. Season, August to September. A good cropper but does not keep and is best eaten as soon after picking as possible. Likes a medium loam soil and forms a moderately weak, drooping tree. May be grown as espalier. Not an orchard fruit. Self-sterile.

Laxton's Advance. A small to medium-sized, round to conical apple, a bright crimson in colour. A cross between Cox's Orange Pippin and Mr. Gladstone, recently introduced. Good flavour, with crisp and juicy flesh. Season, early August. Does not keep and is best eaten as soon as possible after picking. Recommended for garden culture. Self-sterile.

Laxton's Epicure. A medium-sized, flattened, round apple, a pale yellow, flushed and striped bright crimson. Good flavour, tender, yellowish flesh, juicy and sweet. Season, September. Best eaten as soon after picking as possible. Grown in all forms. Suitable for garden culture. Said to be self-fertile.

Laxton's Exquisite. A fairly large-sized, round to oval apple, yellow flaked and streaked red. Fine flavour, tender and juicy, similar to Cox's Orange Pippin. Season, September to October. A good cropper for immediate use. The fruit should be picked as soon as ready and not left too long on the tree. A very good second-early dessert apple. Said to be self-fertile. Susceptible to scab.

Laxton's Fortune. Medium round to conical apple, rosy red when ripe. Very juicy and sweet. Season, October to November. One of the most promising of new varieties. Tree of medium vigour. Suitable for garden culture. Flowers with Cox.

Laxton's Pearmain. A medium to large, round to conical and flattened apple, yellowish, tinted ruddy brown and rosy cheek. Fine flavour, firm, yellowish flesh, sweet and juicy. Season, December to April. Keeps well. Recommended for private garden culture. Said to be self-fertile.

Laxton's Superb. A large to medium-sized, round to conical and flattened apple, green to yellow flushed red and rosy cheek. Fine flavour, crisp, white flesh, juicy, sweet and aromatic. Season, November to March. A good cropper and keeps well. Makes a strong and spreading standard or bush. Also grown as espalier or cordon. Recommended for private garden culture. Has been widely planted in recent years.

Lord Lambourne. A medium-sized, round to conical apple, a rich red flushed over yellow. Good flavour, firm, yellowish flesh, juicy and sweet but greasy. Season, October to December. A good cropper but does not keep long. Makes a fine strong standard or bush, espalier or cordon. Recommended for private garden culture.

May Queen. Medium size, yellow and red with some russet. Good flavour. Very late. Season, November to May. Makes small tree. Suitable for small garden.

Melba. A large round dessert apple, pinkish red with marked bloom, very juicy. Season, end of August. A Canadian variety.

Mr. Gladstone. A medium-sized, round to conical and ribbed apple, yellow flushed and striped dark red. Fair flavour, soft, greenish flesh, juicy and aromatic. Season, July to August. A good cropper for immediate use, preferably eaten as picked. Does well in the Midlands and in Northern localities. Somewhat weak grower and a tip-bearer. Best grown as a bush. One of the earliest dessert apples. Unsuitable for artificial forms of culture. Does not respond well to spur pruning. Said to be partially self-fertile.

Miller's Seedling. A small to medium-sized oval apple, yellow with primrose flush. Season, August to September only. One of the juiciest apples. Much in demand on the London market in some seasons. A weak grower but neat and upright in habit. *Fruit must be thinned.* Suitable for small bush, fuseau or cordon. Recommended for garden culture. Quite unsuitable for standard.

Ontario. See list of Cooking Apples.

Orleans Reinette. A medium-sized, flattened round-shaped apple, somewhat similar to a Blenheim Orange but smaller. A golden russet, flushed deep red. Superb flavour, sweet, crisp and juicy. Some experts maintain this to be the best flavoured of all dessert apples. Season, December to February. A fair cropper and storing well. Makes a strong-growing standard or bush, espalier or cordon. One of the best dessert apples. Said to be partially self-fertile. Somewhat susceptible to canker. Apt to shrivel in store if picked too soon.

Owen Thomas. A small early dessert apple, a cross between Cox's Orange Pippin and Mr. Gladstone. Makes a weak, straggling tree. Good for gardens but unsuitable for orchard culture. The fruit resembles that of Mr. Gladstone, but has a distinct Cox's Orange flavour. Season, August.

Patricia. A large round dessert apple, cricket ball red, very juicy. Season, early September. A Canadian variety.

Pitmaston Pine Apple. Small conical golden russet with yellow flesh. Of exceptional flavour. Described by Bunyard as "honeyed." Now seldom grown, but should do well as cordon, fuseau or bush in small garden.

Ribston Pippin. A medium to fairly large-sized, round to conical, apple, a dull greenish-yellow and brownish-red russet. Superb flavour, firm yellowish-white flesh, crisp, slightly dry and aromatic. Season, November to January. A moderately good cropper and stores well. Does best in sheltered situations and warm soil where ample moisture is available. Makes a moderate-sized standard, espalier, or bush, or may be grown as cordon ; also useful for pot culture. One of the best desserts. Somewhat liable to canker and scab. Needs hard pruning. Self-sterile. (See Triploid varieties, page 191.) Needs diploid pollinator.

Rival. A medium to fairly large-sized, round, flattened and somewhat uneven-shaped apple, a beautiful salmon-carmine and rich yellow. Fair flavour, firm white flesh, crisp and juicy. Season, October to December. A fairly good cropper, keeping well into December. Makes a medium-sized, neat-growing standard or bush, pyramid or cordon. Of decorative value in the garden, recommended for pot culture, good for dessert, or cooking and also grown for market. The bad shape makes it difficult to pack in boxes. Said to be partially self-fertile. "Sulphur shy "—i.e., the leaf is susceptible to scorch when sprayed with lime-sulphur.

Rosemary Russet. A medium-sized, flattened, conical apple, yellow, flushed brick-red and russeted, with a very long, thin stalk. Good flavour, crisp yellowish flesh, juicy and aromatic. Season, December to March. A good cropper and stores well. Makes a moderate-sized standard or bush, or may be grown as espalier or cordon. Suitable for garden culture. One of the best late dessert russets. Self-sterile.

St. Cecilia. A medium-sized, oval apple, a beautiful golden-yellow, striped and flushed crimson. Fine flavour, sweet, juicy and rich. Season, January to March. A good cropper and stores well. Makes a weak, drooping bush. Not suitable for espalier or cordon. Recommended for private garden culture. Self-sterile. The leaf is susceptible to sulphur damage when sprayed.

DESSERT APPLES

St. Edmund's Russet. A small to medium-sized, round and flattened apple, an even, light golden russet all over. Excellent flavour, tender flesh, juicy and aromatic. Season, September to October. A good cropper but does not store and should be eaten as soon as possible after picking. Makes a moderately robust standard or bush. Too much of a tip-bearer for artificial forms. Said to be partially self-fertile. Much recommended as a small garden bush on Number IX stock.

St. Everard. A medium-sized, round-shaped apple, yellow and heavily striped with crimson. " Cox " flavour, tender, yellowish flesh, sweet and luscious. Season, August to September. A good cropper for *immediate* use and best eaten as soon as gathered. Forms a moderate-sized standard, or compact and sturdy bush and is one of the best early dessert apples and a good garden fruit, although a shy cropper. May also be grown as espalier or cordon. Said to be self-fertile. Susceptible to glassiness.

Sturmer Pippin. A small to medium-sized apple, a greenish-yellow with dull russet and rosy cheek. Good flavour, firm, greenish-white flesh, crisp, sweet and luscious. Season, March to May. A heavy cropper and stores well, provided it is not gathered too soon. Forms a compact standard or bush in almost any soil, or may be grown as espalier or cordon. A fine dessert apple. Said to be partially self-fertile. *Must have a warm, sunny situation to finish properly.*

Sunset. Medium, $2\frac{1}{2} \times 1\frac{1}{2}$ inches, round, flattish apple ; golden yellow with bright crimson flush. Stem long in a deep russeted cavity. Eye closed or part open in a shallow, slightly ribbed basin, sepals long. Flesh, yellowish, crisp and juicy, of very good flavour. Season, October to February. Tree vigorous and fertile. Leaves deep green. Mid-season flowering.

Wagener. A medium-sized, flattened, and somewhat irregular, round-shaped apple, yellow with bright crimson cheek. Good flavour, firm, yellowish flesh, juicy and tart. Season, April to June. A good cropper and storing well. Makes a compact-growing standard or bush. A good late cooker. Also used for dessert when fully ripe. Self-sterile.

Wealthy. A medium to fairly large-sized, beautiful round to conical apple, golden, striped and tinted with crimson or pale yellow. Nice flavour, soft and juicy. Season, October to December. A good cropper and keeps into December. Makes a compact-growing standard or bush, espalier or cordon. Useful alike for dessert or culinary purposes. Self-sterile.

White Transparent. Medium to large, round to conical, cooking or dessert. Season, mid-August. A Russian variety.

Winter Queening. Medium size, conical, yellow background almost covered with dark crimson. Handsome, good flavour, yellow flesh. Season December to March. Rather uncertain cropper.

Woolbrook Pippin. A new seedling of promise from Devonshire. A medium-sized round apple, red and yellow with some russet and a wide open eye. Season, after Christmas.

Worcester Pearmain. A medium-sized, round to conical apple, a bright crimson all over. Fair flavour, firm white flesh, crisp, luscious and aromatic. Season, September to early October. A good cropper and cold-stores well. Should not be gathered until well coloured and ripe. Does equally well in the colder districts and forms a medium-sized standard or bush. A good market apple and recommended for private garden culture. Said to be partially self-fertile. A tip-bearer and not suitable for artificial forms. Susceptible to scab and canker but one of the most regular cropping of all apples.

COOKING APPLES

Alfriston. A large-sized, round, flattened and irregular-shaped apple, greenish-yellow and russeted. Yellowish flesh, crisp, sharp and juicy. Delicious when cooked. Season, November to April. A good cropper and storing well provided the fruit is not picked before it is properly mature—early in November. Hardy even in the colder localities and grown in all forms, standard, espalier, bush or cordon. Self-sterile.

Annie Elizabeth. A medium to large-sized, round to conical and irregular-shaped apple, a glossy yellow, striped and splashed with bright scarlet. Crisp, white flesh, sharp and juicy. For cooking or dessert. Season, January to April. A good cropper when established. Makes a strong, upright standard or bush, or may be grown as espalier or cordon. Does well in the Midlands and Northern counties, and is an especial favourite in the Midlands and West Midlands. A good orchard apple. Said to be partially self-fertile. Late flowerer. Slow to come into bearing. Susceptible to scab and canker. Fruit very short on the stalk and apt to blow off. Susceptible to "scald" in store. Should be wrapped.

Arthur Turner. A new large-sized, round, green apple in season in August and September. Strong growing.

Barnack Beauty. See under Dessert Apples.

Bramley's Seedling. A large, flattened, round-shaped apple, green and sometimes tinted or flushed dull red. Fine flavour; firm, yellowish flesh, juicy and sharp. Season, November to March. A heavy cropper and stores well. Does well even in the colder Northern districts and on almost any soil, including heavy and dry soils, and forms a strong standard or bush. One of the best cooking apples. Too strong growing for small gardens or for cordon culture. Susceptible to scab, resistant to canker. Triploid variety, see page 191, and needs cross-pollinating diploid variety.

Crawley Beauty. A beautiful, large, even, round apple, green with red stripes. Good flavour, crisp, white flesh, juicy and tart. Season, March to April. A heavy cropper and stores well. Makes a fine standard or bush for garden culture. *Very late flowering.* Self-sterile.

Crimson Bramley. Similar in shape, size and other characteristics to the well-known Bramley's Seedling, which see, but coloured a bright crimson all over.

Early Victoria (Emneth Early). A medium-sized, conical apple, light green in colour. Good flavour, soft, white flesh, juicy and tart. Season, July to August. A heavy cropper but does not store and should be used as soon as possible. Market fruit should be picked before it is fully grown. Forms a fairly strong standard or bush and is one of the best early codlings for garden culture and market, thriving even in the colder localities. Needs severe fruit thinning. Said to be partially self-fertile. Responds well to spur-pruning.

Edward VII. A large, round to oblong apple, pale yellow with slight reddish-brown flush. Good flavour, firm flesh, juicy and sharp. Season, January to April. A shy cropper, storing well. Forms a strong-growing standard, bush or trained tree and is especially recommended for pyramid form. Good orchard or garden fruit. Late flowerer. Plant with Royal Jubilee, Crawley Beauty, or Court Pendu Plat for cross-pollination.

Emneth Early. See Early Victoria.

Encore. A very large flattened, round to oval apple, yellowish-green in colour and sometimes flushed and striped red. Fair flavour, tender, greenish flesh, juicy and acid. Season, November to June. A heavy cropper and keeps well in store. Forms a strong-growing standard or bush. Good orchard or garden fruit. Said to be partially self-fertile.

Grenadier. A large, flattened, round to conical apple, light green to pale yellow in colour. Good flavour, crisp, juicy and sharp. Season, end of July to October. A good cropper but does not store and should be used as soon after picking as possible. Makes a moderately strong-growing standard or bush and does well even in cold districts and on heavy soils. A popular market apple. A tip-bearer unsuitable for artificial forms. Prune lightly. Said to be partially self-fertile.

Lane's Prince Albert. A beautiful large, round to oval apple, light greenish-yellow, flushed and striped red. Good cooker, tender, white flesh, juicy and sharp. Season, November to April. A heavy cropper and storing well up to six months. A dwarf grower of pendulous habit best grown in bush or cordon form. Hardy even in the colder localities. This is one of the very best of all cooking apples for garden culture in any form. " Sulphur-shy."

Lord Derby. A very large, round to conical and irregular-shaped apple, dark green turning golden-yellow. Firm, yellowish flesh, juicy and sub-acid. Season, November to December. A good cropper and storing well to December. Does well in almost any soil, including heavy and cold land, and in the Midlands and Northern districts. Grown in all forms, standard, bush, espalier, or cordon. Recommended for private garden culture. Said to be partially self-fertile. Susceptible to brown rot.

Lord Grosvenor. A large, round to conical and irregular-shaped apple, a pale yellow turning whitish when ripe. Good flavour, tender, white flesh, juicy and sharp. Season, August to October. A heavy bearer but does not store and should be used as soon after picking as possible. Does well in all districts in almost any soil and may be grown in any form. Needs well thinning. Susceptible to scab. Said to be partially self-fertile.

Mank's Codlin. A conical apple of medium size, greenish-yellow with a slight red flush. Weak growth, but a heavy cropper. A cooking apple ripening in August. Has very beautiful large flowers.

Monarch (Seabrook's). A rather large, beautiful, roundish apple, light green with rosy flush. Good flavour, firm, white flesh, juicy and sub-acid. Season, October to April. A heavy cropper and storing well. Forms a vigorous and spreading standard or bush, or may be grown as espalier. Needs well thinning. Self-sterile.

Newton Wonder. A medium to large-sized, even and round-shaped apple, green to golden and beautifully tinged with red. Good flavour, crisp, yellowish-white flesh, juicy and acid. Season, October to April. A splendid cropper and stores well. A very strong grower. Does well almost anywhere, including the colder Northern districts, and forms a strong, spreading standard or bush. Late flowerer and slow to come into bearing. Too strong growing for cordon or small garden culture. One of the best late cookers and valuable for market or exhibition. Prune lightly. Said to be self-fertile.

Peasgood Nonsuch. A very large, even and round-shaped apple, a pale yellow and bright crimson. Good flavour, soft, yellowish flesh, juicy and acid. Season, October to November. A good cropper, but does not store and should be used as soon as possible after picking. Does well on light and chalky soils, where it makes a medium-sized standard or bush. In cold areas it does best trained on a wall. One of the best exhibition apples. Very subject to canker and brown rot. Self-sterile.

Rev. W. Wilks. A very large, flattened and ribbed, round-shaped apple, a pale yellow with red spots and slashes. Good flavour, tender, white flesh, juicy and sub-acid. Season, October to November. A good cropper but does not keep and should be used as soon as possible after picking. Of dwarf habit but hardy and usually grown as a bush in private gardens. Useful for exhibition. Subject to scab and brown rot. Said to be self-fertile.

Royal Jubilee. A large, beautiful round to conical apple, of clear golden hue. Good flavour, firm, yellowish flesh, juicy and sharp. Season, October to December. A good cropper and stores well. Does well even in the colder localities, forming a sturdy, flat-headed standard, bush or espalier. Recommended for garden culture. *Very late flowerer.* Self-sterile.

Seabrook's Monarch. See Monarch.

Stirling Castle. A medium to large-sized, even, flattened and round-shaped apple, yellow to green in colour. Good flavour, tender, whitish flesh, juicy and sharp. Season, September to October. A good cropper but does not keep and should be used as soon as possible after being picked. On light soil, even in the colder districts, makes a compact, dwarf-growing bush, espalier or cordon. *Should never be sprayed with lime-sulphur. Very prone to canker.* Partially self-fertile.

Transparent de Croncels. A large-sized, round to oblong-shaped apple, a pale whitish-yellow, sometimes slightly flushed red. Good flavour, tender yellowish-white flesh, juicy and sub-acid. Season, October to December. A good cropper but does not keep long after picking. Makes a good standard or bush. Self-sterile.

CRAB APPLES

Underleaf. A roundish apple of medium size, greenish-yellow, with slight russet on one side. Grown as a standard tree in grass orchards in the West Midlands, where it is considered one of the most reliable croppers. A cooking apple in season from November to February. *Very late flowerer.*

Wagener. See Dessert Apples.

Warner's King. A very large, flattened, round to conical apple, a pale yellow in colour. Good flavour, tender, whitish flesh, juicy and sub-acid. Season, November. A good cropper for immediate use. Does not like cold soils. Makes a large, spreading standard or bush, or may be grown in other forms. A good mid-season cooker for the orchard. Very prone to canker. Self-sterile. Triploid variety, see page 191.

Wellington. A medium-sized, flattened, even and round-shaped apple, pale yellow tinged red and russeted. Excellent flavour, crisp, whitish flesh, juicy and sharp. Season, December to March. A good cropper and stores well until March. Forms a moderately strong-growing standard or bush, or may be grown in other forms. Hardy even in the colder Northern localities, but highly susceptible to scab and canker. Self-sterile. Many experts consider it to be the best baking apple.

ORNAMENTAL AND FLOWERING CRAB APPLES

From the decorative point of view no fruit garden or orchard is complete without its ornamental and flowering Crabs. The lovely soft and delicate blossoms are borne in early spring, while the highly-decorative fruits may be made into delicious preserve or jelly. Crabs require cultivation and treatment similar to that of the ordinary apple. Many varieties are highly susceptible to scab.

CRABS WITH DECORATIVE FLOWERS AND FRUIT

Dartmouth. Has beautiful, white-tinted flowers in early spring, followed by medium-sized, plum-shaped fruits with a purplish-red bloom. The fruit is very prolific and makes excellent preserve.

John Downie. Snowed under in early spring with a mass of lovely white flowers, followed by clusters of conical orange and scarlet fruits, which are very beautiful. A prolific bearer, but susceptible to scab.

Paul's Imperial Scarlet. Covered with lovely blossom in early spring, followed by a heavy crop of beautiful crimson miniature apples.

Siberian Scarlet. The masses of lovely blossom, borne in early spring, are followed by a prolific crop of cherry-like, bright scarlet fruits borne on longish stems. Excellent for preserve.

Transcendent. The beautiful and prolific blossom is followed by a heavy crop of very decorative golden-yellow fruits with rosy cheeks, borne on longish stems. This fruit has quite a good flavour.

Veitch's Scarlet. This is a cross between Siberian Scarlet Crab and King of the Pippins Apple. The lovely blossoms are followed by a prolific crop of ovate fruits, a rich crimson-scarlet over golden-yellow, with a pleasant sharp flavour.

CRABS TO GROW FOR DECORATION ALONE

Pyrus Malus aldenhamensis. An attractive tree, 8 to 12 feet or more in height, with masses of wine-coloured blossoms in spring and purple-red fruit in autumn.

Pyrus M. floribunda. The popular " Japanese Crab " is a very attractive tree, rather spreading in habit, reaching some 12 to 15 feet in height and nearly as much in diameter. In April and May it is smothered in lovely blossoms, which are crimson in bud, but open rosy-purple and as they become older turn pale pink to white. The fruit is of little account. *P. M. f. atrosanguinea* is a variety of the above with flowers of a somewhat deeper shade and turning to a rosy-pink.

Pyrus M. Eleyi. Is a beautiful tree 15 to 20 feet in height with vinous-red flowers, which open early and blend with the young, coppery foliage. The bunches of wine-red fruits are an added attraction in autumn.

Pyrus M. Lemoinei. Is a purple-flowering Crab even more intense in colouring than *P. M. Eleyi*, which it resembles in other respects.

Pyrus M. Neidzwetzkyana. The Manchurian Crab is a conspicuous tree some 15 to 20 feet in height and with reddish-purple blossom and fruit. The foliage also assumes a purple hue as the season advances.

Pyrus Sargentii. A native of China, is a delightful, spreading bush, some 5 to 6 feet in height, with clusters of white blossoms, each individual flower being quite large. The fruits which follow are a brilliant scarlet. Budded on standard and half-standard crab stocks, this makes a graceful and attractive tree.

CIDER APPLES

There are three types of apple especially cultivated for the manufacture of cider and these are known as Bittersweets, Sweets and Sharps. All require cultivation and general treatment similar to that given to ordinary apples. Bittersweets are largely used in the production of good-class bottled cider. Sweets, being of a milder flavour and possessing more sugar, are useful for blending purposes ; and Sharps also are useful for blending. No one should attempt planting cider apples without first consulting the National Fruit and Cider Institute, Long Ashton, Bristol, or his county advisory officer.

Bittersweets

Belle Norman. An early variety.

Chisel Jersey. A useful late variety, recommended by the National Fruit and Cider Institute, Long Ashton, Bristol. A good cropper.

Cummy Norman. A mid-season variety.

Dabinett. An excellent cider apple recommended by the Ministry of Agriculture, and the Midland Cider Makers' Association. A good and early cropper. Ready in October.

Eggleton Styre. Can be used without blending. (Mid-season.)

Knotted Kernel. A high-grade crimson cider apple recommended by the Ministry of Agriculture, and the Midland Cider Makers' Association. A regular and heavy cropper, ready in October.

CIDER APPLES

Major. A favourite cider apple with the Devonshire Manufacturers. Early and prolific and recommended by the Ministry of Agriculture.

Royal Wilding. A useful blending apple ready November to December. Recommended by the Ministry of Agriculture, and the Midland Cider Makers' Association. A medium cropper.

Strawberry Norman. A fine-class cider apple, recommended by the Ministry of Agriculture, and the Gloucestershire Agricultural Department. A good cropper, ready October to November.

White Close Pippin. A useful blending apple ready in November. Recommended by the National Fruit and Cider Institute, Bristol. Also useful for jam-making.

Sweets

Killerton Sweet. An early variety.

Slack ma Girdle. An excellent late sweet apple, recommended by the Ministry of Agriculture, and the Midland Cider Makers' Association, and a favourite variety with the Devonshire manufacturers. A good cropper, ready November to December. Also good for jam-making.

Sweet Alford. A highly-recommended cider apple and a favourite in all quarters. Crops well and ready in mid-season (November). Also useful for jam-making.

Sweet Coppin. Another good sweet variety, recommended by the Midland Cider Makers' Association, and the Gloucestershire Agricultural Department. Rich flavour and regular cropper. Ready in October.

White Jersey. A good early sweet apple, recommended by the National Fruit and Cider Institute, Long Ashton, Bristol. A fine and regular cropper. Ready October.

Sharps

Blackwell Red. An early variety.

Cap of Liberty. Also known as Bloody Butcher and Red Soldier. An excellent vintage cider apple, recommended by the Ministry of Agriculture, and the Midland Cider Makers' Association. A good and regular cropper. Ready November. Prefers a heavy soil of the limestone formation.

Crimson King. Another fine mid-season cider apple.

Dymock Red. A mid-season variety.

Foxwhelp. A splendid vintage cider apple, highly recommended by the Ministry of Agriculture, and the Midland Cider Makers' Association. Regular cropper. Ready November.

Kingston Black. Another highly-recommended and much-prized variety. Excellent cropper and ready in November. Susceptible to canker and with definite soil preferences. Can be used without blending.

New Foxwhelp. A mid-season variety.

Ponsford. A late variety recommended by the National Fruit and Cider Institute, Long Ashton, Bristol. Crops well and stores December to April. Also useful for jam-making.

Reinette Obry. Another very highly-prized late cider apple, recommended for all parts. A strong cropper, ready November to December. Also useful for jam-making.

NOTE ON IDENTIFICATION OF VARIETIES

The foregoing notes make no pretence to give a full description of the hundreds of varieties of apples that exist in this country. For this purpose two books of reference are available, which, studied together, should enable the reader to identify any but the most obscure local varieties. These books are E. A. Bunyard's " Handbook of Fruits," Apples and Pears, and H. V. Taylor's " The Apples of England."

When sending apples or other fruits to experts for identification, it is very important to send at least two typical specimens of the fruit, together with specimens of the current year's shoot growth and as full a description as possible of the age and growth habit of the tree and of the conditions under which it is being grown.

The specimens should be packed in such a way as to ensure that they arrive in a fresh condition.

EARLY-BLOSSOMING VARIETIES OF APPLE

Beauty of Bath	(D)	Mank's Codling	(C)
Belle de Boskoop	(D)	Mr. Gladstone	(D)
Duchess's Favourite	(D)	Oslin	(C)
Egremont Russet	(D)	Rev. W. Wilks	(C)
Gravenstein	(D)	Ribston Pippin	(D)
Irish Peach	(D)	St. Edmund's Russet	(D)
Langley Pippin	(D)	Wagener	(D)

LATE BLOSSOMING VARIETIES

American Mother	(D)	Heusgen's Golden Reinette	(D)
Annie Elizabeth	(C)	Transparent de Croncels	(C)
Christmas Pearmain	(D)	White Transparent	(C)
Edward VII	(C)		

VERY LATE BLOSSOMING VARIETIES

Court Pendu Plat	(D)	Royal Jubilee	(C)
Crawley Beauty	(C)	Underleaf	(C)

C = Cooking ; D = Dessert.

A certain limited number of apple varieties will set a fair to good percentage of their blossom in most seasons when planted entirely alone. In spite of this the wisest course is never to plant a single variety in any quantity without making sure that some other variety with a similar blossoming period is planted within easy flying distance of bees and other insects as a " pollinator."

When planting any of the varieties given in the above lists of early and late blossomers, care should be taken to see that the pollinator variety belongs to the same group of blossoming period.

TRIPLOID VARIETIES

As to varieties not included in these lists, there should be no difficulty, as these should usually cross-pollinate.

TRIPLOID VARIETIES OF APPLE

Belle de Boskoop	(D)	Gravenstein	(D)
Blenheim Orange	(D)	Ribston Pippin	(D)
Bramley's Seedling	(C)	Warner's King	(C)

C = Cooking; D = Dessert.

Recent research into the cytology of the apple by M. B. Crane and his fellow-workers at the John Innes Horticultural Institution at Merton has revealed an important difference in the genetical make-up of a small group of apple varieties, a difference in the number of chromosomes or " carriers of the hereditary factors." The majority of apple varieties are " diploids " and have 34 chromosomes, but this small group of " triploids " have 51 chromosomes.*

Crane's experiments in cross-pollinating varieties of these two groups showed that the triploid varieties would not cross-pollinate each other at all well, and were not very good cross-pollinators even for the vast majority of diploid varieties.

In the light of present knowledge, therefore, it would be clearly unwise to plant up an orchard of triploid varieties only or to use them as pollinators for each other. For the commercial grower it would also seem important, when planting *Bramley's Seedling*, to include at least two other varieties, both diploids, to ensure efficient cross-pollination of the *Bramley's Seedling* and of each other.

APPLES SPECIALLY RECOMMENDED FOR GARDEN PLANTING
Dessert

Adam's Pearmain	Heusgen's Golden	Laxton's Superb
American Mother	Reinette	May Queen
Claygate Pearmain	Irish Peach	Miller's Seedling
Christmas Pearmain	James Grieve	Orleans Reinette
Cornish Gillyflower	King's Acre Pippin	Pitmaston Pine Apple
Cox's Orange Pippin	Laxton's Advance	Rosemary Russet
D'Arcy Spice	Laxton's Epicure	St. Edmund's Russet
Duke of Devonshire	Laxton's Exquisite	St. Everard
Egremont Russet	Laxton's Fortune	Sturmer Pippin

Cookers

Arthur Turner	Encore	Monarch
Bramley's Seedling	Grenadier	Peasgood Nonsuch
Crawley Beauty	Lane's Prince Albert	Rev. W. Wilks
Early Victoria	Lord Derby	Royal Jubilee
Edward VII	Lord Grosvenor	Stirling Castle

* This work is lucidly dealt with in " The Apple," by Sir Daniel Hall and M. B. Crane, published in 1933; see also " The Fertility Rules in Fruit Planting," John Innes Leaflet No. 4, published by the John Innes Horticultural Institution, London, S.W.19.

APPLE VARIETIES

DESSERT APPLES FOR GROWING ON WEST WALLS

Claygate Pearmain	Laxton's Exquisite	Ribston Pippin
Cox's Orange Pippin	Orleans Reinette	Rosemary Russet
King's Acre Pippin	Pitmaston Pine Apple	Sturmer Pippin

ORDER OF RIPENING OF SOME GOOD VARIETIES
Early (July–September)

Variety	Garden or Orchard	Dessert or Cooking
Arthur Turner	Garden	Cooking (*Immediate use*)
Early Victoria	Garden or Orchard	Cooking (*Immediate use*)
Irish Peach	Garden	Dessert (*Immediate use*)
Lady Sudeley	Garden or Orchard	Dessert (*Immediate use*)
Grenadier	Garden or Orchard	Cooking (*Immediate use*)
Miller's Seedling	Garden	Dessert (*Immediate use*)
Mr. Gladstone	Garden or Orchard	Dessert (*Immediate use*)
Devonshire Quarrenden	Garden or Orchard	Dessert (*Immediate use*)
Laxton's Advance	Garden	Dessert (*Immediate use*)
Laxton's Epicure	Garden	Dessert (*Immediate use*)

Mid-Season (September–November)

Variety	Garden or Orchard	Dessert or Cooking
American Mother	Garden or Orchard	Dessert
Charles Ross	Garden	Dessert and Cooking
Egremont Russet	Garden	Dessert
Ellison's Orange	Garden or Orchard	Dessert (*Immediate use*)
Golden Noble	Garden	Cooking (*Stores well*)
James Grieve	Garden	Dessert (*Immediate use*)
King of the Pippins	Garden or Orchard	Dessert (*Keeps well*)
Laxton's Exquisite	Garden	Dessert (*Immediate use*)
Laxton's Fortune	Garden or Orchard	Dessert (*Immediate use*)
Lord Derby	Garden or Orchard	Cooking (*Keeps to December*)
Peasgood Nonsuch	Garden or Orchard	Dessert and Cooking
Rev. W. Wilks	Garden	Cooking (*Immediate use*)
Rival	Garden or Orchard	Dessert (*Stores well*)
Worcester Pearmain	Garden or Orchard	Dessert (*Immediate use*)

Ripening Late (November–March)

Variety	Garden or Orchard	Dessert or Cooking
Adam's Pearmain	Garden	Dessert
Annie Elizabeth	Garden or Orchard	Cooking and Dessert
Belle de Boskoop	Orchard	Dessert and Cooking
Blenheim Orange	Orchard	Dessert and Cooking
Bramley's Seedling	Orchard	Cooking
Cox's Orange Pippin	Garden or Orchard	Dessert
Lane's Prince Albert	Garden or Orchard	Cooking
Laxton's Superb	Garden or Orchard	Dessert
Monarch	Garden or Orchard	Cooking
Newton Wonder	Orchard	Cooking
King's Acre Pippin	Garden or Orchard	Dessert
Orleans Reinette	Garden or Orchard	Dessert
Ribston Pippin	Garden or Orchard	Dessert
St. Cecilia	Garden	Dessert
Sturmer Pippin	Garden	Dessert

APPLES—*Belle de Boskoop* (*top*) and *Cox's Orange Pippin* (*bottom*)

APPLE VARIETIES

SELECTION OF GOOD COMMERCIAL VARIETIES

Bramley's Seedling (C)
Cox's Orange Pippin (D)
Early Victoria (C)
Ellison's Orange (D)

Grenadier (C)
James Grieve (D)
Laxton's Superb (D)
Lord Derby (C)

Miller's Seedling (D)
Newton Wonder (C)
Worcester Pearmain (D)

SCAB RESISTANT VARIETIES

Variety	Garden or Orchard	Dessert or Cooking
Belle de Boskoop	Garden or Orchard	Dessert or Cooking
Charles Ross	Garden	Dessert
Court Pendu Plat	Garden or Orchard	Dessert
Duke of Devonshire	Garden or Orchard	Dessert
Early Victoria	Garden or Orchard	Cooking
Grenadier	Garden or Orchard	Cooking
Egremont Russet	Garden	Dessert
King Edward VII	Garden or Orchard	Cooking
Northern Greening	Orchard	Cooking
Wyken Pippin	Garden or Orchard	Dessert

ESPECIALLY HARDY SORTS

Variety	Garden or Orchard	Dessert or Cooking
Alfriston	Garden or Orchard	Cooking
Allington Pippin	Garden or Orchard	Dessert
Beauty of Bath	Garden or Orchard	Dessert
Bramley's Seedling	Garden or Orchard	Cooking
Devonshire Quarrenden	Garden or Orchard	Dessert
Early Victoria	Garden or Orchard	Cooking
Grenadier	Garden or Orchard	Cooking
James Grieve	Garden or Orchard	Dessert
Lady Sudeley	Garden or Orchard	Dessert
Lane's Prince Albert	Garden	Cooking
Mr. Gladstone	Garden or Orchard	Dessert
Newton Wonder	Orchard	Cooking

VARIETIES FOR GROWING IN POTS

Variety	Early or Late	Dessert or Cooking
Calville Blanche	Late	Dessert
Charles Ross	Mid-season	Dessert
Cox's Orange Pippin	Mid-season	Dessert
Ellison's Orange	Mid-season	Dessert
Irish Peach	Early	Dessert
James Grieve	Early	Dessert
Lady Sudeley	Mid-season	Dessert
Laxton's Exquisite	Mid-season	Dessert
Laxton's Fortune	Mid-season	Dessert
Laxton's Premier	Early	Dessert
Melba	Early	Dessert
Miller's Seedling	Mid-season	Dessert
Patricia	Mid-season	Dessert
Peasgood Nonsuch	Mid-season	Cooking
Rev. W. Wilks	Mid-season	Cooking
Wealthy	Late	Dessert
White Transparent	Early	Dessert or Cooking

APPLE VARIETIES

VARIETIES FOR EXHIBITION AT AMATEUR SHOWS

Variety	Garden or Orchard	Dessert or Cooking
Bramley's Seedling	Garden or Orchard	Cooking
Charles Eyre	Orchard	Cooking
Charles Ross	Garden	Dessert
Cox's Orange Pippin	Garden or Orchard	Dessert
Ellison's Orange	Garden or Orchard	Dessert
Fortune	Garden	Dessert
John Standish	Garden or Orchard	Dessert
Laxton's Superb	Garden or Orchard	Dessert
Newton Wonder	Orchard	Cooking
Peasgood Nonsuch	Garden or Orchard	Cooking
Rev. W. Wilks	Garden or Orchard	Cooking
Rival	Garden or Orchard	Dessert
Wealthy	Garden or Orchard	Dessert
Worcester Pearmain	Garden or Orchard	Dessert

BEST-FLAVOURED APPLES

Dessert

Variety	Garden or Orchard	Season of Best Flavour
Adam's Pearmain	Garden	December–March
Blenheim Orange	Orchard	December
Brownlees Russet	Garden	December–March
Claygate Pearmain	Garden	December–March
Cornish Gillyflower	Orchard	December–March
Cox's Orange Pippin	Garden	December
D'Arcy Spice	Garden or Orchard	February–May
Egremont Russet	Garden	October
Irish Peach	Garden	September
James Grieve	Garden or Orchard	September
King's Acre Pippin	Garden	February
Laxton's Exquisite	Garden	September
Laxton's Superb	Garden or Orchard	January–March
Mother (American)	Garden or Orchard	End of October
Orleans Reinette	Garden or Orchard	December–March
Owen Thomas	Garden	August
Pitmaston Pine Apple	Garden	March
Ribston Pippin	Garden or Orchard	November
Rosemary Russet	Garden	February
St. Edmund's Russet	Garden	September
St. Everard	Garden	September

Cookers

Variety	Garden or Orchard	Best time to Cook
Annie Elizabeth	Garden or Orchard	January–February
Bramley's Seedling	Garden or Orchard	January–February
Edward VII	Garden or Orchard	February–March
Grenadier	Garden or Orchard	August
Lane's Prince Albert	Garden	October–November
Newton Wonder	Garden or Orchard	February–March
Rev. W. Wilks	Garden or Orchard	September–October
Stirling Castle	Garden or Orchard	September
Wellington	Garden or Orchard	March

Note.—Those readers who are interested in the best-flavoured varieties of fruits should not fail to read " The Anatomy of Dessert," by E. A. Bunyard.

194

APPLE VARIETIES

SELECTION OF VERY LARGE VARIETIES

Variety	Garden or Orchard	Dessert or Cooking
Beauty of Kent	Garden or Orchard	Cooking
Bramley's Seedling	Garden or Orchard	Cooking
Charles Eyre	Garden	Cooking
Charles Ross	Garden	Dessert
Gascoyne's Scarlet	Orchard	Dessert or Cooking
Gloria Mundi	Garden	Cooking
King of Tompkin's County	Orchard, Pot or Garden	Dessert
Lane's Prince Albert	Garden	Cooking
Lord Derby	Garden or Orchard	Cooking
Mère de Ménage	Garden or Orchard	Cooking
Newton Wonder	Orchard	Cooking
Peacemaker	Garden or Orchard	Dessert
Peasgood Nonsuch	Garden	Cooking
Rev. W. Wilks	Garden	Cooking

VARIETIES SUITABLE FOR PARTICULAR FORMS
Standards or Half-Standards
Plant 30 to 40 feet apart, according to Variety and Soil

Variety	Stock	Dessert or Cooking
American Mother	East Malling XVI or Selected Crab	Dessert
Beauty of Bath	East Malling XVI or Selected Crab	Dessert
Belle de Boskoop	East Malling XVI or Selected Crab	Dessert
Blenheim Orange	East Malling XVI or Selected Crab	Dessert
Bramley's Seedling	East Malling XVI or Selected Crab	Cooking
Crawley Beauty	East Malling XVI or Selected Crab	Cooking
Duke of Devonshire	East Malling XVI or Selected Crab	Dessert
Edward VII	East Malling XVI or Selected Crab	Cooking
Grenadier	East Malling XVI or Selected Crab	Cooking
Laxton's Superb	East Malling XVI or Selected Crab	Dessert
Monarch	East Malling XVI or Selected Crab	Cooking
Orleans Reinette	East Malling XVI or Selected Crab	Dessert

Bushes
Plant 10 to 30 feet apart, according to Stock, Soil and Variety

Variety	Stock	Dessert or Cooking
Adam's Pearmain	East Malling IX, II, I or XVI	Dessert
Barnack Beauty	East Malling IX, II, I or XVI	Dessert
Bramley's Seedling	East Malling IX, II, I or XVI	Cooking
Charles Ross	East Malling IX, II, I or XVI	Dessert
Cornish Gillyflower	East Malling IX, II, I or XVI	Dessert
Cox's Orange Pippin	East Malling IX, II, I or XVI	Dessert
Egremont Russet	East Malling IX, II, I or XVI	Dessert
Ellison's Orange	East Malling IX, II, I or XVI	Dessert
Gladstone	East Malling II, I or XVI	Dessert
Grenadier	East Malling II, I or XVI	Cooking
Irish Peach	East Malling II, I or XVI	Dessert
Langley's Pippin	East Malling II, I or XVI	Dessert
Lord Lambourne	East Malling IX, II, I or XVI	Dessert
Orleans Reinette	East Malling IX, II, I or XVI	Dessert
Owen Thomas	East Malling II, I or XVI	Dessert
St. Cecilia	East Malling IX, II, I or XVI	Dessert
Worcester Pearmain	East Malling IX, II, I or XVI	Dessert

APPLE VARIETIES

VARIETIES SUITABLE FOR GROWING AS DWARF PYRAMID AND CORDON

Plant Single-vertical or oblique cordon 2 to 3 feet apart,
Single-horizontal cordon 10 to 12 feet apart,
Double-U cordon 5 to 6 feet apart, and
Dwarf Pyramid 3 to 6 feet apart.

Variety	Stock	Dessert or Cooking
American Mother	East Malling IX, II or I	Dessert
Cox's Orange Pippin	East Malling IX, II or I	Dessert
Early Victoria	East Malling IX, II or I	Cooking
Edward VII	East Malling IX, II or I	Cooking
Egremont Russet	East Malling IX, II or I	Dessert
Ellison's Orange	East Malling IX, II or I	Dessert
James Grieve	East Malling II or I	Dessert
Lane's Prince Albert	East Malling IX, II or I	Cooking
Laxton's Fortune	East Malling IX, II or I	Dessert
Laxton's Superb	East Malling IX	Dessert
Lord Lambourne	East Malling IX, II or I	Dessert
Miller's Seedling	East Malling II or I	Dessert
Ribston Pippin	East Malling IX, II or I	Dessert
St. Cecilia	East Malling IX, II or I	Dessert

ESPALIERS

Plant about 15 to 20 feet apart.

Variety	Stock	Dessert or Cooking
American Mother	East Malling IX, II or I	Dessert
Belle de Boskoop	East Malling IX	Dessert
Blenheim Orange	East Malling IX	Dessert
Brownlees Russet	East Malling IX, II or I	Dessert
Cox's Orange Pippin	East Malling IX, II or I	Dessert
Crawley Beauty	East Malling II or I	Cooking
Early Victoria	East Malling II or I	Cooking
Edward VII	East Malling IX, II or I	Cooking
Egremont Russet	East Malling II or I	Dessert
James Grieve	East Malling II, I or XVI	Dessert
King's Acre Pippin	East Malling II, I or XVI	Dessert
Lane's Prince Albert	East Malling II, I or XVI	Cooking
Laxton's Superb	East Malling IX	Dessert
Lord Lambourne	East Malling IX, II or I	Dessert
Ribston Pippin	East Malling IX, II or I	Dessert

BEST ORCHARD VARIETIES

Variety	Season	Dessert or Cooking
Beauty of Bath	Early August	Dessert
Belle de Boskoop	Late (Dec.–March)	Dessert or Cooking
Blenheim Orange	Late (Nov.–January)	Dessert or Cooking
Bramley's Seedling	Late (Nov.–March)	Cooking
Duke of Devonshire	Late (March–April)	Dessert
Laxton's Superb	Late (Nov.–February)	Dessert
Lord Derby	Late (Nov.–December)	Cooking
Monarch	Late (Dec.–March)	Cooking
Newton Wonder	Late (Feb.–March)	Cooking
Ribston Pippin	Late (Nov.–January)	Dessert

THE APRICOT *(Prunus armeniaca)*

ORIGIN AND HISTORY

When grown in suitable situations and properly cultivated, the apricot is one of the most delicious stone-fruits that can be grown in the open. It comes from Asia Minor, and is said to have been first planted in England by the gardener of Henry VIII.

SOIL AND SITUATION

The apricot thrives in a good, well-drained calcareous loam and is most suited to cultivation on a sunny, sheltered wall, or may be grown under glass. It will not do well in light, sandy soil.

ASPECT

In the warm south-west districts, the apricot does well almost anywhere, in suitable soil. The early and mid-season apricots bear best when planted against west walls. Late apricots should always be planted against walls facing south. In the south-east, a sunny east wall is to be recommended, for the early and mid-season fruits. In the midlands, a sheltered south wall and in the northern districts a sheltered south-west wall is desirable. In the extreme north and in Scotland this fruit should be grown only under glass.

FORM OF TREE

The apricot is grown as a dwarf or tall fan-shaped tree, trained to a wall, and no other form should be attempted.

Varieties Most Suitable for Growing as Tall Fan-shaped Trees on South Walls.—Hemskirk; large fruit, hardy, fine quality, early August. Moorpark; large, rich, August. Shipley's Blenheim; medium size, earliest of all, very hardy. St. Ambroise; large, mid-August. New Large Early; large, mid-July.

Varieties Most Suitable for Growing as Dwarf Trees.—Breda; fine quality, mid-August. Royal; large, good quality, useful and hardy, early August. Sucré de Holub; medium-growth, vigorous, early August. Peach, fine quality, early.

PROPAGATION

The apricot is propagated by budding in July or August on plum rootstocks. The Brussels is the stock traditionally recommended, but this suckers badly, and experiments are being made in the walled garden at Bradbourne by East Malling Research Station to discover the most suitable stocks for apricots. Brompton and Common Mussel are the present recommendations.

THE APRICOT

PLANTING

The trained trees are best planted in October. Where a number of fan-shaped trees are planted side by side 20 to 25 feet space should be allowed between each. With a 4¼-foot stem a well-grown dwarf tree will be about 9 feet high with a top about 6 feet in diameter. Such trees should be planted 10 feet apart.

PREPARING THE SITE

When planting, prepare the soil about a yard deep, and add a dressing of fine bonemeal. Place some brick or rubble below each tree to improve drainage.

CULTIVATION

The apricot, when in a healthy state, produces more natural spurs than most other trees, and although some kinds will blossom and bear fruit on the young wood, for a crop of fine fruit dependence must be placed on the true spurs. Water should be given liberally in dry weather.

PRUNING

The operations of disbudding, summer pinching, stopping, and laying in of the young fruit-bearing shoots in autumn are carried out as described in detail on page 272 for peaches and nectarines, remembering that the golden rule for apricots is to control the tree as much as possible by *summer pinching and stopping*, and to do as little cutting back as possible in autumn, winter, and spring.

FRUIT THINNING

This process, as with peaches and nectarines, should be progressive. Starting at the " large pea " or " hazel nut " stage, a partial thinning should be carried out on those parts of the tree where fruit has set in large numbers. The final thinning to 5 or 6 inches between fruits should be delayed until the " stoning " process is complete, and the fruits have begun swelling again.

GATHERING

The fruit should be gathered for table as soon as it is fully ripe. If it is going to market, it had better be picked just before this stage is reached. Gather it early in the morning when perfectly dry, and pack and dispatch the same day to catch the following morning's market.

198

MARKETING

Apricots are usually sent up in single-layer trays or boxes holding one to three dozen fruits carefully packed in woodwool, several trays or boxes being tied together in the same manner as those containing peaches.

DISEASES AND PESTS

The apricot is subject to a peculiar form of die-back in which first one branch and then a whole side of the tree dies. The cause of this trouble remains obscure, one explanation being that in a forward season growth starts very early in the spring, frosts occur, and the trees suffer from what is in fact a form of winter injury. Whether this be the true cause or not, apricot trees should always be carefully protected from spring frosts (see page 276).

In addition to the form of die-back already referred to, the apricot shares many of the diseases and pests of the peach and nectarine, but is, on the whole, less liable to the attacks of insects than other fruit trees. Aphides may be somewhat troublesome, and Bark or Trunk Borers may be encountered. Other pests include Scale, Red Spider, Leaf-roller Moth, and Magpie Moth. Such diseases as Blossom Wilt or Wither Tip, Crown Gall, Rust and Silver Leaf are all liable to occur.

For diagnosis table, showing how to recognize at a glance the cause of the various troubles, see Peaches and Nectarines, page 278, and Plums, page 317.

VARIETIES (APRICOTS)

The following is a selection of the most satisfactory varieties. Any one of these may be grown alone, as all varieties are self-fertile.

Blenheim. See Shipley's Blenheim.

Breda. Small to medium-sized round fruit, orange-yellow, flushed brownish-red. Ready in mid-August. Nice flavour and particularly hardy. May be grown as a standard in the open in the milder districts of the south and west.

Early Orange. Medium-sized, roundish to oval fruit, rich orange, with rosy red cheeks. Ready mid-August. Rich flavour, sweet and juicy. Hardy and prolific.

*Hemskirk. Large and round to conical fruit, orange-yellow, blotched with red. Ripe from the end of July to early in August. Delicious greengage flavour. Hardy and a good cropper. Also suitable for pot culture.

Kaisha. Medium-sized and roundish to oval. Pale yellow and red in colour. Ready mid-August. Excellent in flavour. Hardy and a prolific bearer. Also suitable for pot culture.

APRICOT—VARIETIES

Luizet. Large, oval-shaped fruit, deep rich yellow in colour. Ready end of July. Good flavour and a good cropper.

*Moorpark. Large, round fruit, orange-yellow, flushed red in colour. Ready in August and September. Excellent flavour. A strong and vigorous grower and a good bearer. Useful for pot culture.

*New Large Early. Large, oval fruit, orange-yellow and red in colour. Ready from the end of July to early August. Fine flavour, hardy and prolific. Has taken the place of Large Early.

Peach. Large, oval fruit, rich yellow and red in colour. Ready from the end of August to early in September. Rich and pungent in flavour. A good cropper and one of the most widely-grown kinds.

Powell's Late. Large, round to oval fruit, deep yellow, flushed red in colour. Ready in August and September. Nice flavour. A vigorous grower and a good bearer.

Royal. Medium-sized, oval fruit, pale yellow, spotted with purple Ready early in August. Rich flavour, sweet and juicy. Hardy and a good cropper.

Shipley's Blenheim. Medium-sized, oval fruit, rich orange with crimson spots. Ready early in August. Good flavour. Hardy and a prolific cropper. Also useful for pot culture.

St. Ambroise. Large, round to oval fruit, rich yellow and red. Ready mid-August. Good flavour. Hardy and prolific.

* Recommended by the Royal Horticultural Society for cultivation in private gardens.

SELECTION IN ORDER OF RIPENING
Early (End of July till Early August)

*Hemskirk	New Large Early
Royal	Shipley's Blenheim

Mid-season (Mid-August)

Breda	Kaisha
*Early Orange	St. Ambroise

Late (End of August–September)

Moorpark	Powell's Late	*Peach

* Denotes best-flavoured varieties.

SELECTION OF SIX BEST SORTS

Breda	Moorpark	Powell's Late
Hemskirk	New Large Early	Shipley's Blenheim

ESPECIALLY HARDY SORTS

Breda	New Large Early	Shipley's Blenheim
Hemskirk	Royal	St. Ambroise
Moorpark		

VARIETIES FOR GROWING IN POTS (see page 366)

VARIETIES FOR EXHIBITION

Moorpark	Peach

GROWN AS STANDARDS IN MILDER DISTRICTS

Breda	Hemskirk	Shipley's Blenheim

BEST FOR GARDEN CULTURE

Hemskirk	Moorpark	New Large Early

THE BLACKBERRY (*Rubus fruticosus*) AND ITS HYBRIDS

The blackberry grows wild in great profusion in this country, where it is a feature of many hedgerows. When cultivated, it yields very large crops, which are used mainly for canning, bottling or culinary purposes. Some of the hybrid berries are much appreciated for dessert.

SOIL AND SITUATION

The blackberry prefers a really deep, rich, well-drained soil, but it will do fairly well in any soil that is moist and well-drained, and sunny.

PROPAGATION

Blackberries may be propagated from "tips" in the manner described for loganberries (page 262), or they may be raised from suckers dug up from round the base of an established plant.

DISTANCE OF PLANTING

The plants should be from 12 to 16 feet apart, according to the variety, in rows 6 to 8 feet apart. Blackberries will generally continue to carry good crops for periods up to about 15 years.

TRAINING AND PRUNING

There are various ways of training the blackberry, one of the most practical being that known as the Rope Method. Three strands of galvanized straining wire, gauge 10, are stretched on uprights at 2, 3 and 5 feet above ground level, and the canes are tied to the two top wires in autumn as shown in the diagram. As the new canes grow out from the base of each plant the following summer, they are looped together and tied loosely to the bottom wire, shown in the diagram.

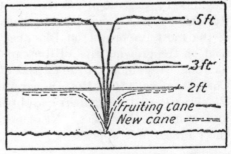

ROPE METHOD OF TRAINING BLACKBERRIES.

With the most vigorous sorts of cultivated blackberry, such as *Himalaya Giant*, it may be advisable to put the top two wires at 4 and 6 feet respectively above ground level, but this will make picking rather more difficult. Most cultivated varieties of blackberries make very strong, prickly canes and are very awkward plants to train, requiring strong leather gauntlet gloves to protect the hands.

MANURING

It is not unusual for cultivated blackberries to carry crops up to 6 or 7 tons per acre, and at the same time each individual plant may put out several new canes up to 16 feet in length. Hence it will be seen that the cultivated blackberry requires generous manurial treatment with plenty of nitrogen and regular dressings of potash. Farmyard dung, 15 to 30 tons per acre, dug in, in winter, is the best form of manure if obtainable, but shoddy, poultry manure, meat and bonemeal are all suitable, provided they are supplemented by sulphate of potash at 2 cwt. per acre. Steamed boneflour at the rate of 5 cwt. per acre is one of the best forms of organic phosphatic manures to apply to blackberries in the spring.

GATHERING AND MARKETING

These berries are usually treated in similar manner to loganberries. (See page 264.)

INSECT PESTS

Raspberry and Loganberry Beetle (*Byturus tomentosus*). (See Loganberry, page 264. Shoot Moth (*Eucosma uddmanniana*). (See Loganberry, page 265.) Greenfly. Of the various species of greenfly which attack Loganberries (page 265), *Macrosiphum rubiellum* is the most important on Blackberries. The aphides cluster and feed on the growing tips of the cane, but can easily be killed with nicotine. Common Green Capsid (*Lygus pabulinus*). (See Black Currant, page 234.) Both generations of this insect feed on the Blackberry and Loganberry, splitting and deforming the leaves and stunting the canes. Nicotine should be applied soon after the damage first appears.

DISEASES

DWARF

A virus disease recognized in spring by the bushy, stunted appearance of the new growths when a few inches high. There are many such growths instead of the usual few strong ones, and the normal purplish colour at the tips is often absent, giving place to light green. The virus, probably carried about by insects, gets into the sap, and the only satisfactory means of checking the disease lies in the prompt removal and destruction of affected plants. Himalaya and the Parsley-leaved are susceptible, as are also the Loganberry and the hybrid Phenomenal Berry.

CANE SPOT (*Elsinoë veneta*)

This disease attacks blackberries and can be controlled as recommended for Loganberries on page 265.

INSECT PESTS: DIAGNOSIS TABLE

Damage	Probable Cause
Shoots and Foliage	*Disease*
New growths light green, bushy and stunted when a few inches high	Dwarf
Foliage	*Pests*
Leaves at tips of new canes spun together	Shoot Moth
Leaves or young tips of shoots attacked by clusters of small aphides	Aphides
Young leaves spotted, becoming brown and torn ; shoots may be stunted	Common Green Capsid Bug
Fruit	
Fruit fails to swell and ripen properly, remaining small, brown, hard and deformed, maggoty	Raspberry Beetle

Note.—Once the trouble has been diagnosed, the reader is advised to consult the paragraph dealing with the particular Disease or Pest, and also the Guide to Spraying, page 142.

VARIETIES (BLACKBERRY)

The best varieties are :

Parsley-leaved Blackberry (*R. laciniatus*). A self-fertile variety, which bears a heavy crop of large black fruit of excellent flavour and, on account of its beautifully-shaped leaves, is extremely valuable for decorative purposes in the garden. Often grown for market.

Himalaya Berry. A strong-growing, heavy cropper, bearing large round black berries, excellent for making tarts and jams. This is usually considered the best variety to grow for market. Thought by some to be synonymous with Black Diamond.

John Innes. (Cross between *R. rusticanus inermis* and *R. thysiger*.) Raised by Mr. M. B. Crane at the John Innes Horticultural Institution, Merton—one of the latest to ripen, having a long picking season. Considered to be very promising.

Merton Thornless. Raised by Mr. M. B. Crane at the John Innes Horticultural Institution. Entirely without prickles. Fruit large with wild blackberry flavour. In season mid-August to end September.

White Blackberry. A new white or transparent sport from the common blackberry. The fruit is juicy and very sweet.

HYBRID BERRIES

Boysenberry. Raised about 1930 in California. A good cropper yielding very large fruits. New to this country.

Japanese Wineberry (*R. phœnicolasius*). A useful species for decorative purposes, bearing small, round, sweet to sub-acid flavoured, bright orange berries, enclosed in a hairy calyx. Hardy and prolific. Useful for dessert or culinary purposes. (See coloured plate facing page 14.)

King's Acre Berry. An early-fruiting variety, bearing large, black, longish fruits of distinct blackberry flavour. Ready from the end of June to early in July. Useful as dessert or for culinary purposes.

Laxtonberry. A cross between a raspberry and a loganberry. It is a strong grower and bears large bright red, raspberry-like fruit. Inclined to be self-sterile and should be grown only in conjunction with other berries. This has now been superseded by the Veitchberry, which see below.

Loganberry. (See page 261.)

Lowberry. This bears long, black loganberry-like fruits with a distinct blackberry flavour.

Phenomenal Berry. The fruit resembles the loganberry and is, perhaps, a little larger. (See page 261.)

Veitchberry. This is a new hybrid berry, obtained by means of crossing a blackberry with the November Abundance raspberry. Its cultivation is, in every way, similar to that recommended for the blackberry. The large, sweet and juicy berries, which are ready after the raspberry season is finished, and before the blackberries are ready, are the colour of ripe mulberries, deep red to bluish black, and shaped like a blackberry but fully twice as large. The plants are said to be self-fertile. (See coloured plate facing page 14.)

Worcester Berry. This is really a hybrid gooseberry. It is said to be the result of a cross between a gooseberry and a black currant. It forms a gooseberry-like bush with large spines and the large, purplish-blue, roundish to oval fruits, which have a slight currant-like flavour, and are borne in trusses like black grapes or bunches of huge currants. Hardy and a prolific cropper. Should be pruned and cultivated in the same manner as the gooseberry.

Youngberry. Not such a strong grower as the loganberry or blackberry. Exceptionally large fruits, which are of excellent flavour. A very promising new introduction from the U.S.A.

THE BULLACE *(Prunus insititia)*

The bullace, which belongs to the same family as the plum, is cultivated in exactly the same manner (see page 305). It makes a small tree, or bush, and in autumn ripens a heavy crop of small grape-shaped purple, greenish-yellow or greenish-white fruits, which are suitable for eating, for culinary purposes, or preserves.

Among the best varieties on the market we would recommend the following, all of which are said to be self-fertile :

Black Bullace. The wild bullace of our woods. Small, round, black fruits with a slight bloom. Slightly bitter in flavour until quite ripe, towards the end of October or early November.

Langley's Bullace. A cross between an " Orleans " plum and a Farleigh damson. It bears a heavy crop of small, purple-black, roundish fruits in November. Good flavour and a prolific bearer. Grown as standard or bush.

Shepherd's Bullace. Bears a heavy crop of large, greenish, round fruits, which are ready for picking in September and October.

White Bullace. Bears a prolific crop of small, roundish to oval, pale yellowish-white fruits, which are ready for picking in late September and in October. Grown as standard or bush. Useful for dessert or for culinary purposes.

DISEASES AND PESTS

The bullace is subject to the same diseases and pests as the plum and needs similar treatment.

BUSH FRUIT

See separate articles in this chapter under the headings : Currant, Gooseberry, Raspberry, etc.

THE CHERRY (*Prunus avium*)

ORIGIN AND HISTORY

Named after Cerasus, a city of Pontus, whence the tree was brought by Lucullus to Rome, about 70 B.C. First planted in Britain, it is said, about A.D. 100. Improved varieties were brought from Flanders and planted in Kent about 1540.

SOIL AND SITUATION

Sweet Cherries.—The best sweet cherries in England are grown on the deep brick-earth soils in North Kent. They always appear to grow and crop best under conditions of moderately light rainfall in soils which are really deep and freely drained, overlying a chalk subsoil. They are always unhappy in very wet soils and seldom do well in sandy loams which dry out early in the season, or in soils with a coarse, sandy or gravelly subsoil. They need shelter from the east winds at times of blossoming and protection from spring frosts. Trees on walls should preferably face south or west.

Sour Cherries.—One variety of sour or " red " cherry known as the *Wye Morello*, much esteemed for the manufacture of Cherry Brandy, grows and crops well on its own roots in Kent on the light, sandy loams of the Folkestone sands. The other varieties of sour cherries, including the ordinary Morello, appear to thrive under the same conditions as the sweet cherries, except that they have the additional advantage of doing well on a north wall.

THE CHERRY

The cherry is usually propagated by means of budding in July or August on cherry rootstocks. The "mazzard," or wild cherry, is the rootstock in general use for both sweet and sour cherry varieties. The mazzards are sometimes dug up in the woods, but in recent years they have been propagated vegetatively from layers (see page 40). The Mahaleb stock, which is easily raised from layers, is sometimes used as a rootstock for sweet cherries, but has been found to be unsatisfactory for the sour cherries. Up to the present no really dwarfing stock for cherries in this country has been discovered, although two acid cherry stocks, the *Stockton Morello* from California, and the *Kentish* from New Zealand, are under trial at East Malling. It is always difficult to grow sweet cherries satisfactorily as wall trees because both the varieties themselves and the rootstock on which they are worked are much too strong growing to conform with the limitations of a wall.

The sweet cherry is happiest when grown in its natural shape as a forest tree, and any attempt to grow it in artificial form will inevitably produce its own problems.

The best compromise appears to be that of the commercial cherry growers, who prefer the standard forms grown in grass orchards. Bush trees are widely grown in America, and if no stock is grazed under the trees, there can be no objection to the bush cherry, which is, moreover, a more economical tree to net against birds. The chief objection to growing sweet cherries as wall trees, as already stated, is the difficulty of keeping them confined to the limits imposed by the wall. If hard winter pruning is resorted to, the result is to stimulate excessive shoot growth at the expense of fruit-bud production.

If means can be found to keep them in check, cherry trees trained as fans on walls have the obvious advantages of shelter from wind and frost. They are, moreover, easy to net against birds, which form one of the chief pests of the cherry.

The Morello, the most popular form of sour cherry in this country, is grown widely for market as a bush tree under conditions of clean cultivation, and for plantations or for large gardens without walls this is probably the best form. On the other hand, the Morello and most of the sour varieties, with the possible exception of the *Dukes*, are so much less vigorous in growth than the sweet cherries that where wall space is available, they are much more suitable for this purpose than the sweet varieties, especially as they will do quite well on the north side of the wall.

PLANTING AND MANURING

PLANTING A CHERRY ORCHARD

When planting cherries commercially, it is well to remember that unless the birds can be kept out of the orchards when the fruit is ripening, there will be no profits, because the birds will get most of the cherries. A man or boy must be constantly walking about from daylight to dark, from the middle of June until the end of July, either shooting blank cartridges or small shot, or beating old tin cans hung on strings from tree to tree. About five acres is as much as one man can conveniently birdscare in this way, and many experienced growers maintain that for this reason it is uneconomical to plant less than this acreage of cherries.

A typical plant is the mixed cherry and plum orchard suggested on page 93. The plum " fillers " should be grubbed from ten to fifteen years after planting, in order to allow space for the cherries.

In planning the layout of the cherry orchard care should be taken to see that varieties which will cross-pollinate each other are planted reasonably close to each other.

Planting may take place any time when the weather and conditions are favourable, between leaf-fall and bud-burst, October and early November for preference, if favourable. So far as possible, varieties should be planted in order of picking in order to facilitate the moving of ladders. This, however, is a secondary consideration when compared with planning for cross-pollination.

MANURING

The cherry may be classed among the fruits which normally require fairly high nitrogen feeding to produce regular crops of good quality fruit. At the same time, potash is undoubtedly necessary as a basic dressing, and in Kent, at any rate, the best cherry growers have always been keen on giving their cherry orchards periodical applications of phosphatic manures. In Kent it used always to be the custom to graze sheep in large numbers in the cherry orchards, feeding them on cake, and managing the grass in such a way that the sheep grazed it closely and evenly all over the orchard. The result was a smooth, fine turf like a tennis lawn, and it used to be the proud boast of the best orchardists, that anyone could throw a threepenny piece as far as he could in the orchard without losing sight of it.

Phosphatic manures such as basic slag or superphosphates at 5 or 6 cwt. per acre were applied every few years, to keep the clovers going, and potash was given at similar intervals as kainit 4 cwt. or as muriate 1 cwt. per acre. The nitrogen, it was reckoned, was provided in the sheep droppings, distributed evenly all over the orchard by the sheep. Doubtless such a method of manuring is almost ideal for grass orchards in districts of relatively low rainfall, and at times when there is money to be made out of sheep. Of recent years there has been a tendency to look for other ways of manuring cherry orchards. Poultry are, perhaps, the best substitute for sheep to supply the nitrogen, but they must not be run too thickly under the trees. Others, again, apply nitro-chalk, nitrate of soda or sulphate of ammonia at rates of from 5 to 10 cwt. per acre, and keep cutting the grass throughout the season with a tractor-drawn " gang-mower " such as is used on golf-courses. In such cases phosphatic and potash manures are given as well, slag, steamed bonemeal, or supers at 5 to 6 cwt., and kainit at 4 cwt. or muriate or sulphate of potash at 1 to 2 cwt. per acre.

Cherry trees grown on walls, especially wall trees, must not be given much nitrogen until they are carrying a really heavy crop of fruit, otherwise they are likely to make too much shoot growth.

It is very widely held by some of the best fruit-growers that cherries, like plums, should not be allowed to be short of lime, and for this reason where cherries are being grown on soils which are known to be deficient in lime, it is probably wise to apply lime at intervals of four or five years. The ideal method is to buy freshly burnt " flare " lime from the kilns in lumps, and spread this out in the orchard at the rate of about 10 cwt. per acre. When the lumps slake down to powder form, the lime is easily spread.

The exact part played by soil moisture in the setting and the development of the cherry is not known, but it is certainly important. Cherries on walls should be given a good mulching of farmyard manure as soon as the fruit is set to conserve the moisture, and the trees should be watered at intervals throughout the hot weather in June and July.

PRUNING SWEET CHERRIES

Once the framework has been formed the less a cherry tree is pruned the better. The silver-leaf fungus is liable to infect pruning cuts made in autumn and winter, so that any pruning should be carried out either in August and September, or in April. In standard trees dead branches and crossing branches should be cut out once a year, preferably in August.

Wall trees or bush trees grown in confined spaces need very careful pruning. Once the tree has been shaped, pruning should be confined to summer pinching of growing shoots to five or six

CHERRIES—*Kentish Bigarreau* (*top*) and *Early Rivers* (*bottom*)

leaves with the finger and thumb, and to the shortening back of these laterals to three or four buds in September. The leading shoots should not be pruned once the tree is shaped. On walls there is always the temptation, when the tree gets to the top of the wall, to cut the leading shoots hard back every winter. If instead of doing this, the leaders are bent over and tied down for a year, the new growth will be weakened, and in the following autumn it is often possible to shorten the leaders back to a weak lateral.

PRUNING THE SOUR CHERRIES

The sour cherries, particularly the Morello, should be pruned differently from the sweet cherry, the object being to promote fresh shoot growth every year. This makes the Morello a peculiarly difficult subject for wall training. The only way is to be ruthless and cut out one or more whole branches from each tree in the early autumn or late spring and to train new shoots in their place. The Morello being very subject to the Brown Rot fungus, there will nearly always be a certain number of twigs killed by the fungus, and these must be cut out before the tree blossoms the following spring.

GATHERING

Cherries should be picked when dry. Early varieties such as *Early Rivers*, about the middle of June, and late varieties such as *Turk*, about the middle of August. The fruit should be gathered with the stalks intact as it reaches the ripening stage, without actually handling the fruit itself. Morello cherries may be clipped off with special thin-pointed scissors. Each tree is usually gone over once or twice, removing those fruits which are ready first, before finally clearing the tree. The fruit should be placed into paper-lined baskets and forwarded to market the same day, clearly labelled with full details.

It is profitable to grade the choicest fruit for market purposes. See also Gathering, page 108.

MARKETING

Cherries are sent to market in strikes (12 lb.) or half-sieve (24 lb.) wicker baskets; in chip bonnets (12 lb.); boxes (6 or 12 lb.); trays of 6, 8 or 12 cartons (12 lb.); chip baskets (2, 3, 4, 6, and 12 lb.). Punnets (1 and 2 lb.) are used in the case of selected choice fruit. See also Marketing, page 117.

INSECT PESTS

CATERPILLARS

See Winter Moth under Apple, page 155.

SLUGWORM *(Caliroa limacina)*

See Pear and Cherry Slugworm, page 289.

CHERRY BLACK FLY *(Myzus cerasi)*

This is a well-known insect of world-wide distribution. It is the only commonly occurring aphis that feeds on the cherry tree.

Masses of these black aphides may be found in the summer feeding on the young shoots and the leaves (which become curled and often turn a reddish colour, finally blackening and falling off), and to such an extent does it suck the sap that affected shoots frequently die. Although it occurs on the bigger trees, it is, fortunately, seldom a serious pest on them. Its chief damage is done to young trees, nursery material and Morello cherries, all of which can be sprayed more easily and efficiently than large orchard trees.

The winter is spent as a shiny black egg on the twigs and branches. From this egg a stem-mother, the ancestor of the summer colonies, hatches out in the spring.

Control.—Summer outbreaks of this pest should be treated with nicotine before the leaves become too tightly curled.

The winter eggs can easily be killed by spraying with tar-oil washes in December. Young trees and nursery material should always receive such a spray, which will obviate the use of much summer spraying.

Watch should also be kept in the summer for the appearance of colonies of the aphis (established by winged aphides flying in from elsewhere) and immediate steps taken to eradicate them with nicotine and soft soap.

CHERRY FRUIT MOTH *(Argyresthia nitidella)*

This insect is not widespread, but is an important pest in some orchards. As soon as the flower buds burst, the small green caterpillars enter them, making pinholes in their sides. Then, when the petals fall, they bore into the developing cherries and destroy them.

In the middle of May the caterpillars drop to the ground and turn to chrysalides in the soil, in small silken cocoons about one-fifth of an inch in length. After about a month the adult moths emerge.

These are small, delicate, white and brown creatures, which fly in a curious dancing manner. They lay eggs on leaf scars, under scales and in crevices, etc. The egg is grey or brown, oblong in shape and attached to the tree by means of a row of little hooks. It is extremely difficult to find, being almost the same colour as the tree and not more than one-twentieth of an inch in length.

The eggs are laid in July and hatch out in September. The minute caterpillars, after feeding for a short while on the leaves, spin cocoons and hibernate in them in crevices and other convenient spots on the trees.

Control.—A few eggs remain unhatched throughout the winter and these are easily killed by tar-oil washes. These sprays will not, however, have much effect on the hibernating caterpillars, which are well protected by their silken cocoons. For these the best treatment is an application of lead arsenate just before the blossoms open.

CHERRY FRUIT FLY (*Rhagoletis cerasi*)

This is a very serious pest on the Continent, but has not yet been found in this country except in imported cherries. Legislation has been introduced with a view to preventing its introduction.

DISEASES

LEAF-SCORCH (*Gnomonia erythrostoma*)

The main characteristic of this disease is that the leaves fail to drop in autumn but persist, dead, on the tree throughout the winter. The new leaves produced in spring are infected by spores shot from fruit-bodies of the fungus in the dead leaves on the tree. The first sign of attack is the appearance of yellowish patches on the leaves. These later turn brown. The fungus passes down the leaf-stalk and prevents the leaf from falling. The disease can be severe in some seasons.

Control.—In young trees it can be controlled by stripping the dead leaves from the trees in winter and burning them, but this is hardly practicable with large trees.

Spraying just before the blossoms open with Bordeaux Mixture 6–9–100 and at petal-fall with the same at 4–6–100 will prevent infection of the new leaves.

BACTERIAL CANKER AND LEAF SPOT (*Pseudomonus mors-prunorum* and *P. prunicola*)

This is a very serious disease, especially in the nursery and in young plantations. The sweet cherry varieties *Napoleon*, *Bigarreau de Schrecken, Florence, Bradbourne Black, Ohio,* and *Early Rivers,* and the acid cherry varieties, are particularly susceptible, while *Frogmore, Turkey Heart,* and *Governor Wood* are much more resistant. The leaves of badly attacked branches turn yellow, often become rolled, and wilt, usually any time from May to August, and the branches eventually die. Inspection will reveal the presence of a cankered area on the branch. Frequently whole trees are killed when intection occurs in the trunk and spreads far enough to girdle it. Infection is often accompanied by copious gumming of a cloudy yellow colour in the region of the canker. Natural recovery is known to occur, for if the branch or tree is not girdled before the bacteria die out, the canker heals. In such cases, although the affected branch or tree may be enfeebled during the ensuing year, it continues to live and eventually recovers. Experiments have shown that infection occurs most readily through wounds in October, November, and December, while the bacteria have usually died out by the following summer when the canker ceases to grow. There is also a leaf-spot phase. Small circular spots, at first pale yellow, and later turning brown, when often surrounded by a yellow translucent halo, are produced on the leaves in spring. These brown areas eventually fall out, thus giving to the leaves a " shot-hole " effect. The organism that causes these leaf-spots is able to produce cankers in the branches.

Control.—Trunks and branches should be thoroughly sprayed during the second or third week in October with Bordeaux Mixture (10–15–100) and again, just before the flower-buds open in spring, with Bordeaux Mixture (6–9–100). This treatment should be continued every year to give the best results, and particularly during the first ten or fifteen years of a susceptible tree's life, when it is most likely to be attacked. It is important to spray susceptible trees in the nursery. The spring spray will help also to control Cherry Leaf Scorch (see page 211).

High-worked trees of susceptible varieties are preferable to low-worked trees because the stock is usually more resistant than the scion.

BROWN ROT BLOSSOM WILT

Acid cherries and certain varieties of sweet cherry, *Governor Wood* in particular, are susceptible to this disease, caused by the fungus *Sclerotinia laxa* (see Plum, page 314). Spores infect the flowers and the fungus grows down the flower stalk and into the young shoot of acid cherry, or spur of sweet cherry, and these, on being killed, become conspicuous in summer when the withered, brown leaves and flower-trusses hanging stiffly show up clearly against the normal green. On bush trees of acid cherries such as the Morello, on which the disease can be very serious, it is possible to cut out and burn the dead shoots in summer when they are best seen, but on standard sweet cherries the cutting-out of affected spurs would be impracticable, and growers must rely on spraying with tar-oil when the trees are dormant, and with Bordeaux Mixture if necessary just before the blossoms open (see Plum, page 315).

Control.—Spraying as well as cutting-out is highly desirable on acid cherries also, the object being to burn up completely (with tar-oil) or sterilize (with Bordeaux) the surface of the greyish fungus cushions or pustules that arise in late winter on the parts killed by the fungus in the previous year. Even where the cutting-out has been thoroughly done on acid cherries, it is very easy to overlook small infections, especially where the attack has been severe, and spraying is a necessary second line of attack.

BROWN ROT (See Plum, page 314).

CHERRY LEAF CURL

This is a similar disease to Peach Leaf Curl (see pages 277/8), and is caused by a similar fungus. Affected leaves are swollen, perhaps curled, and tinged brownish-red. It is rarely serious and can be controlled by the spring spray of Bordeaux (6–9–100) already mentioned for Bacterial Canker and Cherry Leaf Scorch. A disease caused by another closely allied fungus is known as *Witches' Brooms* or *Bull Wood*. It can be recognized by the characteristic cluster of non-fruiting branches reminiscent of a besom. The same Bordeaux spray will help to control this, too.

SILVER LEAF (See Plum, page 315).

DISEASES AND PESTS: DIAGNOSIS TABLE
THE CHERRY

DAMAGE	PROBABLE CAUSE
Branches and Twigs	*Pest*
Small, round holes in trunk	Shot-hole Borers
	Disease
Cankered area on branch or trunk—may be " gumming " (see also Shoots and Foliage)	Bacterial Canker
Shoots and Foliage (*Including Blossom*)	*Pests*
Leaves and blossom attacked by small, " looping," green caterpillars	Winter Moth
Upper surface of leaves attacked in August by black, slug-like larvæ, leaving pale-brown blotches	Slugworm

213

DISEASES AND PESTS: DIAGNOSIS TABLE—*continued*

DAMAGE	PROBABLE CAUSE
Shoots and Foliage (Including Blossom)	*Pests*
Young shoots and leaves curled in summer, infested with masses of black aphides; maybe reddish, turning black and falling off	Cherry Black Fly
	Diseases
Yellowish patches on leaves, which turn brown and fail to drop in autumn, remaining on tree throughout winter	Leaf Scorch
Flower-trusses withered and persistent with surrounding leaves brown and dead. Shoots dead on acid cherries	Brown Rot Blossom Wilt
Leaves swollen, often curled, tinged brownish-red	Cherry Leaf Curl
Leaves turn yellow, may be rolled and withered; small, circular, brown spots appear, fall out, and leave "shot-hole" effect	Bacterial Canker and Leaf Spot
Leaves silvery on branch affected	"Silver Leaf"
Fruit	*Pests*
Small fruits eaten by green, "looping" caterpillars	Winter Moth
Fruit eaten from within and destroyed by tiny, pale-green caterpillars with brown heads	Cherry Fruit Moth
	Disease
More or less concentric rings of "pustules," buff or greyish, appear on fruit, which is rotting	Brown Rots

Note.—Once the trouble has been diagnosed, the reader should refer to the paragraph dealing with the particular disease or pest.

DESCRIPTIVE NOTES ON THE VARIETIES

DESSERT CHERRIES

Amber Heart (Kentish Bigarreau). Medium-sized, heart-shaped fruit; pale yellow with red cheek. Ready mid-July. Good flavour. Hardy and prolific cropper. Grown as standard, bush, or fan. Pollinated by Waterloo, Napoleon and Florence. An old favourite with Kentish growers and still widely grown. Used for canning.

Archduke. Large, heart-shaped fruit; deep red, turning to black. Ready mid-July. Rich sub-acid flavour. A good cropper when grown as a fan on a wall.

Bedford Prolific. Large, heart-shaped fruit; glossy purplish-black in colour. Closely resembles Roundel and Black Tartarian. Ready early July. Good flavour. Grown as standard, bush, or fan on a wall. Free in habit and a prolific bearer. Pollinated by Elton, Frogmore and Waterloo.

Belle d'Orleans. Medium-sized, heart-shaped fruit; pale yellow to bright red. Ready in August. Fine flavour, juicy and sweet. Grown as standard or bush. A good garden cherry. Pollinated by Amber Heart, Early Rivers, Frogmore Early Bigarreau and Waterloo.

Bigarreau de Mezel. A very large, white, sweet cherry, ready in the first half of July. In recent years it has gained favour in Kent as a promising commercial variety.

Bigarreau Gaucher. A large, black, sweet cherry in season in the second half of July. Planted as a commercial variety in some Kentish orchards. Makes a good tree.

DESSERT CHERRIES

Bigarreau Jaboulay. Medium, heart-shaped fruit ; light red in colour. Ready middle of June. Sweet and juicy. Grown as a fan on a wall it crops well. Pollinated by Black Eagle and Bedford Prolific.

*Bigarreau Napoleon. Very large, heart-shaped fruit ; bright red. Ready late July. Rich flavour. Grown as standard, bush or fan. A prolific cropper. One of the most popular cherries in the market, especially among the extra-selected grade. Transports well. Pollinated by Waterloo, Roundel and Florence. Highly susceptible to bacterial canker and silver leaf.

*Bigarreau de Schrecken. Large, roundish, shiny black fruit. Ready late in June. Delicious flavour. Grown as standard or fan on wall. A prolific bearer. Highly susceptible to bacterial canker. Pollinated by Bigarreau de Mezel.

Black Eagle. Large, roundish fruit ; purplish-black in colour. Ready early to mid-July. Rich, sweet and juicy. Grown as standard, bush, or fan on wall. Hardy, a good bearer and travels well to market, where it is a popular cherry. Pollinated by Bigarreau de Schrecken.

Black Heart. Medium to large-sized, heart-shaped fruit ; dark purple to almost black in colour. Ready early in July. Sweet and juicy. Grown as standard or bush. Hardy and a free cropper. Self-sterile. Pollinated by Early Rivers and Elton. An old favourite in the orchard.

*Black Tartarian. Very large, heart-shaped, bumpy fruit ; deep black in colour. Ready end of June to early in July. Fine rich flavour, sweet and juicy. Grown as standard, bush, or fan on a wall. Hardy and a good cropper. At least five different varieties are grown under this name. Pollinated by Noir de Guben and Elton.

Bradbourne Black (Géant de Hedelfingen). A large, black cherry, ready in the second half of July. Has a very good flavour, and makes a strong tree ; very susceptible to bacterial canker.

Caroon. A name given to a number of varieties which differ only slightly in botanical characters, and with many common features. A small, late, black cherry of rather nondescript appearance, and with markedly purple juice. Tree usually very tall ; flowering season usually early, but the fruit is late in season. Bottles well.

Cleveland Bigarreau. Medium-sized, heart-shaped fruit ; pale yellow, flushed red in colour. Ready end of June to early in July. Good flavour. Grown as standard or bush.

*Early Rivers. Large, heart-shaped fruit ; glossy black. Ready from the middle of June to early in July. Rich in flavour, tender and juicy. Grown as standard. One of the best cherries for all purposes. Forces well and keeps well. A popular market cherry and travels nicely. Pollinated by Governor Wood, Noir de Guben, Turkey Heart, Emperor Francis. Hardy and a good cropper. Makes an enormous tree. Probably the most widely planted cherry in Kent.

*Elton. Large, heart-shaped fruit ; pale yellow, mottled bright red. Ready in July. Superb flavour, sweet and tender. Grown as standard, bush, or as fan on wall. A poor cropper in most localities. Not so

* Denotes varieties specially recommended by the Royal Horticultural Society for private gardens.

popular at market as it used to be. Self-sterile. Pollinated by Black Heart and Early Rivers. Highly susceptible to brown rot.

Emperor Francis. Large, heart-shaped fruit ; dark red. Ready in August. Fine flavour, juicy and sweet. Grown as standard or bush. Hardy and a good bearer. One of the best late cherries for market, particularly in northern areas. Pollinated by Turkey Heart.

Florence. Large, heart-shaped fruit ; bright red. Ready early to mid-August. Good flavour, juicy and sweet. Grown as standard, bush, or fan on wall. Pollinated by Bigarreau Napoleon. A good late variety for market. A heavy cropper, but very susceptible to bacterial canker.

*Frogmore Early Bigarreau. Medium, heart-shaped fruit ; pale yellow, tinged with red. Ready early in July. Fine flavour, juicy and sweet. Grown as standard, bush, fan on wall, or pot plant. Hardy and a good bearer. A popular cherry at market, but soft. Self-sterile. Pollinated by Roundel.

Géant de Hedelfingen. See Bradbourne Black.

*Governor Wood. Large, heart-shaped fruit ; bright red over pale yellow, and thin skinned. Ready late June to early July. Moderate flavour, sweet and juicy. Grown as standard, bush, as fan on east wall, or pot plant. Hardy and prolific. A popular market cherry but needs careful handling. Pollinated by Early Rivers, Turkey Heart and Emperor Francis. Highly susceptible to brown rot and cherry leaf scorch.

Kentish Bigarreau. See Amber Heart.

Knight's Early Black. Large, heart-shaped fruit ; dark purplish-black to dead black in colour. Ready late June to early July. Rich and sweet in flavour. Grown as standard, bush, or fan on wall. Hardy and a medium cropper. One of the best black cherries and a market favourite. Transports well. Pollinated by Noir de Schmidt.

Late Duke. Large fruit, roundish in shape, and a bright red in colour. Ready towards the end of August. Rich sub-acid flavour when ripe. Grown as standard, bush, or as a fan on wall. A valuable late variety. Said to be partially self-fertile. Cross-pollinated by Morello.

May Duke. Large, roundish fruit ; deep red-purple in colour. Rich flavour, juicy and sweet. Ready about the end of June. Grown as standard, bush, fan on wall, or pot plant. Hardy and good cropper. Said to be partially self-fertile. Cross-pollinated by Morello. Excellent for bottling.

Napoleon. See Bigarreau Napoleon.

Noble. See Tradescant's Heart.

Noir de Guben. Large, handsome, roundish fruit ; dark reddish-brown. Early flowering. Ready late June. Good flavour and heavy cropper. Suitable for garden or orchard culture.

Noir de Schmidt. A large, black sweet cherry, ready in the first half of July ; a strong grower, not yet widely planted in this country, but said to be promising.

Nouvelle Royale. A distinguished " Duke " in season in the second half of July ; a dark red cherry ; tree grows erect ; cropping fair.

* Denotes varieties specially recommended by the Royal Horticultural Society for private gardens.

Peggy Rivers. A new variety, somewhat similar to Governor Wood, that shows considerable promise. Ready in July.

Ronald's Late Duke. One of the latest of the " Duke " type of clear cherry. A large, dark cherry with yellow flesh, a good cropper.

*Roundel. Very large, heart-shaped fruit ; purplish-black in colour. Ready early in July. Dark red and very juicy flesh. Grown as standard, bush, or as fan on a wall. Hardy and prolific cropper. One of the best flavoured cherries. Transports well. Pollinated by Waterloo.

Royal Duke. Large, heart-shaped fruit ; deep crimson in colour. Ready in July. Good flavour. Grown as standard, bush, or as fan on wall. A garden fruit. Shy cropper. Self-sterile.

Tradescant's Heart (Noble). Large, heart-shaped fruit ; dark red to purple in colour. Ready early in August. Rich flavour, sub-acid. Grown as standard or bush. Unreliable. Pollinated by Napoleon.

Ursula Rivers. A new black variety of good flavour that promises well. Ready in July.

*Waterloo. Large, heart-shaped fruit ; glossy reddish-black in colour. Ready end of June to early in July. Rich flavour, juicy and sweet. Grown as standard, bush, or as fan on wall. Hardy and a fairly regular cropper. An old market favourite. Hangs well on tree after ripening and transports well. Pollinated by Amber Heart, Roundel, Florence, and Bigarreau Napoleon. One of the best flavoured black cherries.

Werder's Early Black. A black cherry notable for its early ripening. In season in early June. Not grown commercially in this country.

COOKING CHERRIES

Belle de Chatenay. A very large, mid-season cooking cherry, turning dark red when ripe ; one of the most vigorous of its kind, but has not a very good cropping reputation.

Belle de Choisy. A large, mid-season cooking cherry ; an erect-growing tree, not a regular cropper.

Carnation. A good representative of the cooking, red, or sour cherry class. Ready in early August. Makes a strong bush tree.

Flemish Red. Rather small fruit, roundish and bright red in colour. Ready about the end of July. Sharp and acid in flavour. Grown as standard or bush. Hardy and grows almost anywhere, producing good crops. Said to be self-fertile.

Impératrice Eugénie.—One of the earliest of the cooking cherries, ready in June ; crops well.

*Kentish Red. Medium-sized, roundish fruit ; deep red in colour. Ready about the middle of July. Sharp, juicy and acid flavoured. Grown as standard or bush. Bears well, particularly when associated with Flemish Red. A good cherry for preserves and cooking. Self-sterile.

*Morello. Large, flattish, roundish fruit ; deep red to black in colour. Ready from August to September. Sharp, juicy and acid in flavour. Grown as half-standard or bush on north, east or west walls. Hardy,

---

* Denotes varieties specially recommended by the Royal Horticultural Society for private gardens.

217

a prolific cropper and said to be self-fertile. Undoubtedly the best of the cooking cherries. A small distinct type known as the Wye Morello is used in the manufacture of cherry brandy.

Reine Hortense. One of the largest and earliest of the cooking cherries. In season from the end of June to July. A poor cropper and hardly to be recommended except under the most favourable conditions.

Triaux. Medium-sized, roundish, bright red fruit, somewhat similar to Flemish Red. Ready about the end of July. Good flavour and a regular cropper. Grown as standard or bush.

Turk or Turkey Heart. Medium-sized, heart-shaped, shining black fruit. Ready early in August. Grown as standard, bush, or as fan on wall. Hardy and good cropper. A good late cherry for market. Transports well. An excellent canning and bottling fruit, unfit for dessert.

POLLINATOR VARIETIES

All the best varieties of sweet cherry are largely self-sterile, so that if any one variety is planted by itself, and there are no wild cherries or sour varieties near by, the trees will blossom freely but will never set a good crop. Hence the absolute necessity for planting pollinator varieties for sweet cherries. Fortunately, most sorts which flower together will cross-pollinate each other, but there is a small group of varieties which have been shown to be inter-sterile, and varieties within this group cannot be relied on to pollinate each other. In choosing varieties to plant together, the following tables should be consulted.

Early Flowering Varieties of Cherry

Variety	Season of Picking
Elton	Early July
Emperor Francis	End of July
Noir de Guben	End of June
Turkey Heart	End of July

Mid-Season Flowering

Variety	Season of Picking
Early Rivers	Middle to the end of June
Bigarreau de Mezel	Early July
Bigarreau de Schrecken	Middle to the end of June
Black Eagle	Early July
Knight's Early Black	End of June
Noir de Schmidt	Early July
Waterloo	Early July

VARIETIES OF THE CHERRY

Late-flowering

Variety	Season of Picking
Bigarreau Napoleon	End of July
Bradbourne Black (Géant de Hedelfingen)	Late July
Florence	End of July
Frogmore Bigarreau	Early July
Governor Wood	Early July
Kentish Bigarreau (Amber Heart)	Mid-July
Noble (Tradescant's Heart)	End of July
Roundel	Early July

Note.—1. *Flemish Red, Kentish Red, Morello* and the *Dukes* are all late-flowering.
Note.—2. From the above lists it will be seen that a variety may flower early and yet be a late season fruit and *vice versa*. This is equally true of some other fruits.

SELECTION IN ORDER OF RIPENING
Early (end of June to early July)

Variety	Colour	Pollinators of same Flowering Period
Early Rivers	Black	Waterloo, Noir de Schmidt
May Duke	Dark Red	Napoleon, Kentish Bigarreau
Frogmore	White	Roundel
Noir de Guben	Black	Emperor Francis
Noir de Schmidt	Black	Bigarreau de Mezel
Bigarreau de Mezel	White	Black Eagle
Elton Heart	White	Noir de Guben
Governor Wood	White	Frogmore

Mid-Season (Mid-July)

Black Eagle	Black	Bigarreau de Schrecken
Kentish Bigarreau (Amber Heart)	White	Waterloo, Napoleon, Florence
Roundel	Black	Waterloo
Waterloo	Black	Roundel, Napoleon, Kentish Bigarreau, Florence

Late (end of July–early August)

Bradbourne Black	Black	Napoleon, Florence, Noble
Emperor Francis	Dark Red	Turkey Heart
Florence	White	Napoleon
Napoleon	White	Roundel, Florence, Kentish Bigarreau
Noble	Black	Napoleon

VARIETIES FOR GROWING IN POTS

Bigarreau Napoleon	Late	White
Bigarreau de Schrecken	Early	Black
Elton	Early	White
Florence	Late	White
May Duke	Early	Red
Noble	Late	Black
Roundel	Medium	Black
Waterloo	Medium	Black

VARIETIES OF THE CHERRY

THE DUKES AND THE SOUR OR "RED" CHERRIES

Variety	Season of Ripening
Impératrice Eugénie	End of June
May Duke	End of June
Archduke	Early to Mid-July
Belle de Chatenay	Early to Mid-July
Belle de Choisy	Early to Mid-July
Kentish Red	Early to Mid-July
Reine Hortense	Early to Mid-July
Royal Duke	Early to Mid-July
Carnation	End of July–August
Flemish Red	End of July–August
Late Duke	End of July–August
Morello	End of July–August
Ronald's Late Duke	End of July–August
Triaux	End of July–August

Note.—1. All these cherries are excellent for bottling
Note.—2. Their flowering season is late, and they should be planted with each other, or with late-flowering sweet cherries for pollination. Morello can be planted alone.

SELECTION OF TWELVE LEADING SORTS

Variety	Season	Colour
Amber Heart (Kentish Bigarreau)	Mid-Season (Mid-July)	White
Bedford Prolific	Mid-Season (Mid-July)	Black
Bigarreau Napoleon	Late (Late-July)	White
Bigarreau de Schrecken	Early (End June)	Black
Black Tartarian	Early (Early July)	Black
Early Rivers	Early (End June)	Black
Frogmore Bigarreau	Mid-Season (Mid-July)	White
Governor Wood	Early (Early July)	White
Kentish Red	Mid-Season (Mid-July)	Red
Morello	Late (End July)	Red
Roundel	Mid-Season (Mid-July)	Black
Waterloo	Mid-Season (Mid-July)	Black

VARIETIES FOR EXHIBITION

Variety	Early or Late	Colour
Bigarreau de Mezel	Early (Early July)	White
Bigarreau Napoleon	Late (Early August)	White
Bigarreau de Schrecken	Early (End of June)	Black
Bigarreau Gaucher	Late (End of July)	Black
Black Eagle	Mid-Season (Mid-July)	Black
Black Tartarian	Early (Early July)	Black
Bradbourne Black (Géant de Hedelfingen)	Late (End of July)	Black
Carnation	Late (End of July)	Red
Elton	Early (Early July)	White
Emperor Francis	Late (End of July)	Dark Red
Florence	Late (End of July)	White
May Duke	Early (End of June)	Red
Noble	Late (End of July)	Black
Noir de Guben	Early (End of June–Early July)	Black
Noir de Schmidt	Early (End of June–Early July)	Black
Roundel	Mid-Season (Mid-July)	Black
Triaux	Late (End of July)	Red

VARIETIES OF THE CHERRY

ESPECIALLY HARDY SORTS

Variety	Season	Colour
Amber Heart (Kentish Bigarreau)	Mid-Season (Mid-July)	White
Bigarreau Napoleon	Late (Late July)	White
Black Heart	Early (Early July)	Black
Caroon	Late (Mid-August)	Black
Early Rivers	Late (End of June)	Black
Emperor Francis	Late (August)	Dark Red
Florence	Late (Mid-August)	White
Frogmore Bigarreau	Mid-Season (Mid-July)	White
Governor Wood	Early (Early July)	White
Morello	Late (End July)	Red
Roundel	Mid-Season (Mid-July)	Black
Turkey Heart	Late (Early August)	Black
Waterloo	Mid-Season (Mid-July)	Black

GOOD MARKET VARIETIES

Variety	Season	Colour
Bigarreau Napoleon	Late (Early August)	White
Black Eagle	Mid-Season (Mid-July)	Black
Early Rivers	Early (End of June–Early July)	Black
Emperor Francis	Late (August)	Dark Red
Flemish Red	Mid-Season (End of July)	Red
Florence	Late (Mid-August)	White
Frogmore Bigarreau	Early (Early July)	White
Governor Wood	Early (End of June–Early July)	White
Kentish Bigarreau (Amber Heart)	Mid-Season (Mid-July)	White
Kentish Red	Mid-Season (Mid-July)	Red
Knight's Early Black	Early (End of June–Early July)	Black
Morello	Late (August–September)	Red
Roundel	Mid-Season (Mid-July)	Black
Waterloo	Mid-Season (Mid-July)	Black

BEST FOR GARDENS

Variety	Season	Colour
Archduke	Mid-Season (Mid-July)	Red
Belle de Choisy	Mid-Season (Mid-July)	Red
Belle d'Orleans	Late (August)	Red
Black Tartarian	Early (End of June–Early July)	Black
Carnation	Late (August)	Red
Early Amber	Early (End of June–Early July)	White
Early Rivers	Early (End of June–Early July)	Black
Elton	Mid-Season (July)	White
Frogmore Bigarreau	Early (Early July)	White
Governor Wood	Early (End of June–Early July)	White
Impératrice Eugénie	Early (Early June)	Red
Kentish Red	Mid-Season (Mid-July)	Red
Morello	Late (August–September)	Red
Noble	Late (Early August)	Black
Noir de Guben	Early (End of June)	Black
Nouvelle Royale	Mid-Season (Mid-July)	Red
Triaux	Late (End of July)	Red
Waterloo	Mid-Season (Mid-July))	Black

VARIETIES OF THE CHERRY

BEST FOR ORCHARDS

Variety	Season	Colour
Early Rivers	Early (End of June–Early July)	Black
Emperor Francis	Late (August)	Dark Red
Florence	Late (Mid-August)	White
Governor Wood	Early (End of June–Early July)	White
Kentish Bigarreau (Amber Heart)	Mid-Season (Mid-July)	White
Kentish Red	Mid-Season (Mid-July)	Red
Roundel	Mid-Season (Mid-July)	Black
Waterloo	Mid-Season (Mid-July)	Black

VARIETIES FOR GROWING AS BUSHES OR PYRAMIDS

(Plant 20–30 feet apart)

Bigarreau de Mezel	Governor Wood
Bradbourne Black	Morello
Dukes	Noble
Early Amber	Kentish Red
Flemish Red	Triaux

VARIETIES FOR GROWING AS FAN-TRAINED TREES

(Plant 20–30 feet apart)

Belle d'Orleans	Kentish Red
Bigarreau Jaboulay	Noble
Carnation	Nouvelle Royale
Dukes	Reine Hortense
Flemish Red	Triaux
Impératrice Eugénie	Werder's Early Black

VARIETIES FOR GROWING AS STANDARDS

(Plant 30–40 feet apart)

Bigarreau Napoleon	Kentish Bigarreau (Amber Heart)
Black Eagle	Knight's Early Black
Early Rivers	Roundel
Florence	Turkey Heart
Frogmore Bigarreau	Waterloo

CHERRIES FOR GROWING ON WALLS

North	South	East	West
Archduke (S)	Amber Heart (S)	Bigarreau Napoleon (S)	Bigarreau Napoleon (S)
Bedford Prolific (S)	Archduke (S)	Bigarreau Schrecken (S)	Bigarreau Schrecken (S)
Kentish Red (T)	Bigarreau Napoleon (S)	Early Rivers (S)	Early Rivers (S)
May Duke (S)	Bigarreau Schrecken (S)	Governor Wood (S)	Governor Wood (S)
Morello (T	Black Eagle (S)	Frogmore Bigarreau (S)	Black Eagle (S)
	Black Tartarian (S)	Morello (T)	
	Early Rivers (S)		
	Elton (S)		
	Florence (S)		
	Frogmore Bigarreau (S)		
	Governor Wood (S)		
	Knight's Early Black (S)		
	Late Duke (S)		
	May Duke (S)		
(S) denotes Sweet.	Roundel (S)		
(T) Tart.	and any of the sour or red		

THE COBNUT AND FILBERT

COBNUT AND FILBERT (vars. *Corylus Avellana*)

ORIGIN AND HISTORY

The cobnut and the filbert are varieties of the common hazel nut *Corylus Avellana*, to be found in our woods and hedgerows. The cobnut is said to have been brought to this country from Constantinople in 1665, but it was not much in favour until early in the eighteenth century, when the introduction of the Kentish Cob aroused enthusiasm, and nut plantations began to prove attractive propositions. In " pre-vitamin " days cobnuts were much in demand on board ship for their ascorbutic properties. As a commercial proposition they are no longer being planted owing to their slow cropping, high cost of production, and severe competition in peace-time from imported shelled nuts of all descriptions. Since 1939 a large acreage has been grubbed in Kent, and very few, if any, fresh plantings have been made.

ASPECT

When planting a cobnut or filbert plantation, a site should be chosen which is sheltered from east and north-east winds. The bushes thrive in sunny, open situations in gravelly and rough, stony ground with a clay subsoil, but good drainage is essential. A shrubbery or hedge of evergreens will form a good wind-screen.

PROPAGATION

This is usually accomplished by layering two-year-old wood in autumn. Young layered plants, when rooted, are separated from their parents and are planted in the nursery garden 10 inches apart in rows 3 feet apart, only one straight stem being allowed to grow. In three years' time this stem should be strong and firm and should carry a crown of five to six sturdy shoots. The young trees may then be planted in their permanent positions.

FORMS AND TRAINING

The nuts are best grown in the form of bushes, with a crown of five to six main shoots supported by a sturdy 15-inch stem.

PLANTING

The trees should be planted 15 feet apart in the late autumn or early spring. After planting the main shoots are cut back to two or three buds, always cutting back to a bud pointing outwards. This procedure is repeated each year until the trees have attained a

223

height of 6 feet, at which height the main shoots are maintained. Ample fruit-bearing laterals soon break from the main shoots.

MANURING

A light dressing of organic nitrogenous manure, preferably shoddy or feathers, should be spread round the trees annually, and the soil should be well dug over each year, preferably in December. Sulphate of potash, 2 to 4 cwt. per acre, and steamed boneflour or superphosphate, 5 to 6 cwt. per acre, if applied at the same time, will ensure a complete manurial dressing. A dressing of lime may be given occasionally.

PRUNING

Cobnuts and filberts are early flowerers, and depend largely on wind for the dispersal of pollen and the consequent fertilization of fruit. They flower in February, and should this month be wet and cold few nuts will be produced. The catkins are long and of a downy yellow appearance. These are the male flowers, the female being small, reddish pink and brush-like, borne on the same or older wood. The male flowers are borne on the last season's wood, the female mostly on the older wood and the lower few inches of the young. It is consequently well not to cut the tree at all until the male flowers have shed their pollen, or there is a great likelihood that the female flowers will not be fertilized. As soon as the pollen is shed, usually early in March, pruning may be begun. Vigorous side shoots should be cut back to a catkin a few inches above the base, some of the oldest wood being cut out each year. The small, twig-like wood of the previous year's growth must be left in, for this bears the fruit. Wood that has borne fruit the previous year should be cut hard back to two or three buds. All sucker growth must be twisted off from the roots in winter and the centre of the trees kept well open. In August all vigorous side-shoots should be " brutted " or broken off by hand about 5 or 6 inches from their base, the ends being left hanging. This will check secondary growth and let light and air in to the centre of the bush.

GATHERING AND STORING

The nuts should not be gathered until they are perfectly ripe, late in September ; they should be left on the bushes until the husks are quite brown, and if they are to be stored, they had better hang until they fall naturally. In any event, after gathering they should be laid out in a dry place for a time before being stored.

RED CURRANT BUSH BEFORE WINTER PRUNING.

  [East Malling Research Station.

RED CURRANT BUSH AFTER WINTER PRUNING.

SHOOT OF A BLACK CURRANT, SHOWING TYPICALLY DISTORTED LEAVES—THE CHIEF SYMPTOM OF " REVERSION "

If the husks contain moisture when the nuts are packed away, they will soon turn mouldy. When quite dry, pack the nuts away in earthenware jars, barrels or tubs, covering each layer with salt before adding another layer. For marketing, however, the nuts are usually picked a little earlier as the nuts then do not so easily leave the husk in which they are marketed.

MARKETING

Cobnuts and filberts are usually marketed in sieves (40 lb.) or half-sieves (20 lb.), wicker baskets. When large quantities are being sent, they may go in 100-lb. sacks. The first pickings are often sent to market in " flats," flat wicker baskets with lids, holding about 20 lb. of nuts.

INSECT PESTS

NUT WEEVIL *(Balaninus nucum)*

There are frequently to be seen nuts that have a small round hole in the side from which the maggot of the nut weevil has escaped. The maggot hatches from an egg laid in the nut by the adult beetle, a brown or greyish creature, about one-third of an inch in length, with long legs and a long, curved snout, the tip of which is furnished with small, powerful jaws. The maggot feeds on the kernel and destroys it. It then leaves the nut and enters the soil, where, the next spring, it turns first to a chrysalis and then to a beetle, in which form it comes out of the soil in June.

Control. The weevils can be collected on tarred boards or sacks by jarring the trees to make them fall. Cultivation exposes some of the hibernating grubs to the attacks of birds. The best method, however, is to spray the trees in June with arsenate of lead to kill the weevils as they feed on the leaves.

GALL MITE *(Eriophyes avellanæ)*

This animal is closely related to the Big Bud Mite of black currants, which it resembles in appearance, in habits and in the damage it does. The nut mite does not, and cannot, attack black currants, although it is often popularly supposed to do so. When sufficiently numerous this pest can do a lot of harm, as the swollen, infested buds are nearly always abortive.

Control.—Lime-sulphur should, if necessary, be applied in May.

CATERPILLARS

These may be of the Winter Moth or the Tortrix families. They eat the foliage, often doing serious damage. The remedy is arsenate of lead, applied earlier than is necessary for the weevil, but this earlier spraying should suffice for both pests.

INSECT PESTS: DIAGNOSIS TABLE

COBNUT AND FILBERT

DAMAGE	PROBABLE CAUSE
Shoots and Foliage	*Pests*
Leaves attacked by "looping," green caterpillars	Winter Moth
Leaves spun together by small brown, green or yellowish caterpillars which quickly wriggle backwards when disturbed	Tortrix Moths
Swollen buds, infested with mite similar to "big bud" in currants, usually abortive	Gall Mite
Nuts	
Holes in side	Nut Weevil

Note.—Once the trouble has been diagnosed, the reader should refer to the paragraph dealing with the particular disease or pest.

VARIETIES

Good varieties include the *Kentish Cob** (Lambert's Filbert), the largest of the cobs, a prolific bearer, largely grown for market purposes ; the *Cosford Cob**, a roundish and thin-shelled nut, a heavy bearer and of good flavour ; *Webb's Prize Cob*, claimed to be of better flavour than the Kentish Cob ; *Pearson's Prolific*, a medium-sized, thick-shelled nut, and a reliable cropper of good flavour ; *Prolific*, a large nut and a good cropper ; *Cannon Ball, Duchess of Edinburgh, Marquess of Lorne* and *Duke of Edinburgh*.

Filberts.—The *White Filbert** and the *Red Filbert** are among the best flavoured filberts, the former so-called on account of its white skin, and the latter on account of its red skin. Other good varieties include *Princess Royal, Prolific**, a very free early cropper, with peculiar long-fringed husks to the nuts, *The Shap, Garibaldi, Daviana, Webb's Prize*, and *Bergeri.** The last-named opens its catkins very early and is therefore a useful variety to plant with other filberts.

* Specially recommended.

CURRANTS *(Ribes)*

The Red Currant is *R. rubrum*, the Black Currant is *R. nigrum*, and the White is a variety of the Red.

HISTORY AND ORIGIN

The name is derived from the Grecian city of Corinth, from whence originally came our dried currants. These are really a

226

small species of grape, but the name was transferred on account of the similarity in size and appearance to our own fruits, which are indigenous to this country.

RED AND WHITE CURRANTS

Red and white currants require the same treatment and can, therefore, be considered together. The black currants needs handling quite differently and must be dealt with separately.

SOIL AND SITUATION

There are few garden soils in which red and white currants cannot be grown successfully, although they prefer a deep loam of medium texture and plenty of sunlight. Shelter from wind is essential to prevent breaking of the shoots, especially in early years. They come into bearing two to three years after planting and should last for fifteen years or longer if kept free from disease.

SUITABLE FORMS

The most usual form is that of the open bush, with eight to ten leaders, shaped like a vase, planted at 5 or 6 feet apart. The red or white currant, when trained in bush form, should invariably be grown on a short leg or stem, forming the head at a height of at least 5 or 6 inches above ground level. This makes it possible to keep the open bowl-shaped bush free of suckers from below. Herein lies one big difference between the training of these fruits and the black currant. As will be seen later, the more sucker shoots that can be induced to grow out from ground level to form the black currant bush or stool, the better. But with the red and white currants the number of leading branches should be strictly limited, and sucker growth firmly discouraged. For late picking these fruits may be trained on a north wall or on wires as single, double or triple cordons at 1, 3 or 4 feet apart respectively in rows 5 to 6 feet apart or as espaliers at 6 to 8 feet apart in the row. In gardens the half-standard form is popular and for exhibition purposes, or where space is limited, the cordon forms are most to be recommended.

PROPAGATION

Red and white currants are easily propagated from hardwood cuttings. These consist of healthy shoots made during the summer, cut off soon after leaf-fall in autumn. They are cut into lengths of 12 to 15 inches and all but the top three or four buds are removed, see diagram, page 230. There are various ways of inserting the cuttings after the soil has been well stirred to a spade's depth. One of the best methods is to dig a narrow trench or " grip " about 6 or 7 inches deep and then to push the cutting vertically down to about 1 inch below the bottom of the trench. After that, the trench is half filled and the soil is trodden firmly down round the base of the cuttings. The trench is then filled up and stamped well down with the heel. Consolidation of the soil immediately around the cuttings is one of the main secrets of success in getting cuttings to strike roots. They are usually spaced about 6 inches apart in the row, leaving about 2 feet to 2 feet 6 inches between the rows. Whereas black currant cuttings are generally planted out into their

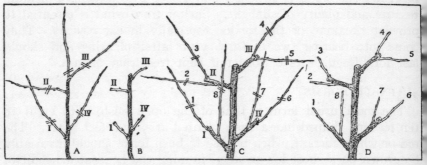

SHAPING RED AND WHITE CURRANTS.

A. A two-year-old plant to be trained as a bush. B. The same cut back to the points indicated in A. C. The same after another season's growth, showing the new shoots and points to cut back to. D. The same, pruned.

permanent quarters as " struck yearlings " at the end of one season's growth in the cutting beds, it is better to spend two years in the preparation of red and white currant bushes. At the end of the first season the yearlings are lifted, and the upper roots are cut clean away in order to prevent suckering. They are then replanted at about 12 inches apart and left for one more season, by which time they will be ready to plant out in their permanent quarters. For cordon and standard forms, the terminal shoot is encouraged to grow on by cutting out the side shoots. For espaliers, the central shoot is cut back by about half its length and the side shoots are cut out.

SHAPING THE BUSH FORM

When a two-year-old plant is planted out to be trained as a bush, there are usually three or four strong lateral shoots as well as the terminal shoot (Fig. A). The latter is cut clean out at the base, and the laterals are cut hard back to within 2 or 3 inches of the base, each to a bud pointing outwards (Fig. B). After one season's growth the young bush will be beginning to take shape as in Fig. C. Eight or nine strong shoots should be selected and cut back hard to outside buds, thus giving a framework of about eight or nine leading branches to the bush (Fig. D). Suckers from below these main leaders must be kept cut out, or they will spoil the shape of the bush.

PRUNING (Illustration facing page 224)

In red and white currants the fruit buds are formed in clusters at the base of the new lateral shoots. These shoots should be pinched back in summer, just as the fruit is beginning to colour, to five or six leaves, and then cut hard back to within half an inch of the base during the dormant season. The leading shoots should be shortened by at least one-half in the dormant season, care being taken to cut back close to a good healthy outside bud. Old wood must periodically, though not too frequently, be cut away to permit young shoots to be trained in to take its place. Summer-pruning must not be too rigorous at one time ; a little should be done each day. The " leaders " must not be summer-pruned. Since birds are apt to peck out the buds in winter the bushes should be " cottoned " with black cotton threaded by means of a bobbin, and pruning should be delayed until just before bud-break in spring.

In exposed places, and particularly with brittle varieties of the *Versailles* group, including *Fay's Prolific* and *Laxton's Perfection*, it is as well to give some form of artificial support to young bushes in the way of stick supports for the branches, to prevent the leaders being broken off by the wind in the summer.

MANURING RED AND WHITE CURRANTS

Potash is generally considered to be much more important for red and white currants than for black currants. Hence sulphate of potash at rates varying from 2 to 4 cwt. per acre (1 to 2 oz. per square yard) should be given according to requirements, poor sandy soils always receiving the larger quantities.

At the same time, red and white currants respond to generous dressings of nitrogenous manures and growers usually like also to apply phosphates in one form or another. Farmyard manure, stable manure, pig dung, shoddy, steamed boneflour, fish-meal and rape-dust or castor meal, all these make useful fertilizers provided the potash basic dressings have been given.

GATHERING AND MARKETING

As for Black Currants, page 232.

BLACK CURRANTS

SOIL AND SITUATION

Black currants prefer a rich soil containing plenty of humus and a high nitrogen content. They have the reputation of doing well on heavier soils than would be suitable for red or white currants, but this does not mean that they can be grown on badly-drained, clay soils. Shelter from east winds at the time of blossoming is important, because with most varieties pollen has to be carried by insects from the anthers to the stigma, and these insects will fly freely only in a sheltered situation. The bushes start to bear from two to three years after planting; their length of life depends on keeping them free from diseases and pests; if well looked after, they should last eight years and may even last longer than this under exceptionally favourable conditions.

SUITABLE FORM

As already stated, red and white currants form fruit buds in clusters at the very base of the young shoots. In black currants fruit buds are formed singly along the whole length of the young shoots. Hence with black currants the main object is to provide for a yearly succession of strong new shoots. Such shoots grow best from the base of the bush and even from buds below the surface of the ground. Thus the best form for the black currant is the stool or bush, rising straight out of the ground without any leg or with as short a leg as possible. Artificial forms are quite unsuitable. Black currant bushes may be planted at distances of from 5 to 8 feet apart, according to circumstances.

CURRANT
CUTTINGS.
A. Red and White.
B. Black.

PROPAGATION

Cuttings are taken from bushes carefully selected in summer for freedom from reversion and big bud (see page 233), and for their good cropping. Such bushes should be labelled late in June as " stock bushes." The cuttings should be taken early in the autumn, preferably in October, and are cut from the lower part of shoots which have just completed one season's growth. They are cut about 8 to 10 inches long and all the buds are left on with the idea of promoting sucker shoots. They are inserted in the ground as described on page 227 for red and white currants, except that with the black currant cuttings only two buds are left above ground level. If the nursery is kept well hoed, these buds should form strong shoots the same season, and the plants can be put out in their permanent positions the same autumn as " struck yearlings."

SHAPING AND PRUNING THE BLACK CURRANT STOOL OR BUSH

As soon as the young plant is put out, whether it be a " struck yearling " or a two-year-old, all the shoots should be cut off to within two inches of their base, with a view to stimulating the growth of more strong new shoots the same season. After that the pruning practice varies only in degree. Every winter a certain number of shoots are cut clean out at the base, choosing always the oldest branches for removal, with the idea of replacing them with strong young shoots. There is no attempt to limit the number of main shoots, nor to keep the centre open. All that is required is a constant succession of strong new shoots to carry fruit the next season. Very often when three or four laterals have grown out on a two- or three-year-old shoot, that shoot can be shortened back to the lowest lateral, thus leaving some fruiting wood, and at the same time stimulating fresh growth lower down.

Needless to say, no summer pruning is necessary for black currants, since each new shoot is needed in its entirety for next year's cropping.

MANURING BLACK CURRANTS

Nitrogen is the chief manurial requirement of black currants, and potash, though necessary in moderation, appears to be a secondary consideration. All forms of animal dung are suitable, good farmyard manure being the best of all. Pig dung is widely used, dry poultry manure, fish manure, guano, hoof and horn, blood, rabbit flick and meat meal, are all used at relatively high rates of application with the object of stimulating strong new shoots. Phosphates are not usually considered essential, but are often applied periodically in the organic forms such as bonemeal or steamed boneflour at rates of from 5 to 6 cwt. per acre. Sulphate of potash at 1 cwt. per acre per annum should provide the necessary basis of potassium. Inorganic chemical forms of nitrogenous fertilizers, such as nitro-chalk, sulphate of ammonia, or nitrate of soda, are often used to supplement light dressings of dung or of organic nitrogenous fertilizers when these are obtainable only in small quantities. The usual practice is to apply these in March or April, but some experts recommend applying them after the fruit is picked. The chemical fertilizers are usually applied at from 1 to 5 cwt. per acre, according to circumstances.

GATHERING

Gathering the fruit for market may commence as soon as a fair proportion of the fruit ripens and colours. The bushes should be gone over again a few days later, and then finally stripped. Or when the whole crop is intended for a jam factory, the grower may prefer to wait and then strip the bushes completely in one picking. The fruit should be gathered in the early part of the day, and on no account should it be picked in a wet condition.

The berries should not be handled, but picked by the strig. Leaves and damaged berries must not be included in the packages. As it is impossible, without serious damage, to grade and sort currants after picking, skilled pickers usually work in advance of the main body, picking only the best bunches of choice berries for the best-grade packages. Where this is impossible, each picker should carry two packages, and grade the fruit as picked.

MARKETING

The old returnable market baskets, the strike, rimpeck, and half-sieve basket at one time in general use for currants have fallen into disfavour and the non-returnable chip baskets (4 lb. and 6 lb.) are the popular market packages for currants to-day. Selected berries may be sent up in No. 2, 3, 4, 6 and 12 chip baskets, while punnets (No. 1 in case) are sometimes used for extra selected. No. 3 and 4 veneer boxes (12 lb. and 6 lb.) are also used, and so are No. 2 bonnet ($\frac{1}{4}$ bushel), as well as the old returnable baskets referred to above.

INSECT PESTS OF CURRANTS

BLACK CURRANT GALL MITE OR " BIG BUD " *(Eriophyes ribis)*

" Big Bud " is, perhaps, the worst pest of black currants, since not only is it so destructive itself, but it is frequently followed by the disastrous " Reversion " disease. Attacked bushes are characterized, as the common name of the pest implies, by the

232

abnormal size of the infested buds. These may swell till they are several times the normal size and globular in appearance. When cut open and examined under a powerful lens, they are seen to contain thousands of minute white creatures, each of which is no more than a hundredth of an inch in length.

Since attacked buds usually fail to open, it can readily be seen that an attack of "Big Bud" soon leads to a falling off in the yield. Moreover, the spread of the pest, once it is established, is rapid and certain.

At blossom time the mites leave the diseased buds and live for a while on the flowers and leaves. Many migrate to other bushes by clinging to insects or by jumping and being carried by the wind. As soon as new buds are formed, the mites enter them, where they reproduce prolifically and soon cause the infested buds to swell.

Control.—Badly-attacked bushes should be destroyed, since for them there is no satisfactory cure. Neither should diseased shoots be used for cuttings, as they will never make satisfactory bushes.

When the flower racemes have appeared, but before the flowers actually open, the bushes should be sprayed with lime-sulphur. The concentration originally employed for this purpose was one part of lime-sulphur to eleven of water. This deals with the mite effectively but is apt to scorch, particularly when used on varieties of the Goliath group, which will seldom tolerate a concentration greater than 1 in 25. When the pest is well under control and spraying is carried out as a routine preventive measure, 1 in 50 suffices to keep the bushes reasonably clean. Only on cutting beds and on bushes exposed to serious risk of infection need the stronger concentration be used.

CURRANT APHIS

Several species of aphides or "greenfly" commonly attack black and red currants and gooseberries. The insects feed on the leaves and stems in early summer, causing, according to the severity of the attack, leaf-curl, shoot distortion and early leaf-fall. An accompaniment of severe aphis attack is the sooty mould which grows on the leaves and fruits on drops of honey dew deposited by the aphides.

Currant Aphis (Capitophorus ribis).—This pest attacks both red and black currants and, sometimes, gooseberries. Often reddish-coloured blisters are seen in the summer on the leaves. The pale green aphides are to be found on the undersides of the leaves, feeding in the blisters. In July or August the insects forsake the currant bushes and breed on other host plants (such as dead nettle) till the autumn, when they return to lay their eggs.

Leaf Curling Currant Aphis (*Amphorophora cosmopolitana*).—This feeds on red and black currants, but may be distinguished from the *Capitophorus* by its darker green colour and by its habit of curling the terminal leaves of the young shoots. The insects hatch early in April from shiny black eggs laid the previous autumn in crevices on the shoots. They then feed on the young leaves till June, when they fly off to other plants (such as sow thistles) and do not return till October.

Currant Root Aphis (*Eriosoma ulmi*).—This aphis infests the roots of gooseberries and currants and much resembles Woolly Aphis in appearance. Winged forms of the insect emerge in the autumn and fly to elm trees to lay eggs. Return migrants fly from the elms to the gooseberry and currant bushes in the summer. It is a comparatively minor pest and does far less damage than either of the other two species.

Control.—Since the leaf-feeding aphides spend the winter on the bushes in the egg stage, infestation can usually be prevented by spraying with a tar-oil wash in the winter. This effectively destroys the eggs but cannot, of course, protect the bushes from infestation by aphides flying in from neighbouring bushes in the summer. If summer spraying has to be resorted to, nicotine and soap or derris and soap should be used.

CATERPILLAR

See Winter Moths, under Apple.

COMMON GREEN CAPSID BUG *(Lygus pabulinus)*

This is a very common and widespread pest with a very large range of host plants. It feeds on the leaves and shoots of blackberries, black and red currants, gooseberries, apples and pears. On currants and gooseberries it makes small brown spots on the young leaves. Affected leaves become " torn " and distorted, and often the shoots are stunted or even killed, excessive side branching then resulting.

The young bugs and the adult insect itself much resemble the Apple Capsid in appearance and habits (page 159). Like that pest, too, the Common Green Capsid lays its eggs beneath the rind of the shoots. These hatch in April and May into the young bugs which cause so much damage to the bushes. When half fed, the bugs frequently leave the bushes and crawl on to neighbouring herbaceous weeds to complete their development. In any case, when mature, they migrate to herbaceous plants, such as potatoes and various weeds, in July, and there produce a second generation. When mature, this second generation returns to the currant bushes or some other suitable woody host in order to lay winter eggs.

Control.—The use of a winter petroleum-oil spray is the most effective treatment for this pest. (See Guide to Spraying, page 143.) If preferred, a tar-petroleum mixture spray can be used with the object of destroying both Capsid and Aphis.

These sprays may safely be used on red or black currants, but have been known to cause severe bud damage on gooseberries and apples.

If it is necessary to spray in the summer, nicotine should be used together with some wetting agent such as soap, and care should be taken that the bushes are well drenched with the spray, or the bugs are apt to fall off and escape killing.

APPLE CAPSID BUG *(Plesiocoris rugicollis)*

Currants, especially reds, are sometimes attacked by this bug (see under Apple, page 159). Its damage is similar to that of the Common Green Capsid Bug and it is amenable to the same remedies.

BLACK CURRANT SHOOT MOTH *(Incurvaria capitella)*

This is a pest sometimes met with. In the spring buds grow out about an inch or so and then wilt. Inside the stem a small caterpillar may be found. The eggs of the pest are laid in the young fruits, but no appreciable damage is done to the fruit by the young caterpillars which feed in them. These spend the winter in the soil as half-grown larvæ in little silken cocoons and emerge in the spring to attack the shoots.

Control.—The only effective measure is to cut the currant bushes down to the ground in the spring, preferably after the larvæ have entered the shoots. This drastic course entails the sacrifice of a year's crop, but the bushes will, in many cases, benefit by being cut down, especially if they are young. Old, badly-infested bushes are best removed altogether ; this should be done during April or May if it is proposed to replant with other black currant bushes the following autumn.

MAGPIE MOTH See under Gooseberry.

CURRANT CLEARWING MOTH *(Conopia tipuliformis)*

Although not frequently met with, this can be a severe pest where it occurs. Mainly red currants but also black currants and gooseberries may be attacked. The moth lays her eggs on the branches in early summer, and the damage is done by the fat white caterpillars which bore into the branches and tunnel in the pith. Affected shoots frequently break off.

Control.—No satisfactory means can be recommended. Where only a few bushes are grown, cut out the infested shoots, although this may involve ruining the shape of the bush with the consequent need to grow fresh shoots.

CURRANT SHOOT MIDGE *(Dasyneura)*

Occasionally, in the summer, the leaves at the tips of the shoots become rolled and twisted and tiny white maggots can be found in them.

There appears to be no remedy, apart from hand-picking, that can be recommended for this trouble.

EELWORM *(Aphelenchoides ribes)*

This pest is not widespread but in some parts of the country has caused a good deal of trouble. The worms, which are microscopic, live and feed in the buds, which if severely affected fail to open. At times the worms migrate and it is then possible to see them congregated together in white cottony masses, protruding from the buds.

Control.—No satisfactory remedy is known. Warm water treatment (20 minutes at 110° F.) should kill the worms in cuttings from suspected bushes, but it is, of course, inadvisable to take cuttings from any currant bush that is not known to be in robust good health.

DISEASES OF CURRANTS

LEAF-SPOT *(Pseudopeziza Ribis)*

This disease sometimes assumes serious economic importance by causing premature defoliation of red, white, and black currant bushes on an extensive scale. It is usually pronounced in wet seasons. It can readily be recognized by the numerous small, brownish, angular spots produced on the leaves, mainly on the upper surfaces. In a severe attack, these spots merge together and the leaves wither and fall off in August, sometimes earlier. The fungus has also been found on leaf-stalks, fruit-stalks, young shoots, and fruits. Infection comes from the old leaves of the previous year, and possibly from the shoots, and is usually first noticed in July.

Control.—It can be controlled by spraying the bushes, immediately after the crop has been gathered, with Bordeaux Mixture made to the formula: 4 lb. copper sulphate, 6 lb. hydrated lime, 100 gal. water.

If the attack is early enough to warrant treatment before the crop is picked—since severe early defoliation causes the berries to shrivel—the bushes should be sprayed with a colloidal copper preparation or dusted with copper-lime dust. Bordeaux Mixture must not be used because it will mark the berries with a lasting, whitish deposit.

RUST *(Cronartium ribicola)*

This disease, sometimes known as " orange rust of currants," is readily recognized in its early stages by the bright orange spots produced by the fungus on the undersides of red, black, and white currant leaves. In severe cases nearly the whole of the underside of the leaf is affected, and premature leaf-fall may result. After a time the orange colour changes to dark brown when the resting-spore stage is reached. The spores protrude in short columns, which gives a rough, hairy appearance to the underside of the leaf. Another stage in the life-cycle of the fungus occurs on the Weymouth Pine (*Pinus Strobus*) and other five-needled pines. Infection of currants comes from the pines and thus completes the life-cycle of the fungus on its alternate host.

Control.—Spraying or dusting as described for Leaf-Spot (see above).

CORAL SPOT *(Nectria cinnabarina)*

This is found on a wide range of hosts, and usually attacks red and white currants through wounds at the base of the bush, probably made during cultivation. An affected branch wilts and dies, and in time becomes covered with bright pink cushions of fungous tissue. These later become studded with small, red, globe-shaped fruit-bodies of the fungus as it passes to its perfect stage.

Control.—Affected branches should be removed and destroyed when the wilting is seen. All dead wood should be cut out and burnt.

DISEASES AND PESTS OF CURRANTS

REVERSION *(Virus)*

This is a serious disease of black currants and is most easily recognized by its leaf-characters in May and June. Reverted leaves, found usually in the middle region of the new growth, are deficient in sub-main veins and marginal serrations as compared with normal leaves (which have five or more sub-main veins) and they are often rather longer and narrower. The blossoms on reverted shoots rarely set fruit, and are of abnormal appearance, the trusses being longer and more highly coloured than healthy ones. The virus is now believed to be transmitted by the " Big Bud " mite (and, perhaps, by other insects), which can be controlled by spraying with 2 to 5 per cent. lime-sulphur, according to severity of attack, at a time when the majority of the flower-trusses look like tiny bunches of grapes. The disease does not always affect a whole bush at first ; reverted branches may be found among healthy ones. Reverted shoots should not be used for propagation, and where whole bushes are affected, they should be destroyed.

Care should be taken to distinguish this disease from " false reversion " found in the lower leaves. Distortion of these is usually caused by injury to the terminal bud during the early stages of seasonal growth.

DISEASES AND PESTS : DIAGNOSIS TABLE

BLACK CURRANTS

DAMAGE	PROBABLE CAUSE
Shoots	*Pests*
In spring buds grow out about one inch and then wilt. Small caterpillars may be found inside shoot	Black Currant Shoot Moth
Shoots break off. Fat white caterpillars in stems	Currant Clear Wing Moth
Foliage	*Pests*
Abnormally large buds, which fail to develop	Big Bud Mite
Leaves, opening buds, and blossom attacked by small " looping " caterpillar	Winter Moth
Reddish-coloured blisters on leaves in summer, pale green aphides on undersides	Currant Aphis
Leaf-curl and shoot distortion, foliage infested by dark green aphides. Sooty Mould on leaves and fruit	Leaf-curl Currant Aphis
Leaves torn and distorted, shoots stunted and may be killed	Common Green Capsid Bug
Leaves, attacked by black-and-white marked caterpillars	Magpie Moth
	Diseases
In May and June reverted leaves appear in the midst of the new growth. These are deficient in main veins and serrations—long and narrow. Blossom abnormal and sets no fruit	Reversion
Small, brownish spots on leaves, mainly on upper surfaces, may merge together, and leaves wither and fall	Leaf Spot
Bright orange spots on undersides of leaves. Premature leaf-fall may follow	Rust

DISEASES AND PESTS

RED AND WHITE CURRANTS (DIAGNOSIS TABLE)

DAMAGE	PROBABLE CAUSE
Branches and Shoots	*Disease*
Branch wilts and dies—becoming covered with raised cushions of fungous tissue of a bright pink colour	Coral Spot
	Pests
Shoots break off. Fat white caterpillars in stems	Currant Clear Wing Moth
Foliage	*Pests*
Reddish-coloured blisters on leaves in summer, pale green aphides on undersides	Currant Aphis
Leaf-curl and shoot distortion, foliage infested by dark green aphides. Sooty Mould on leaves and fruit	Leaf-curl Currant Aphis
Leaves torn and distorted, shoots stunted and may be killed	Common Green Capsid Bug
	Diseases
Small, brownish spots on leaves, mainly on upper sides, may merge together and leaves wither and fall	Leaf Spot
Bright orange spots on undersides of leaves. Premature leaf-fall may follow	Rust

Note.—Once the trouble has been diagnosed, the reader should refer to the paragraph dealing with the treatment of the particular disease or pest and should also consult the Guide to Spraying, see page 142.

RED CURRANT VARIETIES

Variety	Group	Colour	Size	Season	Remarks
Cherry	Versailles (*R. vulgare*)	Deep Red	Large	Early	Good show variety
Comet	Versailles (*R. vulgare*)	Crimson	Large	Hangs till September	Not too acid
Fay's Prolific	Versailles (*R. vulgare*)	Deep Red	Very Large	Early to Mid-season	Long truss—exhibition, even ripening, needs protection from wind. One of the most popular commercial varieties
La Hative	Versailles (*R. vulgare*)	Red	Large	Early	Very early
Versailles (*La Versaillaise*)	Versailles (*R. vulgare*)	Bright Red	Very Large	Early to Mid-season	One of the best red currants for all purposes. Needs protection from wind
Dutch (Red Dutch)	Dutch (*R. vulgare* and *R. macrocarpum*)	Dull Red	Large	Maincrop	Good cropper
Houghton Castle (*New Red Dutch*) (*Abundance*)	Raby Castle (*R. rubrum*)	Red	Medium	Mid-season	Good cropper
Raby Castle	Raby Castle (*R. rubrum*)	Bright Red	Medium	Late	Makes good cordon
La Constante (*Southwell Red*)	Scotch (*R. rubrum*)	Bright Dark Red	Medium	Very Late	Attractive appearance
Scotch (*Westwick Red*)	Scotch (*R. rubrum*)	Bright Red	Medium	Mid-season	Good cropper
Earliest of Fourland	Prince Albert (*R. petrœum*)	Pale Bright Red	Medium	Early	Vigorous, upright grower
Prince Albert (*Rivers' Late Red*) (*Murie Red*)	Prince Albert (*R. petrœum*)	Pale Bright Red	Medium	Very Late	Long truss—useful to prolong the season
Laxton's Perfection	Ungrouped	Very Dark Red	Very Large	Mid-season	Long truss—exhibition, needs protection from wind
Laxton's No. 1	Ungrouped	Shining Scarlet	Large	Mid-season	One of the most promising new varieties
Mammoth	Ungrouped	Red	Large	Late	

239

CURRENT VARIETIES

RED CURRANT VARIETIES—*continued*

Variety	Group	Colour	Size	Season	Remarks
Victoria (*Wilson's Long Bunch*)	Ungrouped	Pale Red	Medium	Very Late	Long truss. Suits all districts

WHITE CURRANT VARIETIES

Variety	Group	Colour	Size	Season	Remarks
Transparent	Ungrouped	Yellowish	Large	Late	Long truss. Exhibition
Wentworth Leviathan	Ungrouped	Deep Yellow	Large	Very Late	Strong growth
White Versailles (*White Versaillaise*)	Ungrouped	Pale Yellow	Large	Early	Sweet

BLACK CURRANTS—GROUPS AND VARIETIES

Group	Variety	Growth	Season	Fruit	Remarks
French	*French*	Vigorous, compact, branched	Mid-season	Truss medium; fruit small to medium, acid; skin tough	
French	*Ogden's Black*	ditto	ditto	ditto	
French	*Seabrook's Black*	ditto	ditto	ditto; fruit large	One of the most widely-planted varieties in this group. Gives large fruit off young bushes
Boskoop Giant	*Boskoop Giant*	Very vigorous, drooping	Early	Truss long; fruit large, sweet; skin tender	Needs shelter. Fruit apt to "run off"
	Prince of Wales	ditto	ditto	ditto	ditto
Goliath	*Edina*	Compact	Mid-season	Truss short; fruit very large and sweet; ripens unevenly; skin tender	Rather susceptible to aphis, and leaf definitely sulphur-shy. (See page 140)
	Goliath	ditto	ditto	ditto	ditto
	Monarch	ditto	ditto	ditto	ditto
	Victoria	ditto	ditto	ditto	ditto
Baldwin	*Baldwin*	Weak, compact	Late	Truss medium; fruit medium, acid; skin very tough	Probably the most widely-grown group. Growth starts very early in season, but fruit hangs very late. Needs best growth conditions
	Black Naples				
	Lee's Prolific				
	Daniel's September	Rather more vigorous than Baldwin	Very Late	Truss medium; fruit medium, acid; skin very tough	
	Hatton Black	ditto	Early to Mid-season	Truss medium; fruit large, sweet; skin moderately tender	
Intermediate Group	*Laxton's Raven*	Vigorous	Early	Truss long; large	
	Wellington Triple X	Vigorous, drooping	Early to Mid-season	Truss long; fruit large, sweet; skin moderately tough	A cross between *Baldwin* and *Boskoop*. A promising variety, but apt to spread too much. Strongly recommended
	Westwick Choice	Moderately vigorous	Late	Truss medium, sweet	
	Westwick Triumph	Vigorous	Late	Truss long, large; skin moderately tough	
	Davison's Eight	Moderately vigorous	Early to Mid-season	Truss medium, large; skin moderately tough	Leaf highly susceptible to sulphur damage
	Mendip Cross	Vigorous, drooping	Early	Truss long	A promising variety from Long Ashton Research Station

FIG : LEAF AND FRUIT.

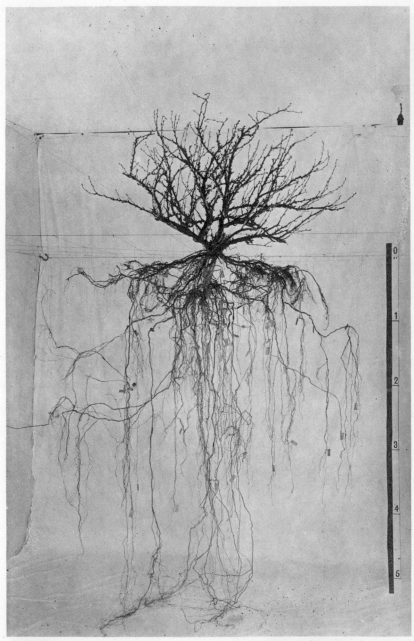

 [East Malling Research Station.
The rootsystem of an eight-year-old gooseberry bush, excavated from sandy soil, and reconstructed to show the positions occupied by the roots when in the soil.

GOOD MARKET VARIETIES
Black Currants

Boskoop Giant (Early)
Davison's Eight (Early Mid-season)
Triple X (Early Mid-season)
Seabrook's Black (Mid-season

Goliath (Mid-season)
Baldwin (Late)
Daniel's September (Very Late)
Westwick Choice (Late)

Red Currants

Fay's Prolific (Early)
Versailles (Early)
Laxton's Perfection (Mid-season)

Laxton's No. 1 (Early Mid-season)
Victoria (Wilson's Long Bunch) (Late)

GOOD GARDEN VARIETIES
Black

Boskoop Giant
Davison's Eight
Seabrook's Black
Goliath (Victoria, Edina)

Westwick Choice
Mendip Cross
Baldwin's Black
Daniel's September

Red

Fay's Prolific
Laxton's No. 1
Laxton's Perfection

Wilson's Long Bunch
Versailles
Prince Albert (Late Red) (Very Late)

White

White Versailles (Early)
White Champion (Late)

White Dutch (Mid-season)

EXHIBITION VARIETIES
Red

Cherry (Early) (Deep Red)
Fay's Prolific (Early) (Deep Red)

Laxton's Perfection (Mid-season)
(Very Dark Red)

White

Transparent Late (Yellowish)

THE DAMSON (Prunus domestica damascena)

ORIGIN AND HISTORY

The damson, a somewhat small, blackish-purple, oval variety of the plum, comes from Damascus, though there does not seem to be any authentic record of the date when it was first introduced into Great Britain.

The fruit is much used for stewing, making tarts and for jam and wine.

SOIL AND SITUATION

Deep, well-drained, strong loam will suit the damson. It also does remarkably well in chalky loams over a clay subsoil. It does not thrive in sandy or gravelly soil, although these may easily be improved to meet the damson's requirements. (See Soil Improvement, also cultivation of the Plum.) The damson is particularly hardy and if planted in a sunny open position, will usually yield heavy crops of fruit in any aspect.

THE DAMSON

FORMS OF TREE

The damson is usually grown as a standard or half-standard, and being particularly hardy, it is frequently planted on the outskirts of a garden or orchard as a windbreak or shelter belt to provide protection to other trees and bushes.

PROPAGATION

The damson is usually propagated by means of budding or grafting on to a vigorous plum stock such as *Myrobolan B*. It can also be grown on its own roots. (See Plum, page 306).

PLANTING

Standard trees should be put in from 15 to 25 feet apart for orchards or plantations. When planted to form a windbreak or shelter belt, they should be planted about 6 feet apart. Damsons require exactly similar treatment to that advised for the plum, and they suffer from much the same diseases and pests. See Plum, page 307.

PRUNING

For the first few years after planting the main branches should be cut back annually until the framework has been formed ; after this it is merely necessary to cut out old and dead wood and to keep the centre of the tree open. The trees will bear for about fifty years if well cared for. Old trees can often be rejuvenated by cutting all the main branches hard back as though the tree were going to be top-grafted. Strong new shoots will then grow out and may be shortened back to form a new framework. (See also Plum, page 307.)

MANURING

The manuring of damsons is the same as for plums (page 307) and will be described in the section devoted to that fruit. Some excellent results have been obtained in damson orchards by running hens and ducks in large numbers under the trees.

MARKETING

(See Plum, page 309.)

DISEASES AND PESTS

(See under Plums, pages 309–312.)

VARIETIES OF DAMSONS

Name	Size	Season	Quality
Aylesbury Prune	Large	October–November	Late bearer. Dependable
*Bradley's King of the Damsons	Large	Mid-September	Almost too large for a damson and without the true damson flavour. Susceptible to bacterial canker
*Farleigh (Crittenden's) or Cluster Damson	Small	Mid-September	Hardy and very prolific. A market favourite, but not the best for canning or preserving
*Merryweather	Very Large	September–October	Very prolific. For cooking or dessert
Prune (or Shropshire)	Large	September	Good cropper. Described by E. A. Bunyard as the " Greengage of Damsons "
Westmoreland	Medium	November	Hangs late. Excellent for canning

Note.—These are all usually grown as standards or half-standards, and are more or less self-fertile.
* Recommended by the Royal Horticultural Society for garden culture.
Note.—Aylesbury Prune is considered by some fruit-growers to be more resistant than other sorts to the attacks of the Silver Leaf Fungus.

THE FIG (Ficus Carica)

ORIGIN AND HISTORY

Historians are uncertain as to where the fig first originated, but it is thought to have been brought gradually westwards from beyond Asia Minor. Whether the Romans first brought it to Britain is not known, but there are records of fig trees having been planted at Lambeth Palace in the second half of the sixteenth century. Two large trees are to be seen close to the Lake in St. James's Park, and visitors to the National Gallery must often have admired the fig trees trained along the walls and iron railings.

SOIL AND SITUATION

The fig should have a situation fully exposed to sun throughout the day, and it must have a free supply of air to enable the branches to ripen. Success depends ultimately upon ripe wood, and this can be attained in the English climate only by root restrictions and the exposure of the wood to the maximum of sunlight. At the same time, the plant should be effectively sheltered so as to preserve as much warmth as possible. Its rooting space should be strictly limited, and it is well to prepare the actual site rather carefully. Indeed, the actual hole, which should be about 3 feet deep and 4 feet square, is often walled in by bricks and cement, so that the roots cannot possibly escape beyond the space allotted

243

to them. At the bottom of this hole should be placed about a foot in depth of broken bricks or gravel. On this should be laid about a foot depth of turves, grass side downwards, and the top foot should consist of a mixture of fibrous loam and broken rubble. Some successful growers, however, prefer to grow in a 12-inch pot and plunge the pot. The roots will climb over the top of the pot and can, if necessary, be pruned at any time.

PROPAGATION

Figs are propagated by means of cuttings made of semi-ripe one-year-old wood, 4 to 6 inches long, and inserted in pots or under a hand-light in September. Or cuttings 10 to 12 inches long, made of firm, woody shoots, may be inserted against a sheltered wall outdoors in autumn. For two years the cuttings are kept in a warm, sunny spot, and are then planted in permanent situation. Suckers are also a possible mode of propagation.

PLANTING

The trees should be planted in late autumn about 9 inches deep. No manure must be added at planting time, nor at any other—save in exceptional circumstances ; excessive root growth must be guarded against. The borders should be liberally watered every ten days in a dry summer. Fifteen to twenty feet should be allowed between trees. The trees will bear for thirty to forty years.

FORMS OF TREE

Fan.—Details for producing a fan tree are given in full on page 75. In training figs to this form each fruit-bearing shoot must be allowed as much sun and air as possible.

Bush.—In the mild climate of the south and west of England figs ripen on bushes in the open, provided they get enough sunlight, but in most localities the fan form is to be preferred.

PRUNING, DISBUDDING AND PINCHING

Winter pruning consists of cutting out last year's fruit-bearing shoots and tying in the replacement shoots in their place. Where space allows the retention of last year's fruit-bearing shoot and its extension shoot, the replacement shoot may be tied in beside the old fruit-bearing shoot. In early summer disbudding should be carried out to limit the number of new shoots arising from each fruit-bearing shoot. Where space allows one is allowed to grow out at the epical end, as an " extension " shoot, and one from the base for replacement. Towards the end of August or beginning of September, these young shoots should be " stopped " by pinching above the fifth or sixth leaf. This stopping, the object of which is to induce the formation of fruit for the ensuing season, is a matter of much nicety. A too-early stopping with most trees will cause a too-early development of fruit, the consequence of which will be that it will not stand through the frost of winter. The fruit for next year must not be much larger than a pea when winter sets in.

ROOT PRUNING

If fig trees are to be induced to crop, their roots must not be allowed to grow too strongly. In the south of France they are often to be seen with their roots growing on what appears to be almost pure rock. In this country it often happens that in spite of root space being restricted at time of planting, the roots succeed in growing over or round the obstruction, and when this happens the tree often grows much too strongly, with the result that there is little or no fruit. For this state of affairs root-pruning is the only remedy. (See Root Pruning, page 61.)

PROTECTION FROM FROST

Severe winter and spring frosts will often kill the shoots of the fig. For this reason the French growers near Paris used to grow the plants as low bushes or stools, burying the entire plant in the autumn in shallow trenches, and uncovering them the following spring when frosts were over. In this country, with the possible exception of the south-west, the fig tree needs protection in severe winter. Wall-trained trees may be covered over with nets, mats, straw or bracken.

GATHERING AND PACKING

The ultimate success in marketing figs depends upon gathering them at a moment when they will arrive on the market in a perfect condition of ripeness. The fruit must be as nearly dead ripe as handling will permit.

It is true that a fig must be picked in such a condition that it will carry, but a fig that is not ripened on the tree is never fit to eat.

The solution of this difficulty lies in careful pulling and more careful packing. Figs must be picked ripe if they are to be worth eating. Perfect flavour depends entirely upon perfect ripeness. They should be packed in shallow boxes in the softest of wool,

THE FIG

or cotton, a single layer in a box, carefully supported on all sides, or better still, in punnets protected in the same manner.

VARIETIES OF FIGS

Name	Colour	Size	Qualities
Black Ischia	Purplish-black	Medium	Sweet and juicy. Hardy
*Bourjasotte Grise	Reddish-brown	Medium–Large	Excellent flavour. Sweet and rich
*Brown Turkey	Brownish-purple	Medium–Large	Prolific. Good under glass, and best for outdoor culture Excellent flavour
*Brunswick	Brownish Red-purple	Very Large	Excellent flavour. Forces well, and good outdoor sort
Castle Kennedy	Light Brown	Large	Hardy. Good and early bearer
Negro Largo	Brown-red	Large	Not hardy enough for outdoor. Good flavour
Osborne's Prolific	Brown-red	Medium	Free bearer. Best for pot culture under glass
St. John's	White-fleshed	Large	Excellent. Early bearer under glass
White Ischia	Pale Yellow	Small	Prolific and well adapted for forcing. Not hardy. Sweet and delicious
*White Marseilles	Pale Yellowish-green	Large	Hardy and prolific. Good pot sort. Forces well. Excellent flavour

* Recommended for outdoor garden culture.

DISEASES AND PESTS

The fig suffers little from pests. Scale insects and Red Spider, should they appear, can be checked with petroleum-oil emulsions.

DISEASES

CANKER *(Phomopsis cinerescens)*

This fungus disease sometimes attacks the branches, gaining entry through wounds. It may cause death of an affected branch, the bark of which is roughened at the seat of the canker, often reminiscent of the markings of an oyster shell. In damp weather the spores of the fungus are released in whitish tendrils from tiny points scattered over the surface of the canker, from whence they can be splashed about by rain.

Control.—Removal and burning of cankered branches, and painting of all wounds with white-lead paint. Branches should be cut out flush so that no snags are left.

DIE-BACK AND FRUIT ROT *(Botrytis cinerea)*

This common fungus, the cause of Grey Mould disease in many plants, sometimes attacks the young shoots and fruits. The young

246

shoots wilt and the developing fruits rot and usually drop off, though they may become mummified and remain on the tree through the winter, producing spores in the following spring for further infections. The fungus can be recognized by its greyish, fluffy felt produced on affected parts in wet weather.

Control.—Affected shoots and fruits should be removed and burnt.

FILBERT (See Cobnut)

THE GOOSEBERRY *(Ribes Grossularia)*

ORIGIN AND HISTORY

The gooseberry belongs to the same group as the currants and is a native of northern Asia and of parts of Europe. It appears to have been introduced into Great Britain in the sixteenth or seventeenth century, and has been extensively cultivated.

SOIL AND SITUATION

Although the gooseberry will grow on a fairly wide range of soils, it must have potash, and cannot stand waterlogged conditions ; hence very sandy soils, lacking in potash, and heavy undrained clay soils, should equally be avoided for the gooseberry. To produce the best bushes and fruit it should be planted in a deep, rich, well-drained loam exposed to full sun and air. The gooseberry starts to bear two or three years after planting, and if it escapes American Gooseberry Mildew, and is well cared for, should remain productive for ten to fifteen years. If neglected, growth soon becomes stunted.

SUITABLE FORMS

The gooseberry is usually grown as a bush on a short leg in the same way as a red currant, but with rather more leading branches, planted at 5 or 6 feet apart in rows, and at the same distance between the rows.

Where space is limited, the gooseberry may be trained as standards, as pyramids, as single, double, or triple-cordons, as grid-irons, or in fan or espalier form. These are planted at the same distances as for red and white currants (page 227).

PROPAGATION

The gooseberry is raised from hardwood cuttings which are inserted before the middle of October, in the manner described for red currants (page 227). After a season, the yearlings are lifted, the upper roots are cut off, and they are replanted for one more season in the nursery. The following autumn they are ready for planting out in their permanent positions as two-year-olds.

SHAPING THE ARTIFICIAL FORMS

Gooseberries and red and white currants can usually be obtained from the nurseries already trained as standards, or in other artificial forms, so that it is not essential to do all the shaping at home. The technique for shaping the tree into these forms is given on page 228.

PRUNING

Pruning for Quantity of Berries.—The gooseberry bears fruit on both one- and two-year-old wood. Hence it can be pruned by either of two methods, according to whether quantity or quality of fruit is required. Where the fruit is to be picked green for jam or bottling, *number of fruits* rather than size of berry is to be considered. In such cases, pruning follows more on the lines of that advised for the black currant, and consists of cutting out whole branches of old wood, in order to keep the bush sufficiently open to allow of easy picking ; at the same time, such cutting back stimulates the growing out of strong new shoots to replace the old ones. As a rule little or no " spurring back " of new shoots is practised when gooseberries are being grown on bushes for jam or bottling, but the extension or " leader " shoot is cut back from one-half to two-thirds according to the general vigour of the bush.

Pruning for Quality of Berries.—When the main object is to get *a really large fruit*, a different method of pruning is employed, more on the lines laid down for the red currant. The number of main branches is strictly limited, and all the new lateral growths on these are shortened or " spurred back " in winter or early spring to within about 2 inches of their base. In commercial plantations summer pruning of gooseberries is seldom practised, but in gardens when time allows, it probably pays to carry out this operation when growing the berries for size on cordon and other artificial forms. Summer pruning in this case consists of spurring back the new laterals to within about 5 inches of their base in June or July. This is followed automatically by the winter spurring previously referred to.

In subsequent years the shoots growing from the ends of these " spurs " are shortened right back to their base.

The treatment of the leader or extension shoot depends very largely on the form of tree used. In bush trees it is usual to cut the leaders back annually about one-half from the time the framework is formed, until the bush is in full bearing. When the bush is large and carrying heavy crops, the leaders may need shortening by two-thirds, but this can be determined only by experience.

Some varieties of gooseberry are of a very drooping habit of growth. The leaders of these varieties should always be cut to an inward and upward-pointing bud. Other varieties have a bad habit of sending up strong " gourmand " suckers from the base. They should be ruthlessly suppressed in the growing season.

Birds are very fond of eating out the buds of gooseberries and red currants, so that it is best to leave the winter pruning of these fruits to the last. Many people cover the bushes all over with black cotton at the beginning of winter by means of a special bobbin which can be bought for the purpose. The birds catch their feet in the cotton, and this acts as a deterrent. Some authorities recommend dusting over the bushes with a mixture of slaked lime and soot for the same purpose.

MANURING

Gooseberries are potash and nitrogen lovers. Potash is the more important element, because, if it is not available in sufficient quantity, the leaf of the plant becomes scorched and brown round the edges and cannot perform its normal functions. This condition is known as " leaf-scorch " (see under Apple, page 171). Potash should be given every winter, preferably in the form of sulphate of potash, broadcast and pricked in at rates of from 1 to 4 cwt. per acre ($\frac{1}{2}$ to 2 oz. per square yard), according to requirements. *The lighter the soil, the more potash will be required.* Provided they have plenty of potash, gooseberries respond to generous applications of bulky nitrogenous manures such as farmyard manure, stable dung, pig dung, shoddy, or meat and bonemeal.

These organic manures help to keep the moisture in the soil through the dry season. It is risky to give very heavy dressings of concentrated nitrogenous fertilizers such as guano, fish manure, dried poultry manure, nitrate of soda, sulphate of ammonia or nitro-chalk, because these promote too rapid growth of young shoots, which are apt to break off in the wind, and which readily become attacked by American Gooseberry Mildew where there is a source of infection.

THE GOOSEBERRY

GATHERING THE FRUIT

In some districts the green berries are gathered as soon as they reach marketable size, three-eighths of an inch in diameter, so as to catch the early market. In the later districts this is inadvisable, it being best to wait until the berries are at least half an inch in diameter. The main crop are usually graded at eleven-sixteenths of an inch in diameter and under eleven-sixteenths of an inch. No damaged berries or leaves should be gathered. The main crop is usually picked into 6-lb. or 12-lb. chip baskets, and is graded afterwards. A start can usually be made with the dessert kinds in July. First all the fruit from the centre of the bush should be gathered, then the large fruit on the lower branches; after this the fruit is picked in successive gatherings as it swells and ripens. Thinning is recommended in the case of special dessert kinds, such as *Leveller*, when large fruit is required for market or exhibition, the berries being carefully thinned in the early stages, when about half to three-quarters of an inch long.

MARKETING

The first early green berries are usually sent to market in 6-lb. chip baskets; the main crop usually in 12-lb. chip baskets. The old half-sieve, rim peck and strike, returnable measures have fallen into disfavour. Select dessert berries go up graded in No. 1 and 2 punnets and in No. 2 chip baskets.

INSECT PESTS OF THE GOOSEBERRY

CATERPILLAR

Caterpillars, chiefly of the Winter Moth group (see page 155), can do a great deal of damage to gooseberries by eating the leaves, blossom and young berries.

Control.—Tar-oil and petroleum-oil sprays, particularly the latter, help to control these pests by killing many of the eggs, but the best plan is to apply lead arsenate or derris immediately after blossoming.

SAWFLY (Nematus ribesii)

This is one of the best-known and most widely distributed pests of gooseberries. About blossom time the eggs can be found laid in rows along the veins on the underside of the leaf—as many as thirty or more often occurring on a single leaf. The eggs soon hatch into tiny green caterpillars with black heads and small black spots on the body. At first they feed on one side of the leaf only and keep very much together. Later, as they grow bigger, they consume whole leaves and spread over the entire bush in search of food. Branches or even entire bushes can rapidly be defoliated by a severe attack of sawfly.

When fully fed and about to leave the bushes, the caterpillars are about two-thirds of an inch long, bluish green in colour with an orange-coloured patch behind the head and another on the tail. By now they have lost the rows of black spots, which are, until the final moult, a very conspicuous feature. Like many other sawflies, they spend their pupal period in the soil, in brown parchment-like cocoons.

Control.—It is advisable to spray for this pest soon after blossoming, as the larvæ are then small and easily killed and have not moved far from the spots where the eggs were laid. Lead arsenate (which will kill other types of caterpillar also) should be used, and an effort should be made to apply the spray to both sides of the leaves. If spraying later in the season becomes necessary (either on account of a second generation of the pest or because the post-blossom spray was omitted), derris root should be used in place of lead arsenate, as the latter may leave an objectionable deposit on the berries.

GOOSEBERRY APHIS *(Aphis grossulariæ)*

The Gooseberry Aphis is the chief greenfly pest. Other species, such as the Lettuce Aphis *(Myzus lactucæ)* occur now and then.

The Gooseberry Aphis is deep green or greyish green in colour, and occurs in colonies on the shoots in May and June. The insects suck the sap and cause the young shoots to become stunted and malformed. Migration to other host plants takes place in the summer, but aphides return in the autumn to lay eggs which hatch in the following spring.

Control.—The pest is not particularly easy to kill with nicotine in the summer, as the leaves serve to protect it from the spray. Fortunately, the eggs are easily killed by means of a tar-oil wash, which can be used at any time in the winter up to the end of February.

COMMON GREEN CAPSID *(Lygus pabulinus)*

Gooseberries are seldom if ever attacked by the Apple Capsid, but do suffer injury occasionally from attacks of *Lygus.* (See Black Currants, page 234.)

DISEASES AND PESTS OF THE GOOSEBERRY

RED SPIDER (Bryobia ribis)

This pest must not be confused with the Fruit Tree Red Spider (*Oligonychus ulmi*), from which it differs greatly both in appearance and in habits. Attacked foliage turns grey or silvery as a result of the sucking of the sap by the spiders. When the attack is severe, the young leaves are stunted ; later many of the leaves fall off, and the fruits either drop or fail to grow out properly.

Both spiders and eggs may be found on the bushes in the winter. The spiders, which are red, green or grey in colour, reach a length of about one-thirtieth of an inch when mature. After June, very little damage occurs. Eggs are then laid on the branches and may or may not hatch before the winter.

Control.—Good results can be obtained by winter washing with a tar-oil preparation ; this kills the hibernating mites. After blossoming, lime-sulphur may be applied at a concentration of 1 in 100.

MAGPIE MOTH (Abraxas grossulariata)

This is one of the minor pests of gooseberries and currants. The caterpillars are marked with black and white, and feed on the leaves. If spraying has to be resorted to, non-poisonous material such as derris should be used.

CURRANT CLEARWING MOTH   (See Red Currants, page 236.)

DISEASES OF THE GOOSEBERRY

AMERICAN GOOSEBERRY MILDEW (Sphærotheca mors-uvæ)

This is most commonly found on the tips of the young shoots and on the berries as a thick felt of " mycelium," white in its summer stage but turning brown by autumn. It can be peeled or rubbed off. Occasionally the disease reaches epidemic intensity, when the results are disastrous, the berries being ruined and the young growths distorted. Affected leaves are white and mealy. The brown felt may remain on the bushes in winter, or it may break up and fall to the ground, thus serving as a source of infection the following spring. *Control.*—There are various ways in which the risk of infection may be minimized.

Correct pruning to remove any affected growths and to allow of free air circulation amongst the bushes is helpful. Heavy nitrogenous manuring should not be practised, for this encourages succulent growth, which is very susceptible to infection. Bad soil drainage also fosters the disease. Affected portions of shoots removed in pruning should be destroyed and not left lying about.

252

Lime-sulphur (2½ per cent.) should be sprayed on to the bushes just before flowering and again (1 per cent.) just after flowering, to protect the new growth from infection. A further application (1 per cent.) may be given if necessary, but the use of this fungicide should be discontinued sufficiently early so that an unsightly spray-deposit does not mar the appearance of the berries at picking-time. The varieties *Leveller, Cousen's Seedling, Yellow Rough* (*Early Sulphur*), and *Golden Drop* should not be sprayed post-blossom with lime-sulphur as they are very sulphur-shy, and will drop their leaves and fruits, especially during hot weather. *Leveller*, indeed, is best not sprayed with lime-sulphur at any period. Alternative sprays are colloidal sulphur or dispersed sulphur at a strength recommended by the makers, or soda-soap solution (20 lb. washing soda and 5 lb. soft soap made up to 100 gallons with water) on lime-sulphur-shy varieties. The last-named is a contact spray and is best applied after the appearance of the disease, in its earliest stages. Its effect does not persist, however; it is readily washed off by rain, and frequent sprayings may be necessary to keep the disease in check.

This disease occasionally affects red, white, and black currants as well as gooseberries.

DIE-BACK *(Botrytis cinerea)*

This disease attacks the main stem and branches of the bush, and is occasionally found on the young shoots, leaves, and berries. An affected bush or branch suddenly wilts and ultimately dies. After death, the bark begins to peel off in flakes and the ashy-grey tufts of the fungus appear profusely all over the dead parts, especially in damp weather. The fungus grows within the host tissues and can spread from one affected branch to another. It is important, therefore, to remove affected branches as soon as they are seen, and to cut out and burn any dead wood. Dying bushes should be dug out and destroyed. In cultivating among gooseberry bushes, care should be taken not to injure the plants, for cracked or wounded branches are frequently attacked by the fungus. The fungus can endure for long periods in a resting stage in the form of small, black bodies embedded in the bark of attacked branches. These are highly resistant to weather conditions, and they can give rise to spores, which spread the disease. The fungus is a very common saprophyte on decaying vegetation, and sources of infection for gooseberries are, therefore, extremely numerous.

DISEASES AND PESTS OF THE GOOSEBERRY

CLUSTER CUP RUST (*Puccinia Pringsheimiana*)

This disease is not very common but it sometimes turns up in the plantation or garden, and can be recognized by characteristic orange-coloured patches mostly occurring on leaves and berries. The patches are usually found as thickened cushions covered in tiny, saucer-like depressions ("cluster cups") with frilled edges, but if found before that stage is reached the cushions may appear to be covered in warts or pimples. The depressions arise when these warts burst open to liberate spores, which, however, infect sedges and not gooseberry. On sedge a rust is produced that is an essential part of the life cycle of the fungus. Certain spores are produced in spring on the sedges, and it is these spores that are capable of causing infection on gooseberries, when the Cluster Cup stage arises again, and so on.

Control.—Good cultivation and drainage to eradicate sedges in the gooseberry plantation is a necessary preliminary. Where the disease persists and is really troublesome the bushes should be sprayed when the leaves first appear with Bordeaux Mixture (4–6–100) or with a colloidal copper preparation.

LEAF SPOT (*Pseudopeziza Ribis*)

This disease, already described for currants (see page 236), is frequently found on gooseberry and can be severe.

Treatment as recommended for currants.

DISEASES AND PESTS : DIAGNOSIS TABLE

THE GOOSEBERRY

DAMAGE	PROBABLE CAUSE
Branches and Stems	*Disease*
Main stem and branches wilt and die	Die-back
Foliage and Blossom	*Pests*
Leaves, opening buds and blossom attacked by small green " looping " caterpillars	Winter Moth
Leaves attacked by green larvæ with black heads ; as these grow, they may cause defoliation	Sawfly
Young shoots stunted and malformed and infested with deep or greyish-green aphides	Gooseberry Aphis
Leaves torn and distorted, shoots stunted and may be killed	Common Green Capsid Bug
Foliage turns grey or silvery, young leaves may be stunted and fall early	Gooseberry Red Spider
Leaves attacked by black-and-white marked caterpillars	Magpie Moth
	Disease
Leaves, berries and young shoots coated with felt of fungus tissue—white, later turning brown	American Gooseberry Mildew
Orange-coloured patches on leaves, covered in warts or saucer-like depressions	Cluster Cup Rust
Small brownish spots on leaves, mainly on upper surfaces, may merge together, and leaves wither and fall	Leaf Spot

254

THE GOOSEBERRY

DISEASES AND PESTS : DIAGNOSIS TABLE—*continued*

DAMAGE	PROBABLE CAUSE
Fruit	*Pest*
Drops or fails to grow	Gooseberry Red Spider
	Disease
Orange-coloured patches on berries, covered in warts or saucer-like depressions	Cluster Cup Rust

Note.—Once the trouble has been diagnosed, the reader should refer to the paragraph dealing with the particular disease or pest, and should also consult the Guide to Spraying (see page 142).

GOOD VARIETIES

Seasons—Early ; End of June to early July.
Mid-season ; Middle to end of July.
Late ; End of July to August.

GREEN

Berry's Early Kent (see Keepsake).

Bright Venus. Medium-sized, slightly hairy fruit of fine flavour. Mid-season.

Glenton Green. Medium-sized, hairy fruit of good flavour. Mid-season.

Green Ocean. Very large, smooth-skinned and of good flavour. Mid-season and of spreading habit.

Howard's Lancer. Medium to large-sized oval, downy-skinned, greenish-white fruit of excellent flavour. Regular cropper. For dessert, cooking or exhibition. Recommended for garden culture and a market favourite. Susceptible to American Gooseberry Mildew. Makes a large, spreading bush. Suckers freely. Should be grown on a leg. Mid-season.

Keepsake. Large, oval, hairy-skinned fruit of excellent flavour. One of the best for picking early for market. A heavy cropper. Recommended for garden culture and is a market favourite. Dessert or cooking. Very susceptible to Mildew. Early.

Langley Gage. Small to medium, rounded, smooth, pale green and very sweet. Strong, upright growth. Suitable for gardens. Mid-season.

Stockwell. Very large, smooth-skinned fruit of fine flavour. A late cropper. Spreading habit.

RED

Crown Bob. Large, oval and slightly hairy, thin-skinned fruit of good flavour. Ripens a dark claret red in mid-season, but may be picked green. Recommended for garden culture, and is a very old market favourite. Spreading habit.

Ironmonger. Smallish, round-oval, hairy fruit of rich flavour. Mid-season. Spreading in habit.

Lancashire Lad. Large, oblong to oval, hairy-skinned fruit of fair flavour. Ripens to a dark claret red in mid-season, but is useful also for picking green. Dessert, cooking and exhibition ; a heavy cropper

255

RED *(continued)*

and a very old market favourite in Kent. Probably the best all-round red gooseberry for garden or market.

London. Very large, smooth-skinned fruit of moderate flavour, ripening to a purplish-red. Late. The champion berry from 1829 to 1867. Very spreading in habit.

Lord Derby. Very large, smooth-skinned fruit of moderate flavour, ripening to a deep red. Late season.

May Duke. Medium to large, roundish, smooth-skinned fruit of excellent flavour when cooked. Ripens a deep red, early, and useful for picking green as early as May. Dessert or cooking. Upright growth.

Red Champagne. Small, hairy fruit of good flavour. Mid-season.

Warrington. Medium-sized, roundish-oval, slightly hairy fruit of good flavour. An old favourite, much esteemed for preserving. Strong, spreading growth. Late cropper.

Whinham's Industry. Medium to large, oval-shaped, hairy-skinned fruit of fine, sweet flavour. Mid-season. Hardy and a good cropper. Good for picking green. Recommended for garden cultivation and is a market favourite. Dessert or cooking and makes excellent jam. Rather susceptible to American Gooseberry Mildew.

YELLOW

Brighton Dessert and **Brighton Mammoth** (see Leveller).

Broom Girl. Very large, roundish-oval, hairy-skinned fruit of fine flavour. Early.

Cousen's Seedling (Sandwich Yellow). Large, oval, slightly hairy fruit of delicious flavour. A clear, pale yellow in colour and a popular market dessert fruit, especially in the Thanet area. Ready very late. Sulphur-shy. Spreading habit.

Early Sulphur (Yellow Rough). Medium-sized, roundish, hairy, transparent-skinned fruit of excellent flavour. Early. A bright yellow. Cannot be sprayed with Lime-sulphur.

Golden Drop. Smallish, oval, downy-skinned, greenish-yellow fruit of very good flavour. Mid-season. Subject to Mildew.

Golden Gem. Medium-sized, smooth-skinned, golden-yellow fruit of good flavour. Mid-season.

Gunner. Large, round-oval, slightly hairy, dull, greenish yellow berry. Good flavour and bears well. Mid-season to late.

Langley Beauty. Large, roundish, hairy-skinned, pale yellow fruit of good flavour. Mid-season.

Leader. Large, roundish-oval, greenish-yellow fruit of excellent flavour. Late. A market dessert favourite.

Leveller. Very large, oval, smooth-skinned, yellowish-green fruit of excellent flavour. Mid-season. Heavy cropper. One of the best dessert fruits. Recommended for garden culture, and much the most sought-after market variety at present. Is also known under other names. Needs rich soil, good drainage, and heavy dressings of potash and of organic nitrogenous manures. *Very susceptible to lime-sulphur damage.*

256

LOGANBERRIES.

R

 [East Malling Research Station.

FRUIT AND LEAF OF RASPBERRY "LLOYD GEORGE."

YELLOW (*continued*)

Trumpeter. Very large, oval to pear-shaped, dull yellow fruits of fine flavour. Mid-season. Susceptible to mildew.

Yellow Ball. Small, roundish, downy-skinned, golden-yellow fruits of fine flavour. An old favourite.

Yellow Champagne. Small, roundish, hairy-skinned, yellow fruit of excellent flavour. Late.

There are red and white varieties of this, known as Red Champagne and White Champagne. Both are mid-season and of good flavour.

Yellow Rough. (See Early Sulphur.)

WHITE

Careless. Very large, oval, smooth-skinned, creamy or whitish-green fruit of excellent flavour. Second early or mid-season. A very heavy cropper and a market favourite, especially in the Eastern counties. Makes a large bush.

Freedom. Very large, oblong, smooth-skinned, white to yellowish and vigorous.

White Lion. Very large, oval, slightly-flattened, downy-skinned, white fruits of excellent flavour. Mid-season. Popular at market. Makes a very large bush.

Whitesmith. Medium-sized oval, smooth and downy-skinned, whitish-green fruits of fine flavour. Mid-season, hardy and crops well. A popular market berry, and one of the best all-round varieties. Recommended for garden culture.

BEST VARIETIES FOR MARKET
Green
*Howard's Lancer (Mid-season); *Keepsake (Early).

Red
Lancashire Lad (Mid-season); *Whinham's Industry (Mid-season); Lord Derby (Late)

Yellow
Cousen's Seedling (Very Late); Leader (Late); *Leveller (Mid-season).

White
Careless (Mid-season); White Lion (Mid-season); *Whitesmith (Mid-season).

VARIETIES WITH SMALL, HIGHLY-FLAVOURED BERRIES

Champagne (Red)	Ironmonger (Red)
Golden Drop (Yellow)	Langley Gage (Yellow)
Warrington (Red)	

BEST VARIETIES FOR CANNING AND BOTTLING

Careless	Warrington
Howard's Lancer	Whinham's Industry
Keepsake	Whitesmith

* Recommended by the Royal Horticultural Society for garden cultivation.

GOOSEBERRY VARIETIES

BEST VARIETIES FOR PICKING GREEN

Careless
Keepsake

May Duke
Lancashire Lad

White Lion

VARIETIES WITH VERY LARGE FRUITS

Green

Green Ocean

Keepsake

Stockwell

Red

Lancashire Lad

London

Lord Derby

Yellow

Broom Girl
Cousen's Seedling

Leader
Leveller

Trumpeter

White

Careless

White Lion

Freedom

All the above are suitable sorts to grow for exhibition

VARIETIES TO GROW AS STANDARDS

Green

Keepsake

Red

Crown Bob
Lancashire Lad

Whinham's Industry
Lord Derby

Yellow

Leveller

Leader

Langley Gage

White

Careless

Whitesmith

VARIETIES SUITABLE FOR SINGLE, DOUBLE or TREBLE CORDONS

Green : Bright Venus, Langley Gage.
Red : Lancashire Lad, Lord Derby, May Duke, Red Champagne.
Yellow : Broom Girl, Golden Drop, Golden Gem, Langley Beauty, Leveller, Trumpeter, Whitesmith, Yellow Ball, Yellow Champagne.

VARIETIES GROWN IN BUSH FORM

All varieties do well in this form, but the following are of drooping habit and when grown as bushes should always be provided with a good " leg " or stem to keep them off the ground :—*Careless, Howard's Lancer, Whinham's Industry* and *White Lion.*

258

FRUIT GROWING

THE GRAPE *(Vitis vinifera)*

ORIGIN AND HISTORY

Previous to the reign of Edward VI, grapes were imported from Flanders in large quantities. The vine was introduced into England in 1552, being first planted at Bloxhall in Suffolk. In former times the grape was much more cultivated in the open air in England than at the present day. Outdoor vineyards of considerable area and apparently satisfactory productivity were attached to many of the monasteries in the fourteenth and fifteenth centuries. Owing, however, to the introduction and popularity of small glasshouses heated and unheated, and the consequent increase of indoor grape culture, this has come to be looked upon as purely an indoor fruit. When carefully grown under glass there can be no doubt that better fruit can be obtained, better varieties grown, and a higher degree of certainty assured, than by open-air culture in a climate such as ours. When grown under glass the grape rejoices in a fairly rich, deep soil, because the luxuriant growth thus produced has there opportunity of ripening and of being kept within bounds. But when grown in the open, better results are obtained when the vine is planted in a poorer and less stimulating soil. For it is found that in these circumstances the growths of more moderate luxuriance ripen the better.

In the gardens of Hampton Court Palace is a vine (Black Hamburgh) stated to surpass any on the Continent. It was planted in 1769. The stem is 13 inches in diameter and the vine measures over 70 feet by 20 feet. In a single season on record it produced 2,272 bunches of grapes, weighing 18 cwt. There is an even larger vine at Cumberland Lodge, Windsor Park, and yet another in Perthshire.

CULTIVATION IN THE OPEN

SOIL AND SITUATION

A situation at the base of a warm, sunny wall facing south, south-east, or south-west, should be selected, and the ground should be broken up to a depth of about 2 feet. Manure should not be added unless the soil is very poor indeed, but it is well instead to incorporate with the soil a dressing of fine bonemeal showing about 4 per cent. nitrogen. A slight topdressing of manure may often, however, be given with advantage. Although vines grow best in a moist atmosphere, the ground in which they are planted must not

259

be wet. If it contains any excess of moisture, it should be well drained. A waterlogged soil causes the footstalks of the berries to shrivel up before the fruit is ripe (known as " shanking "), and thus both colour and flavour are destroyed. Except in the mildest districts a wall facing south is essential if fruit is expected to ripen.

PLANTING

It is well to plant the young vines as single cordons 4 feet apart, about 6 inches distant from the wall and with the roots about 4 inches below the surface, late in October. The roots should be spread out. When planting a vine always tread it in. Select a time for planting when the soil is not too adhesive. About 6 inches of litter or stable manure should be laid on the ground, more to protect the roots from frost than for any manurial value it may have. The young plants should be lightly tied to stakes, but should not be nailed or attached to the wall or fence to which they are to be trained for at least a month after planting.

PRUNING

The rod should be cut back after the first season's growth, to hard ripe wood, at any time after the leaves have fallen but not later than the end of January. During the first year, a strong shoot should be selected for a lead and run straight up. The side shoots on the rod that was cut back may be allowed to extend up to 2 or 3 feet—this will stimulate root action—when they should be stopped. At the end of the year, when the leaves have fallen, these side shoots should be pruned back close to the main stem, and the lead should be cut back to a point where the wood is hard and ripe : this may be from 3 to 5 feet above the ground. The next spring a lead should be taken from the top or near the top of the main rod and the side shoots may be stopped at about 12 inches long. It is very undesirable to fruit a vine at all in its second year, but an odd bunch may be left. The rest should be cut off as they appear. Sub-laterals that may grow on the side shoots after stopping, should be pinched at one leaf. At the fall of the year pruning should be carried out as before, cutting the new main rod back to ripe wood, and the side shoots back to one or two buds. The following year the side shoots may be fruited. Great care must be taken to keep the crop light on young vines. A vine in its third year will carry about six or eight bunches of grapes. It is impossible to get quality with excessive weight. Furthermore, a young vine overcropped will produce no fruit the following year.

The vine may also be trained horizontally and then vertically as also advised for culture under glass. The branches must at all times be kept carefully and closely attached to the wall or fence. For disbudding, etc., see Grapes under Glass. Muslin bags should be used for protecting the ripened grapes from the attacks of flies and wasps. Disease and pests are also dealt with under Grapes under Glass, page 392. The same applies to cutting and marketing.

OUTDOOR VARIETIES OF GRAPES

Name	Colour	Size	Season	Qualities
Black Cluster	Blue-black	Small	Early	Rich and sweet
Black Hamburgh (See Grapes under Glass)				
Chasselas Dorée or Royal Muscadine	White	Small	Early	Rich and sweet
Grove End Sweetwater	White	Small, round	Early	Hardy, but fruit does not keep long

HAZEL NUT (See Cobnut)

LOGANBERRY AND PHENOMENAL BERRY *

The Loganberry is generally considered to be the result of a cross between the blackberry and the raspberry. It was introduced into this country in 1897, and when properly grown is a valuable market and garden fruit, besides being useful for forming a screen in summer to cover unsightly gaps. The Loganberry is a vigorous grower and produces fruit suitable for cooking, bottling and canning. The plants are self-fertile and the fruit resembles a large raspberry.

SOIL, SITUATION AND ASPECT

The Loganberry prefers a well-drained deep, rich loam. Good drainage is essential. Any aspect which gives a fair degree of protection from wind is suitable.

PROPAGATION

If any quantity of Loganberry canes are to be raised, the parent plants may be bought as " yearlings " in autumn and should be planted out at once in a cane nursery at 6 foot square, and cut back to within 6 to 9 inches of the ground. The following spring several young canes will spring up from each " stool " and these will be

* Similar to the Loganberry. The fruits ripen somewhat later and are a little larger.

used for the rather curious method of vegetative propagation known as " tip-rooting." The method consists of bending over the young growing cane until it is nearly perpendicular, and burying the tip in the soil, by digging a hole and heeling it in firmly. The cane continues to grow for a short time underground, growth becoming more and more abnormal as the cane pushes down against the hard soil. The new growth underground becomes short-jointed, swollen and fleshy, and before long adventitious rooting takes place from this region. Then a bud breaks from near the base and forms a shoot which grows upwards and soon emerges above the ground to become the new " tip-rooted " cane. This process is best done in June or July, though in a normal season Loganberry tips can be rooted as late as mid-August and blackberries until the beginning of September. The " tip," as it is generally called, is left in place all through the winter. About February it is severed from the parent cane about a foot above ground level, and is then dug up and planted out in its permanent position. At this time the cane is usually 12 or 18 inches long. When digging up the young " tip," care should be taken to preserve intact as much of its new root system as possible, because the new roots are very brittle and are liable to get knocked off with rough treatment. When all the " tips " have been cut off and dug up in this way, the remaining part of each parent cane is cut back to within 9–12 inches of the base and the cane nursery is ready to produce a new crop of canes for next season's " tip-rooting."

PLANTING AND TRAINING

Loganberries are best planted as " tips " in the spring or autumn in rows 6 to 7 feet apart, the tips being spaced at from 8 to 12 feet apart in the row, according to the method of training to be adopted. No fruit can be expected in the season of planting, but each plant should make from three to six strong new canes in their first year, and up to twelve new canes in subsequent years.

TRAINING

The canes which are to carry next year's crop are usually tied to horizontal wires at 3 feet and 5 feet above the ground level. Of the various training methods employed, the Fan is the most popular for gardens (see diagram). Immediately after pruning (page 263) the new canes are spread out like the ribs of a fan, each cane being tied with soft fillis string to the wires at 3 feet and 5 feet.

The tips of any canes which extend beyond the 5-foot wires are cut back to it. As the new canes shoot up during the following summer, they are taken up through the middle of the fan and tied up along the top wire (6 feet) to right and left. In commercial plantations of Loganberries, the Rope method of training is often used. This is described under Blackberries on page 201.

PRUNING

The pruning of Loganberries takes place as soon as possible after the fruit is picked, and consists of cutting to the ground the

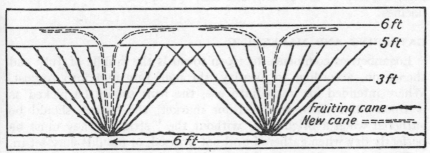

FAN METHOD OF TRAINING LOGANBERRIES.

whole of the cane which has been fruiting during the summer. This should be done with a stout knife or pair of secateurs.

MANURING

The Loganberry, like the raspberry, blackberry, and hybrid berries, has to form fruiting laterals to carry this year's crop as well as new cane for next year. Hence nitrogen is the main manurial requirement.

Experiments with raspberries have shown potash to be essential if the plant is to make full use of the nitrogen, and although there is little, if any, experimental evidence to show this to be the case also with Loganberries, it seems reasonable to suggest that potash should be one of their normal annual requirements. Farmyard manure, which contains nitrogen, potash and phosphates, is the ideal manure for Loganberries, as for all soft fruits, and may be dug in at rates up to 30 tons per acre. Failing this, pig-dung, poultry manure or shoddy may be spread evenly over the ground round the plants in the winter and forked in, or such artificials as guano, hoof and horn, meat meal, castor meal or rape dust may be applied in the same way at about 5 cwt. per acre (2 oz. per square yard), supplemented in February or March with sulphate of ammonia, nitrate of soda, or nitro-chalk, at from 1 to 2 cwt. per acre ($\frac{1}{2}$ to 1 oz. per square yard). Sulphate of potash at 2 to 3 cwt. per acre (1 to 1$\frac{1}{2}$ oz. per square yard) may be applied at any time during the winter and pricked in or dug in. Steamed boneflour at 5 cwt. per acre (2 oz. per square yard) may be applied in the spring as a phosphatic manure for Loganberries.

The ground round the roots of the plants must be hoed throughout the spring and summer to conserve moisture, or as an alternative to summer cultivation a good mulch of old rotted dung, grass mowings, old hay or rotted bracken may be applied after the spring hoeings.

GATHERING AND MARKETING

Loganberries commence to ripen towards the middle of July and thence on, according to locality, through July and into August. Where intended for immediate use, the fruit should be picked as it ripens, but when required for market, the berries should be gathered when a bright red, without the " strig." They must be perfectly dry when gathered and not bruised, or moulds may set in.

The fruit should be roughly graded for size as they are picked. They are usually sent to market in 4-lb., 6-lb., or 12-lb. paper-lined chip baskets.

INSECT PESTS OF THE LOGANBERRY

Loganberries, fortunately, have very few important pests.

RASPBERRY AND LOGANBERRY BEETLE (*Byturus tomentosus*)

This is a pest of long standing and can, if sufficiently numerous, destroy the whole crop. The fat, curved grubs, dirty white in colour and with pale brown patches on the back, are a familiar sight in Loganberry fruits. They hatch from eggs laid in the blossoms by the adult beetle, a small, active, brown or grey creature about one-sixth of an inch in length.

The grubs burrow in the plug and feed on the surrounding drupelets. Badly-attacked fruits of Loganberries and blackberries fail to swell out or to ripen properly, but become, instead, small, brown, hard and deformed. The damage done to the flesh of raspberries, although considerable, is relatively less, since these fruits are much nearer ripening when the larvæ attack them.

Control.—Fortunately, the pest can easily be controlled by the use of derris and soap. This should be applied towards the end

264

of June to both raspberries and Loganberries; this is normally sufficient, but an additional and earlier (mid-June) spraying is often worth while on Loganberries. Blackberries should be sprayed in the middle of July. Thorough spraying is important as it is essential to wet the fruits thoroughly. An alternative method is to apply a derris dust during the blossom period. This is effective, but not good for the bees.

SHOOT MOTH *(Eucosma uddmanniana)*

The fat, dark brown grubs of this moth are to be found feeding in the young tips of the new canes, the leaves of which they spin together in tight bunches. As a rule, the shoots eventually grow out of the attack, but they are then usually distorted and the check to growth is apt to cause excessive side branching.

Control. On a small scale, the pest can be combatted by hand picking. When laterals are attacked, the tip containing the grub may be pinched out, but in the case of main shoots wanted later for training, the bunched tips should be unrolled and the grubs killed. On a larger scale, hand picking is impracticable. Then the young growing canes should be protected by sprayings of lead arsenate applied often enough to maintain a good deposit on the tips until about the middle of May.

GREENFLY *(Aphides)*

Various species of aphides occur on Loganberries, but are not particularly troublesome. The Raspberry Aphis *(Amphorophora rubi)* is large, long-legged and very pale green, and feeds on the undersides of the leaves. *Aphis idaei* is smaller, darker green in colour and clusters at the tips of the shoots.

The Blackberry Aphis *(Macrosiphum rubiellum)* also feeds on the tips of the shoots and is a little larger and paler than *A. idaei.*

Control.—When troublesome, these pests can easily be killed with nicotine or by the derris spray used for the Raspberry Beetle.

RASPBERRY MOTH *(Incurvaria rubiella)*

See Raspberry, page 334.

DISEASES OF THE LOGANBERRY
CANE SPOT *(Elsinoë veneta)*

This is the fungus that causes Cane Spot on the raspberry (see page 335). The symptoms of the disease are similar on the two hosts, but severe infection of the leaves is a more dominant feature in Loganberry than in raspberry. Severely infected Loganberry leaves may be almost covered in rounded, purple-coloured spots, which, as they become older, develop grey centres, so that the spots are very conspicuous. The canes, too, can become so badly attacked that cankers are formed and the ends of the canes are killed. Infection has occasionally been found on the berries. Spores are produced on the spots and splashed about by rain, so that the disease is worst in wet weather.

Control.—The promotion of good conditions for adequate aeration amongst the foliage, and thus quicker drying after wet weather, can be achieved by allowing ample space between plants and rows at planting time, and also by suitable distribution of the canes on the wirework. As the new canes grow, their chances of becoming infected by spores splashed downwards from the current season's fruiting canes are greatly reduced if they are trained above and not below the fruiting canes. First-class control of this disease can be secured if, to the measures already suggested, be added spray-treatment with a copper fungicide. Bordeaux Mixture (4–6–100) should be put on just before the flowers open, and this should be followed by a colloidal copper preparation put into the Derris and soap spray recommended for the control of Raspberry Beetle on Loganberry (see page 264). Bordeaux must not be used on the berries because it would leave a persistent visible deposit on them.

WATERLOGGING

Functional disease.—See Apple, page 170.

DISEASES AND PESTS : DIAGNOSIS TABLE

THE LOGANBERRY

Damage	Probable Cause
Canes, Foliage and Shoots	*Diseases*
Purplish spots on young canes and leaves in early summer ; getting larger and having grey centres	Cane Spot
Apparently healthy canes wilt after bud-burst and fail to grow	Waterlogging
	Pests
Tips of young shoots attacked and leaves spun together by fat, dark brown larvæ	Shoot Moth
Young shoots, about one inch long, wither and die, eaten by small red caterpillars	Raspberry Moth
Undersides of leaves infested with long-legged, pale green fly	Raspberry Aphis
Tips of shoots infested with green fly	Blackberry Aphis or *Aphis idaei*
Fruit	*Pests*
Fails to swell or ripen properly ; is small, hard, brown and deformed ; fat, dirty-white grubs in fruit	Raspberry Beetle

Note.—Once the trouble has been diagnosed, the reader should refer to the paragraph dealing with the particular disease or pest and consult the Guide to Spraying, page 143

MEDLAR *(Mespilus germanica)*

ORIGIN AND HISTORY

The medlar is a native of Europe (possibly Britain) and Asia Minor. It is a highly ornamental deciduous tree, usually between 15 and 25 feet in height, and in late May or early June carries white or pink-tinted solitary flowers, $\frac{3}{4}$ to $1\frac{1}{2}$ inches across. The flowers are followed by peculiar reddish-brown fruits, roundish and indented at the top and crowned by a hairy calyx and leafy segments. As this fruit is not eatable until it is over-ripe, the fruits are allowed to remain on the tree until the advent of frosts. They are then picked and stored until over-ripe or "bletted." In this condition medlar fruits are considered delicious by connoisseurs.

SOIL, SITUATION AND ASPECT

The medlar is one of our most handsome fruit trees. It is easily grown in any good, well-drained but retentive soil. It requires an open, sunny situation where it is protected from cold winds, and in northern districts a protecting wall is necessary.

FORMS AND PLANTING

The medlar may be grown in standard form, allowing 15 to 20 feet between trees, as half-standard, set 15 feet apart, or as bushes or pyramids, set 10 feet apart. The best time to plant is in the late autumn, and the process described for the apple should be followed.

PRUNING

The cultivation of the medlar is almost identical with that advised for the apple. Pruning consists in merely thinning out weak and old wood in winter, and in keeping the tree open. The fruit is borne on old spurs, and on the ends of the branches.

PROPAGATION

Propagation is carried out by means of budding named varieties in July in the open, using the thorn or crataegus as stock. Pear and quince stocks are also sometimes used, and by some grafting may be preferred to budding.

GATHERING AND STORING

The fruits should be gathered about the middle of November, and should be stored in a single layer, "eye" downwards, on some dry silver sand, placed on a shelf in the store room. The stems

267

of the fruit are liable to be attacked by a fungus. The ravages of this mould are said to be prevented if the stems of the medlars are dipped in a strong solution of common salt before placing the fruit on the sand. The stems should point upwards. The fruit should remain on the tree as long as possible, and it is usually necessary to store the medlars for at least a fortnight before they are sufficiently ripe for eating ; that is, when they lose their green tint and become soft.

VARIETIES

The best varieties to grow are *Nottingham* or *Narrow-leaved Dutch*, with small to medium pear-shaped, russeted, yellowish-brown fruits, and *Royal* with medium-sized, roundish, reddish-brown fruits, both of which are of excellent flavour and prolific. *Dutch Giant,* or *Monstrous,* makes a large, spreading tree and produces very big fruits, but the fruit is not so prolific or good flavoured, while *Stoneless* is a variety of somewhat inferior flavour, and without seeds.

DISEASES AND PESTS

The medlar is particularly free from diseases and pests. Should any put in an appearance, the reader is referred to the diseases and pests of the apple.

MELON

See Fruit-growing under Glass, page 394.

MULBERRY *(Morus)*

ORIGIN AND HISTORY

The Black Mulberry (*Morus nigra*) is an attractive, hardy, deciduous and slow-growing tree, attaining a height of from 20 to 25 feet or more. It is thought to be a native of the Orient. A mature tree makes a delightfully picturesque specimen tree for a lawn and is suitable for town gardens and seaside planting. A number of old mulberry trees exist, mostly in the London area and the home counties, which are said to be the survivors of considerable numbers planted during the reign of James II, when an effort was made to establish the silkworm industry in England. It is upon the foliage of the mulberry tree that silkworms feed, though the leaves of the common mulberry (*Morus nigra*) are not so suitable as those of *M. alba*. The unattractive male and female flowers are borne in small cylindrical spikes in May. This tree is rarely

268

planted nowadays for the sake of its fruit. The trees live to a great age, and the fruit, though rather acid in taste, is not unpleasing for dessert and is without equal for tarts, preserves and wine.

SOIL, SITUATION AND ASPECT

The mulberry likes a sunny position and deep, well-drained, rich, moist loam. In the south and most of the British Isles the mulberry can be grown in the open as a bush or standard, but in northern districts it should be grown on a warm south wall.

FORMS AND PLANTING

Mulberries are usually grown as standards, bushes, or wall-trained trees. The best time for planting is in October or November, although the trees may be put in late in February or early in March. They should be planted at least 25 to 30 feet apart. When planting, do not cut back the long, thick roots of this tree, as is usual when planting fruit trees, or they will " bleed " and the tree may die. Also particular care should be taken when transplanting to damage the roots as little as possible.

It is well to plant the mulberry in grass, which should be kept close at fruiting time.

PROPAGATION

The mulberry is easily propagated by cuttings of considerable size which readily root if taken in September and October ; shoots a foot or more in length, root with very little trouble in sandy soil in a cold frame. Layers also root readily if put down in October. Shoots for propagating should not be taken from the base of a tree because this may have been grafted on *Morus alba*.

PRUNING

As the fruit is borne on spurs and on short-jointed young wood, it is well to cut back young shoots to about four or five buds, only removing in winter such as are necessary to keep the tree shapely and from becoming overcrowded. Wall-trees should have their main branches trained some 15 inches apart and should be allowed to grow until they have covered the wall. Side-shoots should be cut back in July to five or six leaves.

GATHERING THE FRUIT

The fruit should be allowed to remain on the tree until it falls from ripeness. Needless to say, it should be carefully protected from birds. Cloths spread under the tree will catch the ripe fruit if the tree is shaken, or hand picking may be preferred. When the tree is heavily laden with fruit, some of the branches may need support, otherwise they are apt to break off.

DISEASES AND PESTS

The mulberry is practically immune from diseases and pests.

CANKER (*Gibberella moricola*)

This fungus disease causes cankers and death of the young shoots, and pale-brown, waxy spore-pustules or cushions appear on the cankers in damp weather.

Control.—All affected parts should be promptly cut out and burnt.

VARIETIES

The *Large Black* is one of the best varieties.

NECTARINE

The nectarine requires exactly the same treatment as the peach (see page 271). The fruit is smaller, smooth-skinned and more delicate in flavour. For best varieties see list below.

VARIETIES (NECTARINES)

Name	Colour	Size	Season	Qualities	Soil, Aspect, etc.
*Dryden	Red and purple	Very large	August	Sweet and juicy	
†*Early Rivers	Bright red	Large	July–August	Good flavour. Excellent cropper	
x*Elruge	Pale green and red	Small	August–September	Good flavour. Very popular. Very sound	
*Hardwicke	Pale green, flushed dark purple	Large	End of August	Good flavour and prolific	Open, deep calcareous soil; not too moist. Aspect East to South-west Winter pruning, autumn; Summer pruning, April–May
†*Humboldt	Orange and crimson	Good size	August–September	Good flavour and sound variety	
x†*Lord Napier	Pale green, red cheek	Good size	July–August	Excellent for forcing. Best of the earlies	
x†*Pineapple	Orange and red	Large	August–September	One of the best flavour	
*Pitmaston Orange	Orange, flushed reddish-brown	Large	Early September	Good flavour and prolific	
x†River's Orange	Orange	Large	September	Excellent for forcing	
Spenser	Dark crimson	Large	Mid-September	Fine flavour. Good exhibition fruit	
x†*Victoria	Yellow, with brownish-red flush	Large	September–October	Prolific. Good flavour	

Note.—* Denotes those kinds which will grow on south walls in the open.
† Denotes a good market variety.
x Denotes recommended for forcing under glass.
Various plum stocks are used for grafting. See notes on Stocks, pages 39 and 94.

NUTS

The principal nuts cultivated in England for their fruit are: the Walnut, the Cob and the Filbert. (See Cobnut, page 223, Filbert, page 247, and Walnut, page 354.)

THE PEACH AND THE NECTARINE
(Prunus Amygdalus Persica)

The nectarine is a smooth-skinned variety of the peach.

ORIGIN AND HISTORY

Opinion is divided as to whether the peach originated in China, Central Asia, or in Persia. It is mentioned by Confucius, and appears to have been established in Persia in the days of Alexander the Great.

SOIL AND SITUATION

The peach and nectarine, like the apricot, need great summer heat to ripen their wood sufficiently to resist injury from frost in winter and spring. For this reason they do best in this country either under glass or on a south wall. In really sheltered situations in the South-West they may be grown in the open on walls facing south-east or south-west, but elsewhere they should have priority of the south aspect.

PROPAGATION

Peaches and nectarines are usually propagated by budding on to plum stocks in the summer. For large trees the Brompton has proved to be one of the best rootstocks, while for trees of medium size the Common Mussel stock is to be recommended. Other Plum stocks making good trees of medium size are Pershore (Yellow Egg) and St. Julien C.

PLANTING

Planting should take place in the autumn. Wall-trained trees should be planted about 4 inches from the wall and not less than 15 feet apart. The bottom of the hole should be made firm previous to planting and all injured roots should be cut away. The roots should then be covered to a depth of at least 6 inches with fine soil, well pressed down, care being taken to see that the union between stock and scion is left uncovered. If a drought should occur during the summer following planting, the ground should be well watered and mulched with old stable manure.

271

PEACHES AND NECTARINES

Peaches and nectarines can be grown in a number of artificial forms and, in extremely sheltered situations, certain varieties, such as Rochester, can even be grown as bush trees. In this country the fan shape is generally considered the most satisfactory form for trees when grown against walls or fences. (See diagrams, page 75 and 76.)

For those who wish to buy maiden trees and do their own training the notes on page 76 will form a guide. But it should be emphasized that the training of a fan tree is essentially a slow process, needing patience and experience to obtain uniformly successful trees, and one which for that reason is best left to the skilled nurseryman.

PRUNING AND DISBUDDING OF TRAINED TREES OF PEACH AND NECTARINE

On peaches and nectarines the best fruits are borne on good shoots of the previous season's growth. Good fruits are sometimes produced on comparatively short and weak growths, but attention should be devoted mainly to shoots from 15 to 18 inches long, bearing in winter mixed fruit and wood buds. These shoots are referred to in the following section as fruit-bearing shoots.

Fruit-bearing Shoots.—The fruit-buds on these shoots will blossom and carry fruits which in due course must be drastically thinned out. The wood-buds on the same shoots, if allowed to grow unchecked, will starve the fruit and smother in the tree, so it is important to know how to deal with them by means of disbudding. The expression " disbudding " in this connection does not mean the actual rubbing out of the bud between finger and thumb, but it means pinching out the tip of the embryo shoot when it is not more than an inch long. This process is vital to the successful control of all wall-trained trees, especially apricots, peaches and nectarines. Disbudding should begin at the top of the tree as soon as the wood buds begin to push out into shoots in the late spring. All " fore-right " shoots, namely, those growing straight outwards from or inwards to the wall, are disbudded first. After that the principle is to restrict the number of shoots so that when these are ultimately tied in to the supporting wires, there will be a clear 5-inch lateral space between each. Most trees on walls are allowed to carry far too many shoots, especially at the top. The only way to avoid this is to lay down a " rule of thumb " regulation for the pruner something as follows :

PEAR " DURONDEAU."

Photos]

PEAR " DOYENNÉ DU COMICE."

[R. A. Malby.

PEAR " CONFERENCE."

PEAR " BEURRÉ HARDY."

Wood-bud for Replacement Shoot.—At the base of every fruit-bearing shoot on which fruit either has or has not set, at least one good shoot must be left to grow. This must be situated at the base of the fruit-bearing shoot, and is known as the "replacement shoot." By the end of the season the fruit-bearing shoot, having done its work and being of no further use, will be cut off just above

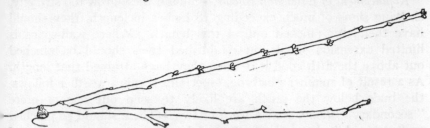

FIG. 1.—Fruit-bearing shoot after fruit is picked, showing replacement shoot ready to replace it.

the replacement shoot which will then be tied in its place to carry out the same function, namely, carrying fruit the next season.*

Extension Shoot.—In early years, when there is plenty of room on the wall, one wood-bud at the end of the fruit-bearing shoot is also retained to form an extension shoot growing in the same direction as the fruit-bearing shoot, its subsequent treatment being the same as described for the replacement shoot.

Shoots next Fruits.—Shoots growing next to fruits left from the final thinning should not be disbudded. These, however, must be pinched out later as described later under Summer Pruning.

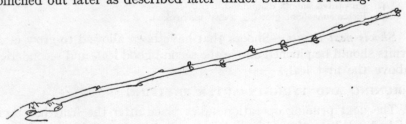

FIG. 2.—Same as above after fruit-bearing shoot has been cut off at base, and replacement tied in to take its place.

All other Shoots growing from Fruit-bearing Shoots.—All other shoots except those mentioned above should be disbudded over a period of two to three weeks. When the process is complete each fruit-bearing shoot should be seen to have either one (or occasionally two) shoots growing strongly away from its base, and one at or

* Some pruners like to leave two wood-buds at the base of each fruit-bearing shoot in order to make certain of having something to replace the old shoot.

near the tip, *where space allows*. No other wood shoots should be tolerated with the exception of those actually next a fruit. At this stage the fruit-bearing shoot should look something like the first of the diagrams on page 273.

SUMMER PINCHING

Replacement of Extension Shoots.—Should these grow too strongly, showing signs of much exceeding 18 inches in length, they should have their tips pinched out at this length. Where wall-space is limited extension shoots on established trees should be pinched out above the fifth good leaf when they have attained that length. As a result of summer pinching, especially if rainy weather follows, the buds below the pinch are likely to send out one or more " secondary " shoots after a week or two. These should be pinched or " stopped " above the first good leaf.

FIG. 3.—Peach Pruning—Pinching and Disbudding.

1. Replacement shoot growing away unchecked.
2 and 3. Fruits, each with one shoot " pinched " to two good leaves.
4. Unwanted shoots disbudded.
5. Extension shoot growing away unchecked.

Shoots next Fruits.—Shoots that have been allowed to grow next fruits should be pinched above the second good leaf, and secondaries above the first leaf.

PRUNING AND TYING-IN AFTER FRUITING

The next pruning operation takes place after the fruit has been picked. Where there is plenty of wall-space available, the extension shoot is tied in, carrying on the direction of the fruit-bearing shoot, and the replacement shoot is tied in beside last year's fruit-bearing shoot. In an established tree, or where wall-space is limited, the old fruit-bearing shoot with its terminal extension shoot is cut off at the base immediately in front of the new replacement shoot. The replacement shoot is then tied in to the space formerly occupied by the fruit-bearing shoot. Thus the replacement shoot of this season becomes the fruit-bearing shoot for next season, and in this way the whole tree is refurnished annually. The pinching programme we have described may be expressed in tabular form as follows :—

SUMMER PINCHING PROGRAMME—PEACHES AND NECTARINES

Replacement Shoot. (At base of fruit-bearing shoot.)
  (1) Terminal bud pinched out at about 18 inches.
  (2) Secondaries stopped at first leaf.
Extension Shoot. (At end of fruit-bearing shoot.)
  (a) *On Young Trees where Wall-space is Plentiful.*
   (1) Terminal bud pinched out at about 18 inches.
   (2) Secondaries stopped at first leaf.
  (b) *On Established Trees where Wall-space is Limited.*
   (1) Terminal shoot pinched out above fifth leaf.
   (2) Secondaries stopped at first leaf.

SUBSEQUENT TREATMENT OF SHOOTS

  (a) *On Young Trees where Wall-space is Plentiful.*
   (1) Extension shoot tied in in the same direction as the fruit-bearing shoot.
   (2) Replacement shoot tied in alongside old last-season's fruit-bearing shoot.
  (b) *On Established Trees where Wall-space is Limited.*
   (1) Fruit-bearing shoot cut back to base.
   (2) Replacement shoot tied in in its place.

The method of disbudding and pinching here described is only one of various systems employed by gardeners, and does not attempt to deal exhaustively with the treatment of all the shoots which may grow in the course of the season. For the sake of simplicity, it has been thought best to concentrate on the treatment of the fruit-bearing shoots, since these are the most important. Shoots arising in other parts of the tree which are not disbudded, and which are clearly not going to be required, are best dealt with by cutting them clean out after the fruit has been picked.

In peaches and nectarines, when tying in, a space of not less than 4–5 inches should be left between all fruit-bearing shoots. In plums and cherries this space may be reduced to about 2 inches.

ROOT PRUNING WALL TREES

One of the difficulties inherent in the maintenance of peaches and other stone fruits in artificial forms and in confined spaces lies in the fact that they are naturally strong-growing trees for which there is no really dwarfing stock. Hence the everlasting problem of what to do with a wall-tree when it gets to the top of the wall. Gardeners on the whole are agreed that the only thing to do is to meet trouble half-way by root-pruning a few years after the trees are planted. A trench 15 to 18 inches deep is dug in winter underneath the tree, and all strong roots are severed at a distance of about 4 feet from the stem.

PROTECTION FROM FROST

Owing to their early flowering, apricots, peaches and nectarines are always liable to be injured by severe spring frosts. Any form of overhead shelter will give a measure of protection, and where this is impracticable, tiffany blinds or a double thickness of fish-netting may be hung in front of the trees every evening from the time of bud-burst throughout the blossoming period. On fine days this shelter should be removed to allow pollinating insects free access to the flowers.

PROTECTION FROM HAIL

Wall trees may be protected to a certain extent from damage by hailstones in March and April by fastening a single thickness of fish-netting, about mid-February, above the top of the wall, and carrying it down and out at an angle of about 45 degrees to the wall. The netting is then fastened to a wire stretched on posts, about 3 feet high, and about 6 feet out from the foot of the wall, as in the diagram on page 105.

MANURING

In the absence of experimental evidence on the subject of manuring outdoor peaches and nectarines on walls, the experience of one of the most successful peach growers may be usefully quoted. Great care must be taken, when making up the border, to work a mixture of woodash, burnt earth, builders' rubble and either bone-meal or other phosphatic fertilizer well into the soil. After this no manure is given unless a tree shows definite signs of poverty, when a generous mulch of well-rotted dung is spread in a semi-circle round the stem about the middle of March.

FRUIT THINNING

Thinning should start when the fruits are the size of a hazel nut, leaving twice as many fruits as will ultimately be required. A natural process known as "stoning" begins when the fruit is about an inch in diameter, and in the course of which many drop off. After stoning, the fruits again begin to swell and thinning should then be continued, leaving the fruits approximately 9 inches apart for peaches, and rather less for nectarines. In the final thinning, only the largest and best-placed fruits should be left on the tree, spaced at about one to every 12 square inches, but leaving more at the top of the tree and less at the bottom.

WATERING

In very hot weather when the fruit is swelling, the trees will benefit from a good watering, but when the fruit is actually ripening, watering must cease.

GATHERING AND MARKETING

The test for time of picking is to feel the fruit at the base, but never to press the sides. When picking the whole hand is placed over the fruits with fingers extended under it. If ready for picking, a slight pull with the fingers will detach the fruit without causing a bruise.

The usual practice is to send peaches and nectarines to market in specially-constructed " peach boxes." These are supplied as returnable packages by the salesman and are lined with cotton-wool to hold 12, 15, or 18 fruits according to size.

INSECT PESTS OF THE PEACH AND NECTARINE

Peaches and Nectarines sometimes suffer from attacks of greenfly, the Green Peach Aphis (*Myzus persicæ*) and the Leaf-curling Peach Aphis (*Anuraphis amygdali*), feeding on the young leaves (causing leaf-curl) and on the blossoms. These can be kept in check with a tar-oil wash in December or with nicotine or derris and soap in spring and summer. Peach Scale (*Lecanium*) may also occur, but can be killed with strong lime-sulphur or with tar-oil washes. Red Spider (*Tetranychus telarius*) is the chief pest. The same species attacks hops and is troublesome on almost all glasshouse plants ; it hibernates as an adult and emerges in the spring and soon causes silvering or browning of the foliage. The lime-sulphur applied at bud-break for Peach Leaf-curl will also destroy this Red Spider.

CATERPILLARS

See Winter Moth, under Apple, page 155.

DISEASES OF THE PEACH AND NECTARINE
LEAF-CURL (*Taphrina deformans*)

This disease is commonly found on peaches grown in the open, and, to a less extent, on those grown under glass. It also attacks nectarines and almonds. Chiefly the leaves are affected. These become crinkled and swollen and, when young, are yellowish in colour with tinges of red. The older the leaf, the more pronounced are the symptoms and the more striking is the red coloration. When the fungus is producing spores, affected leaves develop a whitish bloom mostly on the upper surface. Diseased leaves ultimately wither and die prematurely, and this saps the vitality of the tree, and, in bad cases, causes the immature fruits to drop. The shoots are sometimes attacked; they become swollen and twisted.

Infection of the leaves in early spring is believed to arise from spores that have passed the winter dormant on the tree, possibly entangled in the bud-scales; the disease is favoured by a wet spring. Affected leaves produce large numbers of spores throughout the spring and early summer, and these serve to spread the disease to healthy leaves.

Control.—Good control can be obtained by spraying with lime-sulphur at 3 per cent., or with Bordeaux Mixture at 8–12–100, just as the buds are bursting. The collection and burning of diseased leaves also is helpful.

BROWN ROTS

(See Plum, page 314.)

SILVER LEAF

(See Plum, page 315.)

DISEASES AND PESTS: DIAGNOSIS TABLE

PEACHES, NECTARINES AND APRICOTS

DAMAGE	PROBABLE CAUSE
Branches and Twigs	*Pests*
Reddish-brown scaly formations on branches and twigs	Peach Scale
Foliage and Shoots	
Shoots and young leaves infested with green fly	Green Peach Aphis
Leaves infested with aphis and curled up	Leaf-curling Peach Aphis
Leaves turn silvery or brownish	Red Spider
	Diseases
Leaves crinkled and swollen; when young, yellowish with tinges of red	Leaf Curl
Leaves turn silvery on affected branches	Silver Leaf
Fruit	*Disease*
More or less concentric rings of " pustules " of fungous tissue appear and produce spores	Brown Rot

Note.—Once the trouble has been diagnosed, the reader should refer to the paragraph dealing with the particular disease or pest and should also consult the Guide to Spraying, page 143.

PEACHES AND NECTARINES

PEACHES—GOOD VARIETIES

Name	Colour	Size	Season	Soil and Aspect, etc.	Qualities
EARLY					
†Alexander	Yellow, red flush	Medium	July–August		Very hardy. Sweet and luscious
*Amsden June	Greenish-white, dark red flush	Medium	Early July		Sweet and juicy. Roundish in shape
Dagmar	Yellow, red flush	Medium	Early August		Fine flavour
Dr. Hogg	Yellow, flushed red	Medium to large	August		Excellent flavour
*Duke of York	Bright crimson	Large	Mid-July		Good flavour and forces well
Duchess of Cornwall	Pale yellow	Medium	Mid-July		Good flavour and forces well
Earliest of All	Yellowish, flushed red	Medium	Early July		Earliest to ripen
†*Hale's Early	Crimson	Medium	July–August		Delicious and prolific. Forces well
†*Peregrine	Bright crimson	Large	Early August		Fine flavour and prolific
†*Waterloo	Yellow with red flush	Medium	July–August		Good flavour. Excellent for forcing
MID-SEASON				Open, deep calcareous. Not too moist. Aspect East to South-west. Winter pruning, Autumn ; Summer Thinning and Dis-budding, April–May	
*Crimson Galande	Crimson	Medium	Late August to September		Good flavour and prolific. Roundish in shape
Dymond	Greenish-yellow, red cheek	Large	Early September		Good flavour. Hardy and prolific
Prince of Wales	Greenish-yellow, mottled red	Large	Mid-September		Good flavour and prolific
†Royal George	Pale, speckled red	Large	August and September		Excellent for forcing
Violette Hative	Pale yellow, flushed red	Large	Mid-September		Fine flavour. Hardy and prolific
LATE					
*Barrington	Yellowish-green, marbled red	Large	Mid-September		Good flavour. Excellent for forcing. Roundish shape
*Bellegarde	Dark crimson	Large	Mid-September		Good flavour
Golden Eagle	Lemon	Very large	October		Fine flavour
†Gladstone	Greenish-yellow, slight flush	Large	End of September		Fine flavour
Late Devonian	Greenish-yellow crimson cheek	Large	Mid-September		Fine flavour
†Late Admirable	Yellowish-green, and pale red	Very large	September		Rich and juicy. Usually of poor colour
Princess of Wales	Cream and red	Large	September to October		Excellent, especially for forcing
*Sea Eagle	Pale yellow, crimson flush	Very large	September to October		Good flavour and excellent for forcing
Téton de Vénus	Pale yellow, crimson flush	Large	End of September		Good flavour

Note.—† Denotes the best market varieties.
* Denotes those kinds which may be grown on a south wall in the open.
Various plum stocks are used for grafting. See notes on stocks, page 39.

NECTARINES FOR GROWING ON A SOUTH WALL

Early Rivers (End of July) ; *Lord Napier* (Early August) ; *Humboldt* (Mid-August) ; *Elruge* and *Hardwicke* (End of August) ; *Darwin* (September) ; *Pitmaston Orange* and *Pineapple* (Early September) ; *Victoria* (End of September).

For details of these varieties, see list, page 270.

FRUIT GROWING

THE PEAR (*Pyrus communis*)

ORIGIN AND HISTORY

The pear, which is a member of the same genus as the apple, is a native of Britain. It is also indigenous to Europe and the more temperate parts of Asia. Under cultivation it yields one of our most delicious fruits, but its cultivation calls for careful study and attention if good results are to be obtained, as prevailing climate and conditions have a remarkable effect upon the fruit produced.

SOIL AND SITUATION

The best soil for all varieties of pear is a deep, well-drained medium loam of a " brick earth " type such as is found in the famous cherry districts of North Kent in the neighbourhood of Rainham, Sittingbourne and Faversham. The least suitable are shallow, light soils over chalk or gravel, and cold, badly-drained clays. Most varieties of pear tree can be grown in any good garden soil, but many of the best quality dessert pears, especially later-ripening varieties, can give satisfactory results only when grown in the milder districts of the south and west of England. These varieties are often shy croppers, do not mature properly on the tree, and for this reason are difficult to store. Hence they are seldom found in commercial plantations.

To produce some of these best quality late-keeping pears such as *Joséphine de Malines, Amiral Gervais*, or *Winter Nelis* on the table at their right season, and in perfect condition, is one of the most severe tests of skill in hardy fruit-growing in this country. For such varieties perfect shelter, a sunny position and a warm, dry ripening season are just as important as ideal soil. Unless *all* these conditions are obtainable, it is wise to avoid planting any but the more hardy varieties of mid-season pears. Fortunately, there are many of these which are less particular in their requirements, and which yet deserve to be described as high quality pears. *Laxton's Superb, Williams Bon Chrétien, Dr. Jules Guyot, Souvenir de Congrès, Beurré Hardy, Conference, Doyenné du Comice* and *Emile d'Heyst* are all grown to a certain extent in this country in commercial plantations where natural conditions are favourable. They should, therefore, be reasonably safe to recommend for any good garden conditions even in the colder districts of the north. At the bottom end of the scale are the very hardy varieties such as *Hessle, Chalk, Reine des Poires*, and *Fertility*, which can be grown under a fairly wide range of conditions, and in certain seasons will be found quite profitable at market, in spite of their poor flavour.

280

THE PEAR

ASPECT

It is useless to plant dessert pears in a north aspect, even against a wall, since abundance of sunshine and warmth is essential. One or two stewing varieties such as *Catillac* might succeed on a north wall. Shelter is, of course, required on the east and north. In the case of trees grown against walls, protection from frost may easily be afforded by hanging netting about 9 inches from the face of the wall as in the case of peaches and nectarines (see page 105).

FORMS OF TREES

Pears are naturally more slow to come into bearing than apples and require full exposure to the sun if their flavour is to be of the best. Hence they favour the more artificial forms of tree. In France, the land of pear-growing, the pyramid, the espalier, the fuseau, various forms of cordon, the single and double U, and many forms of candelabra and of palmette Verrier or " grid-irons," are all extensively used for the pear, the open bush or vase being one of the few forms which is seldom used. In this country the bush, cordon, espalier and grid-iron forms are the most popular. For garden trees of small and medium size, the single oblique cordon form is the cheapest to produce, and one of the most convenient to handle, but where space allows, the three- or four-tiered espalier is to be recommended. The standard and half-standard forms cannot be recommended for any but the most vigorous varieties such as *Pitmaston Duchess* or *Catillac*.

PROPAGATION

The pear is usually propagated by means of budding in the open in July and August, and by grafting in March and April, on pear or quince stocks. New varieties may be raised by means of seed, as described in Chapter IV, page 37.

ROOTSTOCKS FOR PEARS

Where space is limited and small trees of any form are required, a quince stock of unknown origin, sent to East Malling Research Station many years ago, and indexed there as *Quince C*, is to be recommended. Maiden trees on this stock are often inclined to be weak, but if planted in good soil and well-cared for, they will make sturdy, healthy little trees which come into cropping one, two, or even three years earlier than on any other known rootstock. For the next size of tree, as bush, pyramid, fuseau, espalier or grid-iron, or for cordons on poor soil, *Quince A*, known in this country as *Angers Quince*, and *Quince B*, or *Common Quince*, appear to be equally suitable rootstocks.

In the case of very weak-growing varieties such as *Olivier de Serres* to be trained as espaliers, for any form requiring strong extension growth, and for all varieties on *chalky* soils, the quince stocks cannot be recommended. In such cases a selected seedling pear stock should be used.

Incompatibility between Quince Stock and Pear Scion.—It has been found by experiment that when certain varieties of quince are used as rootstocks, most varieties of pear, when grafted or budded on them, fail to make good trees. There appears to be some form of incompatibility between the stock and scion as there is when apples are grafted on pears or vice versa.

In some cases the trees remain small and stunted, in others growth is normal for a few years and then suddenly in a gale the whole tree breaks off at the graft union. This phenomenon also occurs with plums on certain stocks. The best safeguard is to ensure that trees to be planted have been worked on one of the more compatible quince stocks such as A, B, or C. There are, however, some varieties of pear, such as *Dr. Jules Guyot* and *Williams Bon Chrétien*, which often show a certain degree of incompatibility when grafted or budded direct on to any quince stocks. For such varieties the method known as " double-working " is advocated for making a good tree. In double-working a scion of a variety such as *Pitmaston Duchess*, *Beurré d'Amanlis*, *Fertility* or *Hessle*, which take well on quince, is first budded or grafted on to the quince stock. When this scion has made one season's growth a scion of the incompatible variety is budded or grafted on to this " intermediate " or " first scion." Varieties which are said to do best when double worked, apart from those already mentioned, are *Souvenir, de Congrès, Calebasse Bosc, Beurré Clairgeau, Beurré Rance, Comte de Lamy, Doyenné d'Eté, Jargonelle, Marie Louise, Monarch, Nec Plus Meuris,* and *Thompson's.*

Scion Rooting in Pears on Quince.—When the trees have been planted with the graft or bud union below ground, or when soil has been drawn up to cover the union, the part of the pear stem so covered sometimes forms strong pear roots which compete with the quince roots to such an extent that these often die. When this happens, the tree grows very strongly, with an upright habit of growth, and shows a disinclination to fruit. When such symptoms suggest scion rooting, it is wise to dig the soil away from round the stem, and if young scion roots are seen to be growing out above

282

the union, they can be cut off flush with the stem. If there is only one scion root and it is of any size, it is risky to cut it off completely, in case the quince roots have already perished. In this case, the single scion root can be cut off about a foot away from the stem, or alternatively the tree can be bark-ringed (see page 60).

When a pear tree on quince is showing the signs of incompatibility between stock and scion mentioned above, and no amount of pruning or manuring will increase its vigour, the balance may be restored either by inarching it with a vigorous seedling pear stock (see page 281) or by inducing the tree to send out scion roots. To do this, the soil should be drawn up to the stem until the union is well covered, and conditions for root growth should be encouraged by mulching the soil round the stem.

PLANTING

Pears, like apples, are best planted in the autumn, but where this is impossible, they may be planted early in spring. Planting should be carried out as in the directions given for apples.

Standards or half-standards on pear stock, unless planted for a shelter belt, should be planted from 18 to 25 feet apart all ways, according to soil and variety. Bush and pyramid trees on quince from 12 to 15 feet apart all ways.

The fuseau can be planted as closely as 6 feet by 3 feet, but a square plant of 6 feet is probably better, and even this is rather close.

Espaliers, and most of the various other forms of wall- or wire-trained trees on pear stock, should be planted at from 15 to 20 feet apart, according to variety and stock, in rows not less than 6 feet apart. Single cordons require 2 feet, double cordons 5 feet, treble cordons (grid-irons) 8 feet in the row.

In the more natural forms, the younger the trees are when planted the better. Bush, pyramid, fuseau and cordon trees should be planted as maidens; standards or half-standards as two-year-olds. The espaliers and other artificial forms, if bought already trained, are likely to be four or five years old. Those who wish to shape the trees into these forms, should plant maidens and follow the directions in Chapter VI.

PEARS FOR GROWING AS ESPALIERS

Belle Julie	Durondeau	Le Brun
Beurré Six	Emile d'Heyst	Louise Bonne d'Avranches
Conference	Glou Morceau	Marie Louise
Doyenné du Comice	Laxton's Superb	Williams (Bon Chrétien)

THE PEAR

PEARS FOR WALL CULTURE

(See page 287.)

PRUNING OF PEARS

Winter Pruning.—In commercial plantations, pears are generally pruned in the winter in the same way as apple trees, the leaders or extension shoots being left uncut, tipped or cut hard back according to the age and vegetative vigour of the tree. The less winter pruning a young tree receives, the sooner it will come into bearing ; when the tree has carried one or two good crops, pruning again becomes necessary to keep up the vegetative vigour of the tree by stimulating fresh shoot growth. Trees which become covered with fruit buds and which set enormous crops will require severe winter pruning.

Trees which grow many strong shoots and produce little blossom should be winter pruned as little as possible until they again come into cropping.

It is generally considered that in winter pruning pear trees, the new lateral side shoots may be cut back or " spurred " fairly drastically without either causing the death of the basal part of the shoots or producing a number of strong new laterals as is too often the case with apples.

Summer Pruning.—Although opinions differ as to the best time for summer pruning pears, it will generally be found that the new green shoots begin to lignify in July, and this is probably the best period at which to cut or brutt them at about the fifth leaf. Leaders, or extension shoots, should never be summer pruned in this way. Lorette pruning in France was concerned mainly with pears, and although the system has been severely criticized in this country, there seems no reason in theory why it should not prove successful in normal seasons, with certain varieties such as *Pitmaston, Beurré Hardy* and *Laxton's Superb*, which make a lot of strong wood-growth. The system depends on stimulating dormant buds at the base of strong new shoots of the current season's growth by cutting those shoots right back to the base when they are beginning to get woody. Lorette fixed more or less arbitrary dates for this under his known climatic conditions at Wagnonville, beginning in May and repeating the process three or four times at intervals of about a month.

Unfortunately it often happens in this country that this short summer pruning does not have the desired effect of stimulating basal fruit-buds, and a whole forest of weak secondary growth springs up. When this happens, the only thing to do is to cut or brutt these secondary growths back and try again the next season.

Lorette advocated pruning each extension shoot or "leader" in the normal way, but he did it late in the spring when the new terminal shoot was already about an inch long. This is probably quite an important part of the Lorette pruning process, and in any case is likely to prevent or weaken the growth of very coarse laterals immediately below the terminal.* (See also page 58.)

PRUNING IN RELATION TO VARIETAL HABIT

Like all fruit trees, pears have marked varietal habits which should be taken into account when pruning or shaping the trees. Upright-growing varieties like *Comice* should have their leaders cut to outside buds, but drooping varieties like *Beurré d'Amanlis* should be pruned to upward buds. Tip-bearing varieties like *Marguerite Marillat* are very difficult to grow as cordons because the fruit is borne at the end of long, slender, twiggy shoots, and if these are "spurred" back, little or no fruit-buds remain on the tree.

PEARS NEEDING HARD PRUNING AT CERTAIN STAGES

Variety	Season	Cooking or Dessert
Beurré Diel	October to November	Dessert
Doyenné d'Eté	July to August	Dessert
Olivier de Serres	February to March	Dessert
Seckle	October to November	Dessert

* The Lorette pruning method was given a thorough trial with apples by the late Mr. A. H. Lees when on the staff at Long Ashton Research Station, and a detailed report of his findings was published in the Annual Report of that station for the year 1920. See also "Lorette Pruning," by Lorette, translated by W. H. Dykes.

PEARS NEEDING LIGHT PRUNING AT CERTAIN STAGES

Variety	Season	Cooking or Dessert
Bellissime d'Hiver	November to March	Cooking
Beurré Clairgeau	October to November	Cooking
Beurré Hardy	October	Dessert
Clapp's Favourite	August to September	Dessert
Conference	October to November	Dessert
Doyenné du Comice	November	Dessert
Durondeau	October to November	Dessert
Hessle or Hazel	September to October	Dessert
Joséphine de Malines	December to February	Dessert
Marguerite Marillat	September to October	Dessert
Pitmaston Duchess	October to November	Cooking or Dessert

CROSS-POLLINATION

It is generally recognized by fruit-growers to-day that however "self-fertile" a variety of pear may be said to be, it is always wise to plant one or more pollinating varieties within easy flying distance for insects, and to ensure that the flowers of these varieties overlap to a certain extent in their blossoming period.

To plant a single pear tree in a garden or plantation without any other variety of pear from which pollen may be carried to it by insects, is a practice which cannot under any circumstances be recommended. In situations of this kind, where space will not permit of the planting of another tree, the difficulty can usually be got over by top-grafting or frame-working one or more limbs of the solitary tree with scions of another variety with a similar blossoming period. From what has been said above it will be realized that a hive of bees in the vicinity of the garden or plantation is an invaluable aid to cross-pollination. (See tables, page 300.)

MANURING

There is very little experimental evidence as to the manurial requirements of pears, but the most successful pear growers are unanimous in recommending generous dressings of nitrogen and potash, and most of them apply phosphates, also, to be on the safe side. Nothing can beat really good farmyard manure dug in round the trees in winter, or failing that, shoddy, pig-dung or poultry manure, meat and bonemeal, rape dust or castor meal dug in during the winter and supplemented in February or March by 2 cwt. per acre (1 oz. per square yard) of sulphate of potash. In the spring, if the trees set a really heavy crop, some growers like to apply, in addition, a complete application of artificial fer-

THE PEAR

tilizers such as would be given for potatoes ; i.e. sulphate of ammonia 1 cwt. per acre ($\frac{1}{2}$ oz. per square yard) ; superphosphates 5 cwt. per acre ($2\frac{1}{2}$ oz. per square yard) ; sulphate of potash 1 cwt. per acre ($\frac{1}{2}$ oz. per square yard).

MULCHING AND WATERING

Trees grown against walls or in very dry situations may find it difficult to hold their crop in a hot summer. Under these conditions a good mulching with some decaying organic matter, such as old compost or lawn mowings, will help to keep moisture in the soil. Before applying the mulch, the ground must be hoed to break any pan that may have formed on the surface.

There are occasions when pear trees on quince carrying a heavy crop of pears, will respond to a good drenching of water, but this should be regarded rather as an emergency measure for wall trees in drought conditions where it is obvious that the tree is wilting for want of moisture. A mulch put on after watering is a great help in preventing rapid evaporation.

THINNING

Fruits should never touch one another on the tree. Each fruit should have ample room to develop.

Varieties bearing small fruit naturally need thinning more drastically than the larger fruiting kinds, which may be allowed to carry two or even three pears on each spur.

PROTECTION FROM BIRDS AND WASPS

Choice individual fruits should be protected whilst still hanging on the tree from the attacks of birds and wasps by means of nets or muslin bags, and if these are tied to the branch or spur, they will prevent the fruit falling and incurring damage.

PEARS FOR WALL CULTURE

Amiral Gervais (South)
Bergamotte d'Esperen (South)
Beurré Diel (South)
Beurré Easter (South)
Beurré Hardy (West)
Beurré Rance (South)
Beurré Superfin (West)
Blickling (West)
Comte de Lamy (South)
Doyenné du Comice (South or West)
Doyenné d'Eté (East)
Emile d'Heyst (West)
Glou Morceau (South or West)
Jargonelle (North, West or N.W.)

Joséphine de Malines (South or West)
Knight's Monarch (South)
Le Lectier (South)
Marie Benoist (South)
Marie Louise d'Uccle (South)
Nec Plus Meuris (South or West)
Nouvelle Fulvie (South)
Olivier de Serres (West)
Passe Crassane (South)
Williams (Bon Chrétien) (North East or East)
Almost any good Dessert variety will do well on a South Wall.

THE PEAR

The fruit of the early and mid-season kinds should be gathered before it easily separates from the tree, when gently raised on a level with the stalk, which means that it is ripe. *Williams* must not be yellow when picked or they will quickly go soft. Early fruit intended for market requires very careful selection, handling and packing. It is best sent away as soon as gathered, though some sorts may be stored a few days. Early fruits for private consumption should be laid out singly and allowed to ripen for a few days, being eaten at once, as few of the early varieties keep. The mid-season and late kinds must be stored for a time, as they are not in condition for use when picked. Pears need to be stored at an even temperature of between 40° F. and 45° F. The fruit is best stored in trays in single layers, and not allowed to touch one another. Every care should be taken not to bruise it. The fruit should be inspected from time to time so that any decayed pear may be removed before it contaminates other pears near it. It is not always easy to tell when pears are beginning to ripen. With several varieties, however, the skin becomes a golden yellow, or the tinge of red, if present, will become brighter. Late dessert pears, especially, need care, and should be allowed to hang on the trees as long as possible. Most of the fruit, however, should be gathered before the beginning of November.

Recent investigations suggest the desirability of keeping pears separately from apples in store. It may even be wise to store pears of different seasons separately, varieties of the season of *Beurré Hardy*, *Conference* and *Doyenné du Comice* being kept away from early varieties like *Williams* and *Laxton's Superb* and from really late-keeping varieties like *Joséphine de Malines*, *Glou Morceau* and *Winter Nelis*.

Oiled paper wraps should not be used for pears which are to be stored for any length of time.

Before attempting to place pears in gas storage, the advice of the county horticultural officer should be sought as to the varieties which can safely be stored in this way, and as to the temperature and gas concentration required for such varieties. (See also instructions for Gas Storage, page 116.)

MARKETING

Pears are sent to market in much the same manner as apples ; cookers in sieves or bushels, and dessert pears in boxes, half-boxes or trays. (See Apple.)

PEARS—*Doyenné du Comice (top)* and *Durondeau (bottom)*

THE PEAR

INSECT PESTS OF THE PEAR

PEAR APHIS *(Yezabura Pyra)*

This is the only one of the several species of green fly occurring on Pears that does much damage. In appearance and habits it very much resembles the Rosy Apple Aphis (see Apple, page 156), and it is amenable to the same remedies.

COMMON GREEN CAPSID *(Lygus pabulinus)*

Sometimes corky, dimpled patches are found on pear fruits and are caused by the feeding of this Capsid Bug, which is best known as a pest of bush fruits. (See Currants, page 234.)

APPLE BLOSSOM WEEVIL (See Apple, page 157.)

CATERPILLARS (See Winter Moths, under Apple, page 155.)

CODLING MOTH *(Cydia pomonella)*

The habits of this pest are much the same on this fruit as they are on apples. On pears there is a greater tendency for the larvæ to enter the eye rather than at the side, making control somewhat easier. Arsenical sprays should be applied late in June or early in July. (See also Apple, page 160.)

PEAR AND CHERRY SLUGWORM *(Caliroa limacina)*

The black slug-like larvæ of this pest occur on pears and cherries in August, and feed on the upper surface of the leaves, eating away the tissue to leave pale brown blotches. Badly-attacked leaves turn brown and fall, and small trees have been known to be almost defoliated as a result. The " slug " is really the young stage of a sawfly and hatches from an egg laid in the leaf tissues. Although green in colour, it exudes a very dark green slime which makes it resemble a black slug. When fully fed it spins a cocoon in the soil (much after the style of the Apple Sawfly larva) wherein it pupates and whence the adult sawfly ultimately emerges the following July.

Control.—This pest, which can be very serious, is, fortunately, easy to destroy. Almost any kind of dry powder such as Derris dust or nicotine dust will get rid of it since it absorbs the slime and dries up the larva.

If preferred, a spray of lead arsenate may be used and is very effective.

INSECT PESTS OF THE PEAR

PEAR MIDGE *(Diplosis pyrivora)*

In some districts this insect is a very serious pest and considerably reduces the yield of fruit, since fruitlets attacked by it invariably fall off. An attack of this pest is readily diagnosed soon after the fruit has set. Infected fruitlets swell abnormally, often becoming deformed. Within a few weeks they begin to crack and decay and drop off the trees. The centres of such fruits will be found to consist of wet, black debris together with a number of small, white, legless maggots, up to about one-sixth of an inch in length.

These maggots escape when the attacked fruits fall to the ground and burrow into the soil, their curious jumping powers enabling them to travel short distances. They pupate in the soil and emerge as small, inconspicuous midges the following April, ready to lay eggs in the pear blossom.

Control.—This is an extremely difficult pest to deal with. On small trees in gardens the infected fruit can be collected and destroyed. It is little use doing this, however, if the pest is allowed to go unchecked in neighbouring gardens.

In commercial orchards little can be done beyond frequent cultivation in June and July and stocking with poultry in April, May and June.

Some pears suffer to a greater extent than others, e.g., *Williams* are often badly attacked, whilst late-flowering varieties usually escape altogether.

PEAR LEAF BLISTER MITE *(Eriophyes pyri)*

This pest causes pimples or blisters on the young leaves, first noticeable in the spring, which often are reddish in colour. Severely attacked leaves may eventually turn brown and fall. When numerous, the pest attacks the fruitlets, which may die as a result or become deformed.

The animal responsible for the damage is a mite of microscopic dimensions (less than one-hundredth of an inch in length) which spends the winter under the bud scales and comes out in spring to feed on the leaves and fruits. Eggs are laid in the blisters which the mites give rise to and within which the mites feed and multiply during the whole summer. In the autumn they return to the shelter of the bud scales.

Control.—Either lime sulphur or a petroleum-oil spray should be applied to the trees as soon as the leaves have fallen or when the buds open in the spring.

DISEASES AND PESTS OF THE PEAR

MINOR PESTS

Generally speaking, pears are not so prone to attack by the host of minor pests which infect the apple. Occasional cases may be encountered of the Social Pear Sawfly (*Pamphilus flaviventris*), the black and yellow caterpillars of which live in a " tent " much after the fashion of those of the Lackey Moth.

Sometimes also an attack of Leaf-curling Midge (*Dasyneura pyri*) may be seen.

DISEASES OF THE PEAR

PEAR SCAB (*Venturia pirina*)

Much of what is written under Apple Scab applies also to Pear Scab, but the two diseases are quite distinct biologically; that is, the Pear Scab fungus cannot infect apples, and vice versa. The symptoms of the two diseases are similar, but, with Pear Scab, the fruits are usually infected before the leaves, which, until blossom time, are tightly rolled and present very little surface on which spores can alight and cause infections. Infection of young pear shoots, especially of the variety *Fertility*, is often much more severe than with apples, and the individual " pustules " are much larger and more open. They present a ready means of entry for the canker fungus, and indeed areas are known where it is impossible to grow *Fertility* pears unless very efficient spraying for Scab-control is carried out ; they succumb to Canker.

Control.—Unlike most apple varieties, pears can safely be sprayed with Bordeaux Mixture in most seasons. Many pear varieties, however, are injured by lime-sulphur, especially when this is applied post-blossom. To control the disease, a spray should be applied at the same periods of tree development as recommended for Apple Scab, that is, twice before, and at least twice after blossom. Lime-sulphur at 2½ per cent. pre-blossom, followed by Bordeaux Mixture at 4–6–100 post-blossom, or a colloidal copper preparation, is an effective combination, or the copper spray can be used pre- and post-blossom quite satisfactorily. Copper spray is likely to russet the fruits, but this is not a serious blemish in pears, provided the injury is not severe enough to cause cracking of the young fruits. The russeting is more extensive in a wet summer than in a dry one, but it is preferable to the risk of severe leaf-burn and fruit-drop consequent upon the use of lime-sulphur strong enough to be fungicidally effective. The variety *Conference* is highly resistant to Scab in most districts. *Fertility, Comice,* and *Clapp's Favourite* are among the most susceptible.

DISEASES AND PESTS OF THE PEAR

BROWN ROTS *(Sclerotinia fructigena and S. laxa)*
(See Plum, page 314.)

CANKER and EYE ROT *(Nectria galligena)*
(See Apple, page 165.)

SOOTY BLOTCH *(Glœodes pomigena)*
(See Plum, page 316.)

ARMILLARIA *(Armillaria mellea)*
(See Apple, page 168.)

BITTER PIT *(Functional)*

This disease appears to be of similar origin to that on apple (see page 173), though some workers now suspect that it may be a virus disease. It differs in appearance from that on apple in that the pits are usually deep so that an affected fruit is dimpled and misshapen. The pits consist of very hard areas that resist the knife when an attempt is made to cut them open, and a badly affected fruit is ruined as a dessert pear.

WATERLOGGING *(Functional)*   (See Apple, page 170.)

DISEASES AND PESTS: DIAGNOSIS TABLE
THE PEAR

DAMAGE	PROBABLE CAUSE
Branches and Twigs	*Diseases*
Cankerous formations—patches of small, whitish pustules or crimson spherical bodies grouped together	Canker
Sheets of fungous tissue under bark at base of trunk. Long, black strands like "boot-laces" on roots and in adjacent soil in autumn. Tree dies	Armillaria Root Rot
Shoots and Foliage. (Including Blossom)	*Pests*
Leaves, opening buds and blossom attacked by small "looping," green caterpillars	Winter Moths
Leaves spun together by small, brown, green or yellowish caterpillars, which wriggle quickly backwards when disturbed	Tortrix Moths
Leaves curled and infested by masses of small, bluish-purple aphides. Young shoots twisted, stunted and deformed	Pear Aphis
Flower buds eaten from within in April by black-headed white grub. Blossom remains "capped," turns brown, drops	Apple Blossom Weevil
Leaves torn and distorted, shoots stunted and may be killed	Common Green Capsid Bug
Intervenal tissue of leaves eaten by black, slug-like larvæ in August; leaving pale brown blotches; foliage may turn brown and fall	Pear and Cherry Slugworm
Pimples or blisters on young leaves in spring, often reddish; may turn brown and leaves fall	Pear Leaf Blister Mite
	Diseases
Blister-like "pustules" on shoots and possibly on bud scales in spring. Circular, olive-green spots, turning corky and scab-like later	Pear Scab
Blossom trusses and surrounding foliage of apparently healthy tree wilts about blossom-time	Waterlogging

292

DISEASES AND PESTS: DIAGNOSIS TABLE (*continued*)

DAMAGE	PROBABLE CAUSE
Fruit	*Pests*
Small fruits eaten by green, " looping " caterpillars	Winter Moth
Maggoty. May drop just before picking-time	Codling Moth
Fruitlets swell abnormally, are deformed, crack, decay and drop—centres, wet black débris and white maggots	Pear Midge
	Diseases
Circular, olive-green spots, velvety at first, turning corky and scab-like in spring and summer	Pear Scab
Brownish, roughly circular, indefinite smudges on skin (usually near picking-time)	Sooty Blotch
Deep pits giving fruits a dimpled appearance ; fruits often misshapen ; brownish pockets in flesh after picking	Bitter Pit
Brown, soft rot of fruit either on the tree or in store; buff spore pustules or cushions mostly in concentric form	Brown Rot

Note.—Once the trouble has been diagnosed, the reader should refer to the paragraph dealing with the particular disease or pest, and should also consult the Guide to Spraying, see page 144.

VARIETIES OF PEARS

Before deciding which varieties to grow, it is advisable to make a careful study of local conditions, and if possible to find out which varieties are most satisfactory. This is best done by consulting the county advisory officer and local fruit growers.

DESSERT PEARS

Amiral Gervais. A medium-sized, round oval pear, dark russet green ripening to yellowish green. Excellent flavour and good cropper.

André Desportes. A medium-sized, conical pear, pale yellowish-green with reddish-brown flush. Growth moderate ; good cropper. May be used to cross-pollinate Doyenné du Comice. Late bloomer ; season, August to September.

Belle Julie. A small to medium-sized, oval pear, a russeted golden-brown, flushed red. Of excellent flavour and recommended for garden culture as a cordon, bush, or espalier. Hardy and prolific. Ready for use in October and November. Self-sterile.

Bergamotte d'Esperen. A medium-sized, roundish, flattened, dark green pear, of roughish appearance, turning yellow when ripe. Of delicious flavour. Ready for use from January to March. A choice garden fruit for a warm wall. Said to be self-fertile.

Buerré Alexandre Lucas. A large, roundish, conical fruit, a patchy russeted yellow when ripe. Of juicy and aromatic flavour. Ready November and if gathered before ripe, will store up to January. Recommended for culture as cordon or bush. Self-sterile. Triploid.

Beurré Bachelier. A good quality pear, roundish in shape and green in colour ; makes an upright-growing tree of medium vigour and crops well. Season, November to December. Susceptible to scab.

Beurré Bedford. A fine, large, pyriform and tapering pear, of recent introduction. The result of a cross between Marie Louise and Durondeau ; crimson and russet on yellow. Said to be of excellent flavour and a good cropper in all forms. Ready in October. Said to be self-fertile.

Beurré d'Amanlis. A medium to large, round, pyriform, yellowish-green fruit with reddish-brown cheek. Of excellent flavour and a good cropper. Growth very spreading. Hardy and recommended for the Midlands and northern districts. Ready September. Self-sterile. Triploid.

Beurré de Capiaumont. A small to medium-sized, oval, pale yellow, russeted and flushed fruit of medium flavour, and useful for dessert or cooking. Hardy in all forms. Ready October.

Beurré Diel. A very large, roundish, oval, pale green pear turning yellow with russet spots and reddish-brown flush. Of excellent sweet aromatic flavour when grown as bush or pyramid on the quince stock. Ready October to November. Prefers a warm sheltered site and needs a wall in colder districts. Prune hard. Triploid.

Beurré Easter. A medium to large, roundish, oval, yellow-green pear, with russet patches. Of excellent flavour. Hardy and reliable cropper in all forms. Likes a warm, sheltered situation and should be grown against a wall in colder districts. Should be gathered before it is ripe and stored for use from January to February. Prune lightly. Self-sterile.

Beurré Giffard. Medium in size. Yellow with brown flush. Fair flavour. Weak and straggling growth. Very hardy. Ready in August.

Beurré Hardy. A medium, round to conical, brownish, russet-spotted fruit, that does well as an espalier on a west wall on quince stock. Very vigorous grower. Of excellent flavour and should be gathered just before it is ripe. Ready October. Prune lightly. Mid-season flowering. Usually considered a shy cropper. Self-sterile.

Beurré Rance. A large, pyriform, deep green fruit with russet markings. Of fine flavour. Ready for use from December to March. Hardy and prolific, but must have good soil and preferably a position on a south wall. Self-sterile.

Beurré Six. A large, pyriform, light green pear, changing to russety-yellow. Of good flavour. Ready for use in November and December. Hardy and prolific. Self-sterile.

Beurré Superfin. A medium-sized, pyriform, golden-yellow fruit, patched with russet, that thrives on west walls in espalier form. Does well on quince stock and is a fine garden fruit. Prune regularly. Of excellent flavour. Ready October. Requires to be picked early and eaten while still firm. Early flowering and rarely self-fertile.

Blickling. A small, roundish, russety-green pear of very good flavour. Keeping well for use from December to January. Hardy and prolific. Self-sterile.

Bon Chrétien (Williams). A medium-sized to large, pyriform, uneven, pale green fruit turning yellow, with faint red lines and russet spots, when ripe. Of delicious musky flavour. Recommended for garden culture by the Royal Horticultural Society. Does well as a cordon, on a north or east wall, as a half-standard, standard, trained tree, or bush. Ready September. *Should be picked green.* Mid-season flowering and said to be self-fertile. Prune lightly. Should be double worked on quince. (See page 282.)

Calebasse Bosc. A long "calabash-pipe" shaped pear; dark brown russet. September to October. Superb flavour but most unreliable cropper and very subject to scab. Should be grown as espalier and sprayed carefully. Sometimes wrongly called Beurré Bosc.

Chalk. A small, roundish, light green pear, russeted and flushed. Of poor flavour. Ready early August. A hardy and regular cropper that is frequently planted as a half-standard to act as a screen. The fruit, although of poor flavour, is marketable and should be picked just before it is ripe. Very strong grower with drooping habit. Not a garden fruit.

Charles Ernest. A very large, oval, pyriform, golden-yellow pear, with red flush. Fine rich aromatic flavour. Ready for use in October and November. Hardy and prolific in all forms and does well on quince and pear stock. Good for top-grafting. Self-sterile.

Clapp's Favourite. A medium-sized, pyriform, light yellow fruit with red or bronze cheek, and striped red. Of good flavour. Hardy and prolific in all forms. Ready late August to September and should be picked just before it ripens as it does not keep. A popular market fruit. Late-flowering and said to be self-sterile. Prune lightly.

Comte de Lamy. A small, roundish, greenish-yellow and russeted fruit of delicious flavour. Ready October to November for immediate use. Crops well in all forms but needs a sheltered situation in the warmer counties. A fine wall fruit. Rarely self-fertile.

Conference. A medium-sized to large, pyriform, long-necked, handsome, deep green fruit russeted reddish-brown. Of delicious and aromatic flavour. Ready for picking in late September and a very valuable market pear from October to November. Hardy and a reliable cropper in all forms and on most soils, particularly when grown against a south or west wall. Recommended for garden culture by the Royal Horticultural Society. Said to be self-fertile and a useful pollinator to mix with second-early flowering, self-sterile varieties. *This pear is highly scab resistant.*

Directeur Hardy. A large, pyriform, russeted yellow fruit with flushed cheek. Of fine juicy flavour. Ready from late September to November. Hardy and prolific in all forms. Small tree. Self-sterile.

Dr. Jules Guyot. Large, oval, pyriform, yellow fruit with small black dots and slight flush, very similar to Williams (Bon Chrétien) in appearance. Delicious flavour and a hardy and reliable cropper. A popular market pear, but it must be picked before it ripens as it does not keep long. Ready early in September. Self-fertile. Should be double-worked when on quince. (See page 282.)

Doyenné d'Eté. A small, roundish, yellow fruit, but flushed with reddish-brown, of excellent flavour and ready July to August, but does not store. The earliest pear, but somewhat delicate. Recommended for cultivation as bush, cordon or espalier against an east wall. Self-sterile. A weak grower. Prune hard. Best on pear stock.

Doyenné du Comice. A medium-sized, oval, pyriform, golden-russet fruit of delicious flavour. Does best as cordon, or espalier against a warm and sheltered south or west wall in a deep brick-earth soil. The best-flavoured market dessert pear. Ready for picking early in October and does not keep long after November in ordinary storage. Recommended for garden culture by the Royal Horticultural Society. Late flowering and self-sterile. Highly susceptible to scab. Pollinators recommended are Glou Morceau, Nouveau Poiteau, Laxton's Superb, Winter Nelis, Beurré Bedford, Clapp's Favourite, André Desportes. One of the most difficult of all pears to induce to crop. Subject to scab.

Durondeau. A large, pyramidal, brown russet fruit flushed red, of good flavour, that is popular at market. Hardy and prolific in all forms and recommended for garden culture. Ready in September, and stores until October and November. Early flowering ; sometimes self-fertile. Prune lightly. Highly susceptible to scab.

Easter Beurré. See Beurré, Easter.

Emile d'Heyst. A medium-sized, long, oval, yellow, russeted pear, of excellent flavour that is ready for picking in September, and is popular at market in October and November. Recommended for garden culture by the Royal Horticultural Society and does well in all forms and in all soils on a pear or quince stock, particularly against a west wall. Hardy and prolific in northern counties. Mid-season flowering. Rarely self-fertile.

Fertility. A small to medium-sized, round-conical, yellow fruit with russet cheek. Of fair flavour. Ready in September and October and does not store. Hardy and prolific in all forms on quince and pear stocks, and even in poor soil. Mid-season flowering. Self-sterile. Highly susceptible to scab and canker. A best seller at seaside markets.

Fondante d'Automne. A medium-sized, roundish, yellow fruit, patched with russet. Of delicious aromatic flavour. Ready in October for immediate use. Hardy and prolific in all forms and in its season one of the best. Self-sterile.

Fondante de Thirriot. A large, conical, clear yellow fruit, with russet spots and rosy-flushed cheek. Of fine flavour. Ready for use in November and December. Hardy and prolific in all forms except standard. Has a very long stalk. Self-sterile.

Glou Morceau. A large, roundish light green to greenish-yellow fruit of rich flavour. Hardy and prolific as espalier on warm south or west wall and in light soil. Late blossomer and a good pollinator for Doyenné du Comice. Ready for picking late October and stores until December or January. Very difficult pear to finish. Self-sterile. A strong grower. Prune regularly.

Hessle or Hazel. A small to medium-sized, roundish, yellow to brownish fruit of fair flavour, and always popular at market. Ready September to October for immediate use. Hardy and prolific in all forms and districts including the north. Self-fertile. Prune lightly.

Jargonelle. A medium-sized to large, long, conical, greenish-yellow fruit with faint red cheek. Of fine flavour. Hardy and a good bearer in all forms, even in the colder districts of the north. Best when grown as a trained tree on a north, west or north-west wall, but also does well as a standard. Must be picked and eaten straight off the tree. *Will not store.* Early flowering. Prune lightly. Self-sterile. Triploid.

Joséphine de Malines. A small, conical, greenish-yellow pear russeted round the stem. Of delicious flavour and probably the best of the late pears, particularly for market, where it is popular. Hardy and prolific, especially when grown as an espalier against a wall. Recommended for garden culture by the Royal Horticultural Society. Ready early in October and keeps well for use from December to February. Self-sterile. Prune lightly.

Knight's Monarch. A medium-sized, round, conical, russeted, yellow fruit of delicious aromatic flavour. Stores well and ready for use from January to March. Hardy and prolific when grown in the warmer districts. Self-sterile.

Lammas. A small, conical fruit, of second-rate flavour, somewhat similar to Hessle. Ready in August for immediate use. Strong, upright grower. Often grown as a half-standard for shelter. Not a garden fruit.

Laxton's Superb. A fair-sized fruit of good flavour obtained by means of a cross between Beurré Superfin and Williams (Bon Chrétien). Ready August. Hardy and prolific. Precocious cropper. Partially self-fertile.

Le Brun. A long pear, rather like Conference, but with only a small amount of russet. Grows and crops well, but not of first-class flavour. Season, October.

Le Lectier. Medium to large; greenish-yellow; strong, upright growth; cropping moderate. Good flavour, but needs a wall. Season, December to January. Self-sterile.

Louise Bonne d'Avranches (Louise Bonne of Jersey). A medium-sized to large, handsome, conical, yellowish-green pear, with a dark red cheek. Rich flavour. A heavy and regular cropper, especially in the milder districts and in any form. Recommended for garden culture by the Royal Horticultural Society and useful for pot culture. Ready October, but must be picked before it is ripe. Mid-season-flowering. Partially self-fertile.

Marguerite Marillat. A very large, long, uneven-shaped, golden-yellow pear, tinged red and russeted. Of fair flavour. It should be gathered before it is ripe and stored for use in September and October. Recommended for culture as a bush. Hardy and prolific in warm and sheltered positions. Early flowering. Said to be self-fertile. Prune lightly, leaving tip-bearing laterals full length in early years.

Marie Benoist. A large, uneven-shaped pear russeted over yellow; of fair flavour and a valuable late fruit. Given favourable conditions on a south wall or in a warm, sheltered situation, it is a good cropper, but otherwise results may be very disappointing. Should be gathered late in October and stored for use in February. Self-sterile.

Marie Louise. Long, oval fruit, pale greenish-yellow. Good flavour. Straggling growth and makes many spurs. Season, October to November.

Self-fertile. Makes a small tree ; very suitable for garden culture, but subject to scab.

Marie Louise d'Uccle. A large, pyriform, pale green to yellow fruit with russet patches. Ready October to November. Of delicious flavour. Hardy and prolific in all forms. In colder districts requires wall protection. Should be picked before it is ripe if for market as it does not keep long. A tip-bearer. Subject to scab. Mid-season flowering. Self-fertile.

Moor Fowl's Egg (Muirfowl's Egg). Small to medium-sized, yellowish-green fruit russeted and rosy cheeked. Ready in October. Of fair flavour. A hardy and prolific cropper even in the north and Scotland.

Nec Plus Meuris. A small to medium-sized, greenish-yellow fruit, slightly russeted and of delicious flavour. Stores well, and is ready for use from February to March. Hardy and prolific as bush, cordon, pyramid or espalier. Difficult to ripen in the open, except on wall. Self-fertile.

Nouvelle Fulvie. A medium to large, conical, green fruit, turning yellow, russeted with flushed cheek. Of rich flavour. Stores well and is ready for use from December to February. Hardy and prolific but requires a position on a warm wall in the colder districts. Rarely self-fertile.

Nouveau Poiteau. A large, greenish-yellow pear with reddish russet, and of excellent flavour. Has been recommended as pollinator for Comice. Season, November. Late flowering.

Olivier de Serres. A medium-sized, flattish, round, russeted yellow pear of delicious flavour. Stores well when gathered late and ready for use from February to March. Hardy and prolific in all forms except as a standard, in which form it is unreliable in this country. The shelter of a west wall is desirable. Self-sterile. Prune hard. A very weak grower.

Passe Colmar. A medium-sized, yellow and reddish-brown fruit of good flavour. Ready for use in November and December. Hardy and prolific in all forms. Rarely self-fertile.

Passe Crassane. A large, flattish, round, russeted green fruit of fine flavour. Stores well for use from January to March. Hardy and prolific in favourable conditions in a mild climate and good pear soil. Self-sterile.

Pitmaston Duchess. A very large, long, pyriform, golden-yellow, russeted pear of good flavour for dessert or cooking. Ready for use in October and November, but should be gathered towards the end of September. Hardy and very vigorous in all forms. Too vigorous for small gardens. A popular market and exhibition pear. Late flowering. Partially self-fertile. Prune lightly. A shy cropper in many districts. A triploid and therefore not to be recommended as a pollinator for other varieties.

Princess. A large, handsome, yellow fruit, tinged with red. Of first-rate flavour. Ready for use in November and December. Hardy and prolific in all forms. Self-sterile.

Roosevelt. A very large, roundish, green pear, flushed red. Of fair flavour. Ready about the middle of October and marketed in November. Hardy and prolific in all forms and particularly attractive in blossom. Said to be self-sterile.

Seckle. A small, spotted, brownish-red fruit of honey-like sweetness. Ready for use from October to November. Hardy and prolific in all forms. Rarely self-fertile. Very weak growing.

Souvenir de Congrès. Very large, handsome, pyriform, yellow fruit, russeted and rosy cheeked. Fine flavour. Best when double grafted on quince stock. Ready for use from August to September. Hardy and a good bearer in all forms. Rarely self-fertile.

Thompson's. A medium-sized, uneven-shaped, yellow fruit slightly russeted. Of delicious flavour and crops well as a standard. Ready from October to November. Self-sterile. A good pear, now seldom grown.

Triomphe de Vienne. A medium-sized, conical, russeted, yellow fruit, flushed red. Of good flavour. Ready in September, but best picked before it is ripe. Hardy and prolific in all forms in good pear soil. Rarely self-fertile.

Williams. See Bon Chrétien.

Winter Nelis. A small, dull-green pear, changing to yellow and spotted with black specks. Of delicious flavour and a market favourite. Ready for picking early in October, and stores for use from December to January if gathered before it is ripe. It is hardy and a good cropper if grown in warm and sheltered situations and makes a good wall fruit or espalier. A weak grower. Difficult to ripen. Rarely self-fertile.

COOKING PEARS

Bellissime d'Hiver. A large, yellow fruit with red flush, and of good flavour when cooked. Ready November to March and stores well. Hardy and prolific as a pyramid or standard, and may also be grown as a cordon or bush. Prune lightly. Said to be self-fertile.

Beurré Clairgeau. A large, handsome and remarkably fertile, oval, lemon-yellow to golden-brown fruit, flushed orange and red. Ready from November to December. Hardy and prolific even in the northern counties. Stores well for a short time and is a profitable market pear. Makes a large upright bush or standard on pear stock and needs only light pruning. Said to be self-sterile.

Beurré de Capiaumont. See Dessert Pears.

Beurré Naghin. A medium-sized, round, bright green pear with a long stalk. Medium growth ; good cropper and excellent quality.

Catillac. A large, roundish, dull green pear, tinged reddish-brown and ripening to a deep reddish-brown. Ready to pick in October and stores well. A profitable market fruit from December to April. Recommended for garden culture by the Royal Horticultural Society. Does well as standard, espalier, pyramid, or trained tree on north or east walls. Hardy and prolific, but an uncertain cropper on some soils. Mid-season flowering. Self-sterile. Triploid. Prune lightly. Too vigorous grower for small gardens.

VARIETIES OF PEARS

General Todleben. A very large, greenish-yellow and russeted pear, of exceptional flavour. May be worthy of dessert sometimes. Ready early in October, and stores well into January. Does well in all forms and needs only light pruning. Self-sterile. Difficult to ripen.

Vicar of Winkfield. A large, longish, bright green fruit, turning yellow. Of excellent flavour and may be used for dessert. Ready early in October and storing for use from November to January. Hardy and prolific in all forms. Prune lightly. Triploid.

Many dessert pears, if gathered when they are hard and green, cook splendidly, and when the trees are cropping heavily, it is wise to thin out and cook a quantity, and thus give the remaining fruit more chance to develop into choice specimens. For the small grower the following three varieties make a highly satisfactory combination: **Conference, Laxton's Superb** and **Dr. Jules Guyot.** If only one tree is to be selected, it had better be the first of these.

THE CROSS-POLLINATION OF PEAR VARIETIES

When only one pear tree is planted, it is essential to select one of the self-fertile varieties, unless, of course, other pear trees, flowering at the same period, are growing in other gardens close by.

SELF-FERTILE VARIETIES

Early-flowering	Mid-season-flowering	Late Bloomers
Bergamotte d'Esperen	Bellissime d'Hiver	Dr. Jules Guyot
Conference	Beurré Bedford	
Durondeau	Bon Chrétien (Williams)	
Marguerite Marillat	Marie Louise	

PARTIALLY OR SOMETIMES SELF-FERTILE

Early-flowering	Mid-season-flowering	Late Bloomers
Beurré Superfin	Laxton's Superb	Hessle or Hazel
	Louise Bonne of Jersey	Pitmaston Duchess

The John Innes Horticultural Institution have proved that Beurré d'Amanlis cannot be cross-pollinated by Conference, nor Louise Bonne by Conference. Apart from these any of the fertile or partially self-fertile varieties planted in conjunction with self-sterile varieties, flowering at the same time, will cross-pollinate the self-sterile varieties. Early-flowering sorts will also cross-pollinate mid-season flowers and mid-season bloomers cross-pollinate late bloomers, as the flowering seasons overlap somewhat.

VARIETIES OF PEARS

SELF-STERILE AND RARELY SELF-FERTILE VARIETIES

Early-flowering	Mid-season-flowering	Late Bloomers
Beurré d'Amanlis	Catillac	Calebasse Bosc
Beurré Clairgeau	Emile d'Heyst	Clapp's Favourite
Beurré Diel	Joséphine de Malines	Doyenné du Comice
Beurré Hardy	Winter Nelis	Fertility
Comte de Lamy		Glou Morceau
Doyenné d'Eté		Nouveau Poiteau
Jargonelle		Passe Colmar
Souvenir de Congrés		

14 GOOD VARIETIES OF PEAR

Variety	Garden or Orchard	Dessert or Cooking
Beurré Superfin	Garden or Orchard	Cooking or Dessert
Bon Chrétien (Williams)	Garden or Orchard	Dessert
Conference	Garden	Dessert
Doyenné d'Eté	Garden	Dessert
Doyenné du Comice	Garden	Dessert
Durondeau	Garden	Dessert
Emile d'Heyst	Garden or Orchard	Dessert
Glou Morceau	Garden or Orchard	Dessert
Jargonelle	Garden	Dessert
Joséphine de Malines]	Garden	Dessert
Laxton's Superb	Garden or Orchard	Dessert
Louise Bonne of Jersey	Garden	Dessert
Pitmaston Duchess	Garden or Orchard	Cooking or Dessert
Winter Nelis	Garden or Orchard	Dessert

PEARS FOR LARGE OR MEDIUM GARDENS

Variety	Dessert or Cooking	Season
Belle Julie	Dessert	October–November
*Bergamotte d'Esperen	Dessert	January–March
Beurré Easter	Dessert	January–February
*Beurré Hardy	Dessert	October
Beurré Six	Dessert	November–December
Beurré Superfin	Dessert	October
*Bon Chrétien (Williams)	Dessert	September
Conference	Dessert	October–November
Doyenne d'Eté	Dessert	July–August
*Doyenné du Comice	Dessert	November
Durondeau	Dessert	October–November
*Emile d'Heyst	Dessert	October–November
*Jargonelle	Dessert	August–September
*Joséphine de Malines	Dessert	December–February
Laxton's Superb	Dessert	August–September
*Louise Bonne of Jersey	Dessert	October
*Olivier de Serres	Dessert	February–April
Seckle	Dessert	October–November
Vicar of Winkfield	Cooking	November–January
*Winter Nelis	Dessert	December–March

* Recommended for Wall.

VARIETIES OF PEARS

SELECTION OF PEARS IN ORDER OF RIPENING
Early (August–September)

Variety	Garden or Orchard	Dessert or Cooking
Bon Chrétien (Williams)	Garden or Orchard	Dessert
Clapp's Favourite	Garden or Orchard	Dessert
Doyenné d'Eté	Garden	Dessert
Dr. Jules Guyot	Garden or Orchard	Dessert
Hessle	Garden or Orchard	Dessert
Jargonelle	Garden	Dessert
Laxton's Superb	Garden or Orchard	Dessert
Souvenir de Congrés	Garden	Dessert

Mid-Season (October–November)

Variety	Garden or Orchard	Dessert or Cooking
Beurré Clairgeau	Garden or Orchard	Dessert or Cooking
Beurré d'Amanlis	Garden	Dessert
Beurré Diel	Garden	Dessert
Beurré Hardy	Garden or Orchard	Dessert
Beurré Superfin	Garden	Dessert
Conference	Garden or Orchard	Dessert
Doyenné du Comice	Garden	Dessert
Durondeau	Garden	Dessert
Emile d'Heyst	Garden	Dessert
Fondante d'Automne	Garden	Dessert
Louise Bonne of Jersey	Garden	Dessert
Marguerite Marillat	Garden	Dessert
Marie Louise	Garden	Dessert
Marie Louise d'Uccle	Garden	Dessert
Pitmaston Duchess	Orchard	Cooking or Dessert

Late Season (November–December, etc.)

Variety	Garden or Orchard	Dessert or Cooking
Beurré Alexandre Lucas	Garden or Orchard	Dessert
Beurré Easter	Garden or Orchard	Dessert
Beurré Naghin	Garden or Orchard	Cooking
Beurré Rance	Garden or Orchard	Dessert
Catillac	Garden or Orchard	Cooking
Glou Morceau	Garden or Orchard	Dessert
Joséphine des Malines	Garden	Dessert
Passe Colmar	Garden	Dessert
Nec Plus Meuris	Garden or Orchard	Dessert
Vicar of Winkfield	Garden or Orchard	Cooking
Winter Nelis	Garden or Orchard	Dessert

PEARS FOR FORCING

Variety	Season	Dessert or Cooking
Beurré Hardy	October	Dessert
Beurré Superfin	October–November	Dessert
Doyenné du Comice	October–November	Dessert
Louise Bonne of Jersey	October	Dessert

VARIETIES OF PEARS

SOME GOOD-FLAVOURED DESSERT PEARS

Variety	Garden or Orchard	Season
Beurré Superfin	Garden	October
Beurré Hardy	Garden or Orchard	October
Bon Chrétien (Williams)	Garden	September
Calebasse Bosc	Garden	September–October
Comte de Lamy	Garden	October–November
Doyenné du Comice	Garden	November
Joséphine de Malines	Garden	December–February
Marie Louise	Garden	October–November
Olivier de Serres	Garden	February–March
Seckle	Garden	October–November
Thompson's	Garden	October–November
Winter Nelis	Garden or Orchard	December–March

SOME PEARS FOR MARKET

Variety	Season	Dessert or Cooking
*Beurré Clairgeau	October–November	Cooking or Dessert
Beurré d'Amanlis	September	Dessert
*Catillac	December–April	Cooking
*Clapp's Favourite	August–September	Dessert
*Conference	October–November	Dessert
Dr. Jules Guyot	September (Early)	Dessert
Doyenné du Comice	November	Dessert
*Durondeau	October–November	Dessert
*Emile d'Heyst	October–November	Dessert
*Fertility	September–October	Dessert
Fondante de Thirriot	November–December	Dessert
*Hessle or Hazel	September–October	Dessert
*Joséphine de Malines	December–February	Dessert
Laxton's Superb	October	Dessert
Louise Bonne of Jersey	October	Dessert
Marie Louise	October–November	Dessert
*Pitmaston Duchess	October–November	Cooking or Dessert
*Roosevelt	November	Dessert

* Varieties suitable for orchard cultivation as standards.

ESPECIALLY HARDY PEARS

Variety	Garden or Orchard	Dessert or Cooking
Beurré Hardy	Garden or Orchard	Dessert
Beurré Superfin	Garden or Orchard	Dessert
Catillac	Garden or Orchard	Cooking
Chalk	Orchard	Dessert
Conference	Garden or Orchard	Dessert
Emile d'Heyst	Garden or Orchard	Dessert
Hessle or Hazel	Garden or Orchard	Dessert
Jargonelle	Garden	Dessert
Louise Bonne of Jersey	Garden or Orchard	Dessert
Lammas	Orchard	Dessert
Pitmaston Duchess	Garden or Orchard	Dessert or Cooking

PEARS FOR GROWING IN POTS (See page 367)

VARIETIES OF PEARS

PEARS FOR STORING

Variety	Gather	Ready for Use
Bergamotte d'Esperen	October	January–March
Beurré Alexandre Lucas	October (before ripe)	November–January
Beurré Clairgeau (C)	Late September	November
Beurré Easter	October	January–February
Beurré Naghin	October	January–March
Blickling	October	December–January
Catillac (C)	Early October	December–April
Conference	Late September	October–November
Doyenné du Comice	Early October	November
Durondeau	Late September	October–November
Emile d'Heyst	Late September	October-November
General Todleben (C)	October	December–January
Joséphine de Malines	Early October	December–February
Marie Benoist	Early October	February
Nec Plus Meuris	October	February–March
Nouvelle Fulvie	October	December–February
Olivier de Serres	October–November	February–March
Passe Crassane	October	January–March
Pitmaston Duchess	Late September	October–November
Roosevelt	Mid-October	November
Vicar of Winkfield (C)	Early October	November–January
Winter Nelis	Early October	December–March

(C) Denotes Cooking.

PEARS FOR EXHIBITION

Variety	Season	Dessert or Cooking
Beurré Bachelier	November–December	Dessert
Beurré Clairgeau	November–December	Cooking
Beurré Hardy	October	Dessert
Beurré Naghin	December–April	Cooking
Catillac	December–April	Cooking
Charles Ernest	October–November	Dessert
Conference	October–November	Dessert
Doyenné du Comice	November–December	Dessert
Marguerite Marillat	October	Dessert or Cooking
Pitmaston Duchess	October–November	Dessert or Cooking

PERRY PEARS

Advice on the best varieties of perry pear to suit the district should first be sought from the County Advisory Officer or Long Ashton.

Perry pears are not now much grown in Devonshire and Somersetshire, but in Herefordshire, Gloucestershire and the Midland cider districts, they are much in demand. They are usually grown as standard trees on seedling pear stocks. Among the best varieties are :—

Barland. A favourite perry pear with a peculiar flavour of its own.

Butt. A medium-sized, conical, green fruit which makes a strong, rough perry. Mid-season to late in flowering. Hardy and prolific. Fruit ready mid-season.

Moorcroft (Malvern Hills). A large, rosy-cheeked, orange and russeted fruit which makes a strong perry. Flowers early to mid-season. Fruit ready late September to early October.

304

PLUMS—*Bryanston Gage* (*top*) and *Giant Prune* (*bottom*)

Oldfield. A small to medium-sized, greenish-yellow fruit with russet spots which produces a strong, sweet perry and is quite one of the best pears for this purpose. It is hardy and prolific, and flowers mid-season. Fruit stores well and is profitable at market.

Taynton Squash. Another good perry-making pear, small, russeted over dull yellow with rosy cheek. Hardy and prolific. Flowers early and fruit is ready early in September.

THE PLUM *(Prunus domestica)*

ORIGIN AND HISTORY

The plum is a member of the prunus family, to which the peach, almond, apricot, and cherry belong. Several varieties of the wild plum, including the sloe and bullace, are to be found growing in our woods and hedgerows, but there is a vast difference between these and the many varieties of cultivated plum introduced into this country from Italy and Flanders, early in the sixteenth century.

SOIL AND SITUATION

Plums are nitrogen lovers and in general do well on soils which produce strong growth in trees. Rich garden soil, old hop gardens, loams of the brick-earth type, all these, provided they are well but not excessively drained, will grow good plum trees. In some districts plums do well on stiffish loams over a chalk subsoil, and on chalky loams over a clay subsoil. In other districts they appear to do equally well on acid soils containing a fair proportion of sand and fine silt. In fact, so long as they are not planted on the most extreme forms of clay, sand, or chalk, plums can be made to do well on almost any well-drained soil, provided the soil is kept well cultivated and the trees are given plenty of nitrogenous manure.

On high open land they are less liable to frost damage when in blossom, but need shelter from the east winds. On low land, however sheltered they may be from the wind, they are always liable to frost damage in April. Wall trees may be artificially sheltered by some form of protective covering as recommended for peach trees (page 105).

FORM OF TREE

The plum, like the cherry, produces fruit spurs freely on one- and two-year-old wood. Hence the best form is that in which plenty of new shoots can be allowed to grow full length every year without unduly crowding the tree. Since there is no definitely dwarfing rootstock for plums or cherries, as there is in the case of apples, a plum or cherry tree, whether budded, grafted, or on its own roots, will always tend to make rather a bigger tree than is really suitable for the artificial forms. The bush, half-standard and standard are the most suitable forms where large yields and regular cropping is required. Where fruit size and quality are the first consideration, as in the case of *Coe's Golden Drop*, *Kirke's Blue* and other plums of the highest flavour, the more artificial forms of tree may be useful, though difficult to keep within bounds. Of these the fan-trained tree on a south wall is likely to give the best results, always remembering that the wall should be as high as possible, and that the tree should be allowed as wide a spread fanwise as space will permit. Nothing is easier or more productive of bad results than to under-estimate the space required by stone fruits when planted against a wall. The espalier and cordon forms are sometimes used for plums, but for the reasons given above they are not to be recommended for any stone fruits. The annual hard cutting back of new laterals to maintain tree shape in these very artificial forms reduces the number of fruit-buds, unduly stimulates excessive growth of new laterals, which are useless because they will again be cut hard back, and provides a large number of pruning wounds for possible infection by the Silver-Leaf fungus.

PROPAGATION

The usual nursery practice is to bud plums in July or August on to plum stocks raised either vegetatively or from seed. Experiments at East Malling Research Station have shown that stocks raised vegetatively are more uniform than stocks raised from seed. Both at East Malling and at Long Ashton a selected seedling of the Myrobolan group of plums, known as *Myrobolan B*, has shown itself to be the most satisfactory stock where strong growth, combined with regular cropping, is required. The *Pershore Plum* or *Yellow Egg* gives a rather less vigorous tree, combined with good cropping, but this stock is difficult to produce in quantity and trees worked on true Pershore are difficult to obtain. The *Mariana Plum* has given most promising results in recent years at East Malling, but trees on this stock are not available in any quantity. The *Common Plum* has a partially dwarfing effect and can be safely recommended for the variety *Victoria* as a suitable stock for a wall tree or for planting as bush trees at comparatively close distances such as would be suitable for garden culture. This stock, however, cannot be universally recommended because certain varieties, notably *Czar*, the popular cooking variety, show marked incompatibility between stock and scion when worked on it.

PLANTING

The operation of planting a plum tree is the same as for other tree fruits (see page 98). Wall trees should not be tied up until the soil has had a chance to settle round the roots. Trees should be planted at distances of from 15 to 30 feet apart according to the variety, form, and rootstock. (See Table, page 107.) The trees to be planted should be as young as possible ; i.e., bush, pyramid and half-standard trees may be safely planted as maidens and the head formed when and where desired. Standards may be planted as two-year-old or three-year-old trees, but should not be older than this. The artificial forms of trained tree, such as the fan, if bought already trained to the required shape, are likely to be four or five years old when they come from the nursery and will require correspondingly greater care in looking after for the first year or so.

PRUNING

In general, plum trees, like cherries, should be pruned as little as possible in the winter. Both these fruits are susceptible to attack by the Silver-Leaf fungus, the spores of which frequently infect the tree in wet weather through the wounds caused by large cuts. Such shoot pruning as may be necessary for plums and cherries should be carried out in late spring, and branch-thinning in summer when large wounds heal best and conditions are least favourable for infection. Some well-known plum growers leave their plum trees unpruned after the first year or two, allowing them to grow as they will, and relying on clean cultivations and high nitrogen manuring to stimulate fresh shoot growth every year. Needless to say, this system is impossible for the artificial forms of tree. On wall trees, when fan training is completed as in the manner described in Chapter VI (page 76), the main pruning operation consists of summer pinching out the tips which are not needed for tying in. This pinching should be done when the shoots have made from six to eight leaves. As soon as possible after the crop has been picked, the extension shoots, the replacement shoots, and those for which there is still space on the wall, are tied in, all dead shoots are cut off, and the superfluous shoots which were pinched back in summer are cut back to short stubs of a few inches in length.

ROOT PRUNING

Plum trees grown on walls or against fences will have to be root-pruned, if they are to be kept within reasonable bounds. On a 6-foot wall they should be root-pruned about three years after planting, and again in three or four years' time, as described for peaches.

MANURING

Plums, like all the stone fruits, give the best results under high nitrogen conditions. Rich nitrogenous soil, heavy dressings of organic nitrogenous manures, and clean cultivations are therefore the three main ways of manuring plums. If it is not possible to get ample supplies of dung, shoddy, meat-meal, hoof and horn or other organic nitrogenous fertilizers, light dressings of one form of these should be applied in the winter, supplemented in the spring by sulphate of ammonia, nitrate of soda, nitro-chalk or some similar form of inorganic nitrogenous fertilizer applied at the rate of $1\frac{1}{2}$ to 2 cwt. per acre ($\frac{1}{2}$ to 1 oz. per square yard) and pricked in lightly. Cases of potash deficiency have been known in plums, but this is the exception rather than the rule. On sandy soils sulphate of potash at the rate of 2 cwt. per acre (1 oz. per square yard) should be applied at any time in the winter and dug in.

THINNING

Experiments with half-standard trees of *Victoria* in a plum plantation have shown that on trees which have set a very heavy crop, ultimate fruit size may be increased by thinning out the young fruits when they are about half an inch long, leaving one fruit to every $2\frac{1}{2}$ to 3 inches length of shoot. On wall trees gardeners like to make thinning a gradual process, first removing misshapen and badly-placed fruits, then reducing the clusters to singles, and lastly spacing these out to $2\frac{1}{2}$ to 3 inches apart.

The weight of the heavy crops which plum trees at times bear—especially in the case of the *Victoria* plum—will often cause overhanging and weak branches to snap and thus provide an entrance for fungus disease. To obviate this, strong wooden supports, with a pad between them and the branches they support, should be placed firmly under the branches that appear liable to suffer from an extra heavy crop of fruit.

This should be done early in the season, before the fruit becomes too heavy.

PLUMS AND DAMSONS

GATHERING AND STORING

Dessert fruit should be left on the tree until thoroughly ripe and never gathered too soon. Each individual fruit should be snipped off with scissors with the stalk attached and carefully placed in the picker's basket with as little handling as possible. On no account should the fruit be gathered wet. Cooking plums are gathered as soon as they begin to turn colour, the trees being gone over several times and the largest fruits only being removed, until the plums are eventually all picked. Dessert fruits, if gathered a few days before they are dead ripe, may be stored for a few days, laid out and not touching in the store room. Cooking fruit is usually sent straight off to market.

MARKETING

Most plums are now sent to market in 12-lb. chip baskets. Some growers pack in a non-returnable wooden box resembling a tomato box and holding 14 lb. of plums. Cheap cooking plums are still marketed in half-sieve wickers holding about 24 lb.

INSECT PESTS OF THE PLUM AND DAMSON

See also Guide to Spraying, page 144.

LEAF-CURLING PLUM APHIS *(Anuraphis padi)*

The young of this greenfly hatch out in February and March from the small, black shining eggs which were laid on the twigs the previous autumn. They give rise to successive generations which feed on the leaves till midsummer, when they migrate to other plants, returning to the plum only in the autumn.

This insect, by its feeding, causes the leaves to curl. Attacked shoots are stunted and the fruit remains small or drops to the ground.

Control.—Although these aphides are easily killed by contact with nicotine sprays, it is not always easy to wet them, as they are largely protected by the curled leaves. The winter eggs are, however, easily destroyed by means of tar-oil washes. A winter application of tar-oil should never be omitted from plums and damsons. *Victoria* plums rarely suffer from aphis.

MEALY PLUM APHIS *(Hyalopterus arundinis)*

Although less harmful than the Leaf-curling Aphis, this insect can be very troublesome. It becomes abundant in the middle of

309

the summer, and produces large quantities of a sticky, waxy secretion which falls about on the leaves and fruits.

Control.—Although the Mealy Aphis does not curl the leaves, it is nevertheless not particularly easy to wipe out with nicotine sprays, since the mealiness serves to some extent as a protection. Like the Leaf-curling Aphis, however, it spends the winter in the form of an egg on the twigs and is thus easily killed by winter washing with tar-oil sprays.

HOP DAMSON APHIS *(Phorodon humuli)*

This pest occurs on sloes and damsons, rarely on other plums. The eggs are laid on the twigs in autumn. The aphides hatch in the spring and feed on the leaves until May or early June. Then appear winged forms which migrate to hops and do their most serious damage on that crop. Return migrants lay eggs on the damsons in the autumn.

Control.—The eggs of this, like those of the foregoing species, are readily killed by tar-oil winter washes.

The summer generations on the hop have to be tackled by means of nicotine sprays.

RED SPIDER *(Oligonychus ulmi)*

The life history of this pest has been described in the chapter on apple pests (see page 162). It is even more serious on plums than on apples ; in bad cases the fruit fails to develop properly and premature leaf and fruit drop occurs.

Control.—Lime sulphur at a concentration of 1 per cent. can safely be applied to plums about ten days after petal-fall (at the time when most of the apple petals have fallen). This spray should not be omitted where Red Spider is at all troublesome. The eggs can be killed by spraying in winter (say in February) with a winter petroleum-oil emulsion, which, unless new invasions of spider occur in the following summer, provides the most effective means of getting rid of the pest.

SAWFLY *(Hoplocampa flava)*

In some districts Plum Sawfly takes a heavy toll of the crop. In appearance and habits it resembles the Apple Sawfly. The eggs are laid in the flowers at blossom time and the resulting grubs feed within the growing fruits, passing from fruit to fruit and leaving holes in their sides from which wet, black frass exudes. Attacked fruits invariably drop off whilst they are small and green. When fully fed the larvæ enter the soil, where they construct cocoons similar to those of the Apple Sawfly and spend the winter in them, pupating in the spring, and emerging as adult " sawflies " at blossom time.

Control.—The best results have been obtained by spraying twice with Derris root, once about a week after petal-fall (when the " cots " or receptacles are beginning to split) and again a week later. Care should be taken to wet the developing fruits very thoroughly with the spray.

CATERPILLARS

See Winter Moths under Apple, page 155.

RED PLUM MAGGOT *(Cydia funebrana)*

This pest is related to the Codling Moth and has somewhat similar habits. Eggs are laid on the fruits early in July. From these arise minute caterpillars, which enter the green fruits and tunnel within them in an inconspicuous manner. Usually no sign of the pest is apparent until one eats a ripe fruit of perfectly sound appearance, when a mass of frass is discovered near the stone and usually a large, red maggot.

Control.—It is not safe to apply arsenical sprays for the control of this pest. Any spraying carried out should be confined to non-poisonous materials such as Derris. Affected fruit ripens prematurely and thus some good can be done by collecting and destroying the first fruits which drop.

Some of the larvæ can also be caught in sack bands placed around the tree trunks.

SHOT-HOLE BORERS

Small, round holes in the trunks of the trees are made by various species of wood-boring beetles, which have at times been regarded as major pests of plums. There seems little doubt now that such beetles are a secondary trouble only, since they undoubtedly show a preference for trees in an unhealthy state.

MINOR PESTS

Case Bearers, Leaf-eating Weevils *(Phyllobius spp.)*, and one or two other pests sometimes occur in sufficient numbers to cause alarm, but the damage they do scarcely justifies the trouble of spraying.

DISEASES OF PLUMS AND DAMSONS

BACTERIAL CANKER AND LEAF SPOT *(Pseudomonas mors-prunorum)*

This serious disease of young plum trees is very similar to Bacterial Canker of cherry, caused by the same organism, but there are a few important differences. It is less usual in plum to get cankering of individual branches ; the tree stem is more commonly attacked, though branch cankers do occur. Gumming at the site of the canker is not nearly as copious in plum as in cherry, and the leaf-spot phase usually does not appear in quantity till summer. Inoculation experiments have shown that infection, as with cherry, is most likely to occur in late autumn and winter. The canker does not become readily visible, however, until spring, when normal stem thickening begins and the dead, cankered area is then revealed as flattened and slightly sunken. It can usually be felt quite readily then by running the fingers around the stem, and incisions at the edge of the cankered area will show a very sharp line of demarcation between the brown, diseased area of the canker and the healthy adjacent tissue. Bacterial Canker can be suspected when the foliage on some or all of the branches is yellow, sickly, and wilting soon after growth starts in spring. As with cherry, the bacteria, which are swarming in the bark at the edge of the canker in early spring, usually die out when summer comes, and thus the canker is annual. If the tree is not girdled in the one season it will probably recover, though its vigour will be curtailed for a time. Trees that have recovered from stem cankers can often be recognized by a deep depression, sometimes several feet long, surrounded by vigorous new callus growth, running more or less vertically up the stem and frequently with a slight spiral twist. The varieties *Victoria, Czar, Giant Prune,* and *Early Laxton* are very susceptible, particularly during their early years before cropping. Whole plantations can be jeopardized because the bacteria are so prone to attack the young stems, which are rapidly girdled, thus killing the trees.

Control.—The method of attack suggests the means of prevention of at least the serious stem-canker phase, and experiments have proved its value. It is the use of a resistant " stem-builder " variety on which the susceptible variety required for cropping is high-worked. *Myrobolan B* has proved highly resistant and a satisfactory nursery stock. This should be run up to the required height, usually that of a 5 or 6 feet standard, in the nursery, and be allowed to form the initial branch-system, which is then top-grafted with the susceptible variety. If some root-system other than *Myrobolan B* is required, *Myrobolan B* can be low-worked in the usual way on to it, and the susceptible cropping variety super-imposed at standard height as before, though a more expensive nursery tree will result from this method. The stem-builder method is of use only where new plantations are contemplated ; for existing plantations containing susceptible varieties some other means of treatment must be employed. Up to the present a satisfactory spray-programme has not been developed, since the spray-treatment recommended for cherry (see page 142) does not appear to meet the requirements of plum. Summer spraying, beginning towards the end of May, has proved effective in controlling Leaf Spot, and Bordeaux Mixture at 4–6–100, though likely to cause some leaf-spotting in wet weather, is recommended. The addition of 6 pints per 100 gallons of edible cotton-seed oil will render the spray safe, though this commodity is not available under restricted war-time conditions. For further sprayings that may be desirable during the summer, Bordeaux Mixture should not be used on cropping trees within six weeks or so before picking, since this spray will leave an unsightly deposit on the fruits ; a colloidal copper pre-paration should be used instead at not more than 0·03 per cent. of copper when diluted, otherwise severe spray-damage to the foliage may result.

Since the bacteria are readily able to invade wounds made in autumn and winter, branch-thinning and the cutting-out of dead or dying wood, which leaves large wounds, is best done during the " safer " summer months when the risk of infection is greatly reduced (see also Silver Leaf, page 315).

BACTERIAL SHOOT WILT *(Pseudomonas prunicola* and *P. mors-prunorum)*

A disease of young, green, sappy shoots, the causal organisms (especially *P. mors-prunorum*) are the same as those of Bacterial Canker in cherry, and plums. The bacteria obtain entry into the leafy shoots, especially in damp weather, and cause long black streaks to appear, often on only one side of the shoot. When infection girdles the shoot, it droops at the tip and dies, and is in this phase very similar to Wither Tip caused by one of the Brown Rot fungi (see page 314). It is rarely of economic importance, but could be controlled by spraying the trees with Bordeaux Mixture (4–6–100) as soon as the petals have fallen. All wilted shoots should be cut out and burnt.

DISEASES OF PLUMS AND DAMSONS

BROWN ROTS *(Sclerotinia fructigena* and *S. laxa)*

Fruit Rot.—This is caused by *S. fructigena* and *S. laxa.* Infection usually occurs through a wound, such as an insect puncture, and this acts as the centre for a progressive soft rot which ultimately invades the entire fruit. More or less concentric rings of cushions or " pustules " of fungous tissue (buff-coloured with *S. fructigena* and greyish with *S. laxa)* appear on the fruit, and produce innumerable spores that serve to carry the disease to healthy fruit. A diseased fruit is able to infect a healthy one by persistent contact, so that one diseased fruit allowed to remain in a bunch can rapidly result in the loss of them all. Bunches of " mummied " fruits are often seen hanging on the trees long after the sound fruits have been gathered. The early collection and destruction of such fruits is strongly advised to reduce the losses caused by this disease.

Wither Tip and Spur Blight.—These are caused by *S. laxa,* which infects the leaves, usually through a wound. The fungus grows down the leaf-stalk and into the main stem, causing it to wilt. The tip of the stem droops, thus giving rise to the " wither-tip " condition. The tissues harden and the leaves turn brown and persist throughout the winter. In early spring, greyish " pustules " of the fungus appear and produce spores which are able to bring about infection of the new season's leaves, flowers (see " Blossom Wilt ") and fruits. It is therefore important that diseased shoots should be removed before the fungus fructifies on them. Spur Blight is caused in a similar manner to Wither Tip ; infected leaves occur on a spur arising from a branch. The fungus may then grow down the spur into the branch, causing it to canker and die.

Blossom Wilt and Twig Blight.—These are caused by *S. laxa,* which infects the flowers and grows back into the spur and sometimes into the young twigs and branches on which the flower-trusses are borne, often girdling and thus killing them above the seat of infection. A similar disease attacks cherries, especially Morellos (see page 212).

Control.—Perhaps the best way to control diseases caused by *S. laxa* is, where practicable, to remove and burn the dead and dying twigs and shoots in the summer and autumn before leaf-fall. Once the leaves have fallen, it is very difficult to distinguish the dead shoots, which, if left on, will carry the " pustules " of the fungus during the following spring. All " mummied " fruits should also be removed and burnt for the same reason, but these can best be seen in winter when the trees are bare.

In plantations where the losses from *S. laxa* are serious and cutting-out is impracticable, winter spraying with a tar-distillate wash (5 per cent.) and pre-blossom spraying (just before flowering) with Bordeaux Mixture (6–9–100) or lime-sulphur (2 per cent.) will give good control, provided the applications are thoroughly made so as to wet the " pustules " and thus to sterilize them. The application of tar-distillate must be made when the trees are quite dormant, but the later in the dormant period the better. Even then all the fungus " pustules " might not have pushed through the bark, and the spring spraying would probably be necessary in addition to the winter one to sterilize the more recently-formed " pustules." The spray treatment recommended for the control of diseases caused by *S. laxa* are ineffective against Fruit Brown Rot caused by *S. fructigena.*

SILVER LEAF (*Stereum purpureum*)

The foliage produced by an infected branch, or possibly by a whole tree if infection has entered the trunk, is characteristically of silvery sheen, the silvering being caused by the presence of a layer of air just below the upper surface of each leaf. A brown stain will be found in the wood of an affected branch, though this stain may occur only in the lower part of the branch remote from the silvered leaves. The presence of the brown stain serves to distinguish the true Silver Leaf disease from False silver leaf, a condition that may arise as a result of some growth disturbance in the tree.

The fungus can cause infection only through wounds. Death does not always result ; natural recovery is known to occur, especially under good cultivation and manurial treatment when the trees are induced to grow strongly.

Affected branches or trees should be removed only when wilting occurs, but before death ensues. Silvered leaves are not sources of infection. Fructifications of the fungus occur *only on dead wood*, particularly in autumn after wet weather. These are most commonly in the form of overlapping brackets horizontal to the branch, and often thickly placed along most of its length. They can frequently be seen on the trunk of a dead tree as well as on the branches. The brackets are leathery, they have a wavy edge, and are up to 2 inches across. The upper surface is yellowish- or greyish-brown, often showing concentric zones of colour, and it is rough and slightly hairy. The lower surface is smooth and, when fresh, purple in colour. Occasionally flattish brackets are found, attached more closely and more nearly parallel with the branch, and showing the purplish, spore-bearing surface outwards. Many other kinds of fruit trees and bushes, as well as forest trees (e.g., Poplar) and shrubs (e.g., Rhododendron,) are attacked, among them apple, pear, cherry, gooseberry, currants. Certain other, and comparatively harmless, fungi produce fructifications not unlike those of *Stereum purpureum* in some respects, so it is important that *Stereum* be correctly identified. Spores are produced in large numbers from the purple surfaces of the fructifications, and these serve to spread the disease. During June, July, and August, infection does not readily occur, for the tree is then best able to resist attack by the formation of a " gum-barrier," which prevents the fungus from progressing in the host tissue.

All dying and dead wood should, therefore, be removed and burnt early in summer ; The Ministry of Agriculture's Silver Leaf Order of 1923 makes it compulsory to do this by 15th of July every year. It is important to cut back well into healthy wood, for brown-stained wood contains the fungus-mycelium. The wounds should immediately be protected with a white-lead paint. Professor F. T. Brooks and his co-workers, who have specially studied the disease for many years, recommend a white-lead paint made up as follows : To 2 lb. white-lead paste (as bought) add 2 teaspoonfuls of paste driers and 2 tablespoonfuls of linseed oil. Mix, then add 2 tablespoonfuls of turpentine and mix well. Stockholm tar is not satisfactory.

Victoria and *Czar* are the two most susceptible plum varieties, while *Yellow Egg*, *Purple Pershore*, and *Green Gage* are resistant though not immune.

Trees on the Common Plum rootstock are said to show a measure of resistance.

SOOTY BLOTCH *(Glœodes pomigena)*

This disease is entirely superficial and resembles Scab in that it is seen as shadowy, circular areas on the skin of the fruits, usually in late summer. Affected fruits look as if they had been handled with sooty fingers. The disease can rapidly assume epidemic proportions during wet weather in summer, and its effects can be serious. It is most likely to occur in overcrowded plantations, and especially where the soil is badly drained. It is not of common occurrence in dry summers.

Prevention is the best control, and this can most satisfactorily be ensured by allowing the trees plenty of light and air to avoid stagnation and to promote rapid drying after rain. Lime-sulphur, in 1 per cent. solution and applied post-blossom, is often used to control Red Spider, and will protect the trees from Sooty Blotch, but this spray, on account of its persistent deposit, should not be used within one month before picking the fruit. Colloidal sulphur, or dispersed sulphur, used at a strength recommended by the makers, might be used with advantage, for this leaves no unsightly deposit on the fruit.

Bordeaux Mixture (4–6–100) or a colloidal copper preparation, as suggested for the control of Bacterial Canker and Leaf Spot (see page 312) and for Plum Rust (see below), would probably be helpful.

RUST *(Puccinia Pruni-spinosæ)*

This disease is very widespread in some districts, and, occasionally, is severe enough to cause premature defoliation. Small, slightly-raised, orange-yellow spots are produced on the leaves, mainly on the undersides. These spots later turn dark brown, when the fungus enters a resting stage, and they may almost cover the under surfaces of the leaves. The fungus has another essential host, the anemone (*Anemone coronaria* and *A. nemorosa*) on which it passes part of its annual cycle. Affected anemones are malformed and rarely flower.

Control.—Spraying the trees with Bordeaux Mixture or with a colloidal copper preparation as suggested for Bacterial Canker and Leaf Spot (see page 312) will keep the disease in check. The destruction of diseased anemones in the vicinity would help to control the disease on plums, but this is a counsel of perfection hardly feasible in most circumstances on account of the ubiquitous nature of the anemone.

DISEASES AND PESTS : DIAGNOSIS TABLE
THE PLUM

DAMAGE	PROBABLE CAUSE
Branches and Twigs	*Pest*
Small, round holes in trunk	Shot-hole Borers
	Disease
Cankered area on trunk or branch, sometimes with gumming ; tree may wilt and die if trunk cankered	Bacterial Canker
Shoots and Foliage (including Blossom)	*Pests*
Leaves, opening buds and blossom attacked by small, green, " looping " caterpillars	Winter Moth
Leaves spun together by small brown, green or yellow-ish caterpillars, which wriggle quickly backwards when disturbed	Tortrix Moth
Leaves curled, shoots stunted and infested with aphides	Leaf-curling Plum Aphis or Hop Damson Aphis

317

THE PLUM

DISEASES AND PESTS: DIAGNOSIS TABLE (continued)

DAMAGE	PROBABLE CAUSE
Shoots and Foliage (including Blossom)	*Pests*
Sticky, waxy secretion on leaves and fruit in summer	Mealy Plum Aphis
Leaves turning brownish; premature leaf-fall	Red Spider
	Diseases
Leaves turn yellow and wilt in spring and summer. Leaf-spot phase—small, circular, brown spots, which eventually fall out and leave " shot-hole " effect	Bacterial Canker and Leaf Spot
Young green, sappy shoots droop at the tips and die	Bacterial Shoot Wilt
Tips of shoots and leaves on spurs droop and wilt; leaves turn brown and persist often throughout winter	Brown Rot Wither Tip and Spur Blight
Blossoms wilt, spurs and young twigs become cankered and die, dead leaves and flowers hang stiffly	Brown Rot Blossom Wilt and Twig Blight
Small, slightly raised, orange-yellow spots, later turning dark brown, mainly on undersides of leaves	Rust
Silvery sheen foliage on affected branch—brown stain in lower part of wood	Silver Leaf
Fruit	*Pests*
Remains small and drops	Leaf-curling Plum Aphis or Red Spider
Sticky waxy secretion on fruit	Mealy Plum Aphis
Fruits drop when small and green—hole in side with wet mass of black frass exuding	Sawfly
Early-matured ripe fruit drops; mass of frass near stone and large red maggot	Red Plum Maggot
	Diseases
More or less concentric rings of " pustules " of fungous tissue on fruit, may be grey- or buff-coloured	Brown Rots
Shadowy, circular areas on skin of fruit, usually in late summer	Sooty Blotch

Note.—Once the trouble has been diagnosed, the reader should refer to the paragraph dealing with the particular disease or pest, and should also consult the Guide to Spraying, page 144.

DESCRIPTIVE LIST OF VARIETIES

DESSERT PLUMS

Angelina Burdett. A medium-sized to large, roundish fruit, a dark crimson-purple. Of rich, sweet, juicy, gage-like flavour. Ready late August to September. Prolific and hangs well. Suitable for growing on a north or east wall, or as a bush or standard in a sheltered garden. Self-fertile.

Belgian Purple. See list of Cooking Plums.

Bryanston Gage. A medium-sized, roundish, greengage-like plum, a yellowish-green, spotted with red when ripe. Of delicious, sweet flavour. Ready mid-September. Hardy and prolific in all forms, especially on a west wall. Early flowering. Self-sterile. Cross-pollinates with Green Gage.

Cambridge Green Gage (Chivers). A medium-sized, roundish, greengage-like fruit, commonly grown in the Cambridge area, and recommended for general garden culture by the Royal Horticultural Society. Of delicious flavour. Ready early in September. A heavy cropper when grown as fan on a wall and netted against birds. Early flowering. Partially self-fertile. Probably a seedling of Green Gage.

DESSERT PLUMS

Coe's Golden Drop. A medium-sized to large, oval, golden-yellow fruit, spotted with red, with marked constriction at the stalk end. Of delicious flavour. Ready late in September and will keep in a cool fruit room for some little time. Suitable for culture on east, south or west walls even in the northern districts, or as a bush or standard in the open in the warmer districts. Recommended by the Royal Horticultural Society for general garden cultivation. Early flowering. Self-sterile, but cross-pollinates well with Cambridge Gage, President, or Comte d'Althan.

Comte d'Althan's Gage. A medium-sized, roundish, red-purple plum, of fine, rich gage-like flavour. Ready mid-September. Crops well when grown on a wall in sheltered gardens, even in the north. Early flowering and self-sterile. Cross-pollinates well with Rivers Early, Coe's Golden Drop, or Jefferson. Incompatible with Myrobolan B rootstock when budded.

Cox's Emperor. See list of Cooking Plums.

Denniston's Superb Gage. A medium-sized, round, yellowish-green fruit. Of excellent greengage-like flavour. Ready in August. Hardy and prolific in all forms, even in the northern districts, and especially recommended for a north or east wall in sheltered gardens. Self-fertile.

Early Transparent Gage. A small to medium-sized, round fruit, a rich yellow and crimson spotted. Of delicious, sweet flavour. Ready mid-August. Hardy and prolific as a trained tree on a north, south or east wall, and in all forms in sheltered gardens, even in the northern districts. Recommended for general garden cultivation by the Royal Horticultural Society. Early flowering and self-fertile.

Golden Transparent Gage. A very large, roundish, golden-yellow fruit dotted with red. Of delicious gage-like flavour. Ready early in October. Suitable for wall culture in sheltered gardens. Self-fertile.

*Green Gage (Reine Claude). A medium-sized, round fruit, green, spotted with red when ripe and flattened at the ends. Of delicious flavour. Ready August to September. Makes a strong tree. Notoriously unreliable cropper. Best grown on garden walls and netted against birds. Recommended for general garden culture by the Royal Horticultural Society. Early flowering and partially self-fertile.

Jefferson's Gage. A large, oval, golden-yellow fruit, spotted with red. Of delicious rich, sweet, gage-like flavour. Ready in September. Hardy and prolific on a south, north or west wall in sheltered gardens and as a bush or standard even in the northern districts. Early flowering and self-sterile. Cross-pollinates well with Rivers Early, Monarch, Victoria. Recommended by the Royal Horticultural Society.

* The Green Gage is the English name for Reine Claude. This is probably one of the oldest fruits in cultivation, and is grown under one name or another all over Europe. It is thought to have originated in Central Asia, and to have been taken thence by way of Asia Minor to Italy. Princess Claudia is said to have taken it with her from Italy to France on her marriage to Francis I. Since the fruit comes fairly true to seed it is not unlikely that many of the famous Reine Claude varieties now grown in Europe arose as selfed seedlings from Reine Claude. Green Gage is so-called in this country after the Gages of Firle Park, Sussex, who are said to have been responsible for introducing or re-introducing it to England. There are now three or four Green Gage varieties in England, showing slight differences in size of blossom, fertility, season, etc., but all having much the same kind of fruit.

Kirke's Blue. A medium to large roundish, dark purple fruit, of excellent sweet flavour. Ready mid-September. Of moderate growth, but in sheltered gardens as a bush, or fan on a south, an east or west wall, and in warm soil, it crops well. Recommended by the Royal Horticultural Society. Mid-season flowering and self-sterile. Pollinated by Cambridge Gage, Golden Transparent and Oullins Gage. Needs root pruning periodically.

Late Transparent Gage. A large, roundish, oval, yellow fruit, golden russet. Of delicious rich juicy flavour. Ready towards the end of September. Self-sterile. Pollinated by Denniston's Superb or Early Transparent. Hardy and prolific in sheltered gardens when grown on a warm wall, and in bush or half-standard forms in the warmer districts. Makes small tree.

Laxton's Gage. A medium-sized, oval, yellow fruit, the result of a cross between the old Greengage and Victoria plum, and somewhat resembling Transparent Gage. Ready late in August, a hardy and prolific cropper in all forms. Late flowering and self-fertile.

Magnum Bonum. See Warwickshire Drooper.

Ontario. Medium to large, roundish oval, marbled yellow, vigorous. Ready mid-August. Very prolific. Gage flavour.

Oullins Golden Gage. A medium to large, roundish, oval, golden-yellow fruit, of gage-like flavour. Ready mid-August. Picked early, it is excellent for cooking and bottling. Hardy and prolific on a north or east wall in sheltered gardens or as bushes in the open in the warmer districts. Especially recommended for private garden or market culture. Late flowering and self-fertile. Incompatible with Myrobolan B when budded. Grown commercially in Kent.

Pond's Seedling. See list of Cooking Plums.

Red Myrobolan (Cherry Plum). A small, round, red plum of pleasant flavour. Makes a strong tree useful for shelter belts. Will not stand tar-oils. Flowers earlier than any other plum ; hence very susceptible to frost. Crops freely when the flowering season is mild and fine. Ready in July. Self-fertile. A good plum for bottling and canning. Can be grown on its own roots or budded on Myrobolan B.

Reine Claude de Bavay. A large to medium-sized, roundish, oval, greenish-yellow fruit, of delicious gage-like flavour. Ready late September to October. Hardy and prolific as a wall plant even in the northern districts. Mid-season flowering and self-fertile.

Rivers Early Prolific. See list of Cooking Plums.

Schwitchen Quetsche (Zwetsche) (German Prune). The Schwitchen is a species of plum common to eastern Europe. It produces a small, longish, oval, dark blue plum of good flavour when cooked in September. It is much grown in Germany and used chiefly for cooking and bottling. Has been planted in Kent for market purposes.

Transparent Gage (Reine Claude Diaphane). A medium-sized, roundish-oval, greenish-yellow fruit flushed with pale violet. Of delicious gage-like flavour. Ready in September. Hardy and prolific on a wall in warm soil and sheltered aspect or may be grown as a bush or standard in the warmer districts. Mid-season flowering and self-sterile. One of the best of all gages. Pollinated by Denniston's Superb and Early Transparent.

Victoria. A large, oval, pinkish-red fruit of delicious flavour when ripe and excellent for cooking or preserving. Ready in August. Hardy and prolific in all forms and almost anywhere. Especially partial to a chalky clay mixture. The most popular market plum. But highly susceptible to silver leaf. Mid-season flowering and self-fertile. Susceptible to bacterial canker.

Warwickshire Drooper. Known as Magnum Bonum in parts of the West Midlands, although not the true White Magnum Bonum. A medium-sized, roundish, oval plum, greenish-yellow dotted with red. Of gage flavour but not of the highest quality. Very hardy and prolific, but makes a very drooping tree. An early blossomer. Plant with Rivers Early, Early Laxton, or Denniston's Gage for cross-pollination. Plum hangs to September. Cans and bottles well and is also a good dessert plum in September.

Washington Gage. Large, flat at both ends, golden yellow with red flush and spots. Early September. Excellent flavour, but uncertain cropper.

COOKING PLUMS

Autumn Compote. A very large, oval, handsome, red fruit, of good quality. Ready late in September. Suitable for wall culture in the garden. Self-sterile. Good for preserving.

Belgian Purple. A medium-sized, roundish, oval, deep purple plum, juicy and sweet when ripe and useful for dessert or cooking. Ready in August. A heavy cropper even in the northern districts and suitable for garden culture on a north wall, or as a bush or standard. Mid-season flowering and partly self-fertile.

Belle de Louvain. A large, egg-shaped red plum, ripening to a dark purple. Of juicy, rich, acid flavour. Ready late in August. A hardy and prolific cropper even in the colder northern districts when grown as a fan on a north or east wall, or as a bush or a standard, and a profitable market fruit. Recommended for general garden culture by the Royal Horticultural Society. Late bloomer and self-fertile. Very strong grower. Does well on heavy soils.

Blaisdon Red. A medium-sized, oval, red plum, much grown in Gloucestershire for jam. Ready in September. Hardy and prolific and almost immune from silver leaf. A fine market fruit for orchard cultivation on grass. Easily propagated by means of suckers. Mid-season bloomer and self-fertile.

Cox's Emperor. A very large, roundish, oblong, bright red plum, spotted yellow. Of excellent flavour and suitable for dessert when ripe. Ready late in August to early in September. Hardy and prolific even in the northern districts in all forms. Late flowering and partially self-fertile. Cross-pollinates well with Czar and Belle de Louvain.

Czar. A medium-sized, roundish, oval, purple-black fruit of splendid flavour. Ready early in August. A reliable and prolific cropper in all forms even in the colder northern districts. Recommended for general garden culture by the Royal Horticultural Society. Also suitable for orchard culture and for marketing. Late-season flowering and self-fertile. Susceptible to bacterial canker.

Early Laxton. A small to medium-sized, oval fruit, yellow, flushed red, sweet and juicy. Ready mid-July, being the earliest of all plums. Recommended for wall culture or as a bush or half-standard in the open. Suitable for marketing. Early flowering and partially self-fertile. Subject to bacterial canker.

Early Prolific. See Rivers Early Prolific.

Giant Prune. A large, longish, oval, deep reddish-purple fruit of moderate flavour. Ready towards the end of September. Hardy and prolific as a bush or standard and recommended for market culture. Mid-season flowering and self-fertile. A good pollinator of many self-sterile sorts. Highly susceptible to bacterial canker and brown rot.

Gisborne's Prolific. A medium-sized, roundish, oval, yellow plum, spotted red. Of sharp, acid flavour. Ready mid-August. A very old orchard and market favourite. Hardy and prolific, in standard or half-standard form, even in the colder northern districts of Great Britain on light soils and chalk. Late flowering and self-fertile.

Kentish " Bush " or Waterloo. A medium-sized, roundish-oval, purple plum. Of good quality. Ready September to October. Very hardy and prolific and a market favourite in Kent. Useful for planting as a wind-screen. Self-fertile. Makes a very high tree.

Monarch. A very large, round, dark purple plum, of fine flavour, good enough for dessert when ripe, and one of the best for cooking. Ready in late September. Hardy in all forms, especially in districts which suit it, and a favourite market fruit. Early flowerer and self-fertile. A very uncertain cropper in Kent.

Pershore (Yellow Egg Plum). A medium-sized, egg-shaped, yellow plum, of fine quality. Ready towards the end of August. A hardy and prolific cropper in all forms and one of the most profitable market plums. Usually propagated by means of suckers. Late flowering and self-fertile. One of the most noted plums for jam, canning, and bottling.

Pond's Seedling. A very large, longish, oval, deep red plum, of excellent flavour, and when ripe good enough for dessert. Ready late in September. Hardy and prolific in all forms in districts which suit it. A highly-recommended and profitable market fruit, but it has certain drawbacks. In wet weather the fruit is somewhat liable to crack, and it is susceptible to brown rot and silver leaf. Late flowering and self-sterile. Cross-pollinates with Czar and Belle de Louvain.

President. A very large, oval-shaped, deep purple plum, with yellow spots. Of excellent flavour when ripe. Ready in October. Hardy in all forms in heavy soil, even in the northern districts of Great Britain. Early flowering and self-sterile. Cross-pollinates with Coe's Golden Drop or Cambridge Gage. Extremely uncertain cropper. Makes a large tree.

Purple Pershore. A medium to large-sized, egg-shaped, deep purple fruit, of fine quality, somewhat similar to Pershore, but purple instead of yellow. Ready mid-August. Hardy and prolific in all forms and a profitable market fruit. Late-season flowering and self-fertile. One of the plums which respond to potash manuring. Widely planted.

VARIETIES OF PLUMS

Rivers Early Prolific. A small to medium-sized, oval-shaped, deep purple-black plum, of good flavour, for cooking, bottling, or jam making, and when ripe, considered good enough for dessert. Ready late in July or August. Hardy in all forms in districts which suit it—calcareous clay and gravel soil mixed—a profitable market fruit. Seems almost immune from silver leaf. Early bloomer and almost self-fertile. Cross-pollinated by Monarch and Warwickshire Drooper. An uncertain cropper. Plant with early-blossoming varieties.

Victoria. See list of Dessert Plums.

Waterloo. See Kentish " Bush."

Wyedale. A small to medium-sized, oval, reddish-purple fruit of good quality. Ready in October. Hardy and prolific in all forms and all districts. A popular market fruit. Recommended for general garden culture by the Royal Horticultural Society. Self-sterile.

FERTILITY GUIDE TO ENSURE CROSS-POLLINATION

When only one plum tree is planted, it is essential to select one of the self-fertile varieties, unless, of course, other plum trees, flowering at the same period, are growing in other gardens close by.

SELF-FERTILE VARIETIES

Early Flowering	Mid-season Flowering	Late Flowering
Denniston's Superb Gage	Blaisdon Red	Belle de Louvain
Early Transparent Gage	Egg Plum	Czar
Monarch	Reine Claude de Bavay	Golden Transparent
Warwickshire Drooper	Victoria	Laxton's Gage
		Oullins Golden Gage
		Pershore
		Purple Pershore

PARTIALLY SELF-FERTILE

Early Flowering	Mid-season Flowering	Late Flowering
Cambridge Green Gage	Old Greengage	Belgian Purple
Early Laxton	Reine Claude Violette	Cox's Emperor
Rivers Early Prolific		Farleigh Damson

Any of these fertile or partially self-fertile varieties planted in conjunction with self-sterile varieties, flowering at the same time, will cross-pollinate the self-sterile varieties. Early-flowering sorts will also cross-pollinate mid-season flowers, the mid-season bloomers will cross-pollinate late bloomers, as the flowering seasons overlap somewhat and the plum blossoms last a long time.

SELF-STERILE VARIETIES

Early Flowering	Mid-season Flowering	Late Flowering
Black Diamond	Bryanston Gage	Kirke's Blue
Coe's Golden Drop	Transparent Gage	Pond's Seedling
Comte d'Althan's Gage		
Jefferson's Gage		
President		

VARIETIES OF PLUMS

SELECTION OF TWELVE LEADING PLUMS FOR THE GARDEN OR PRIVATE ORCHARD

Variety	Dessert or Cooking	Ready
Czar	Cooking	August
Denniston's Superb Gage	Dessert	August
Early Transparent Gage	Dessert	August
Giant Prune	Cooking	September
Oullins Golden Gage	Dessert	August
Pershore (Yellow Egg Plum)	Cooking	August
Rivers Early Prolific	Cooking	End of July
Schwitchen	Cooking	September
Victoria	Dessert or Cooking	August
Warwickshire Drooper	Dessert or Cooking	September
Wyedale	Cooking	October

SELECTION OF PLUMS IN ORDER OF RIPENING
DESSERT

Variety	When Ready	Colour
Denniston's Superb Gage	August	Yellowish-green, tinged Red
Early Transparent Gage	Mid-August	Yellow and Crimson spotted
Oullins Golden Gage	Mid-August	Golden-yellow
Laxton's Gage	Late August	Yellow Fruit
Green Gage	August–September	Green, spotted Red
Cambridge Green Gage	Early September	Green, spotted Red
Victoria	Early September	Pinkish Red
Washington Gage	Early September	Gold, Red spots
Bryanston Gage	Mid-September	Yellowish-green, spotted Red
Reine Claude de Bavay	September–October	Greenish-yellow
Comte d'Althan's Gage	Mid-September	Red-purple
Kirke's Blue	Mid-September	Dark Purple
Jefferson's Gage	September	Golden-yellow, spotted Red
Transparent Gage	September	Greenish-yellow
Coe's Golden Drop	Late September	Golden-yellow
Late Transparent	End of September	Yellow
Golden Transparent Gage	Early October	Golden-yellow

COOKING PLUMS

Variety	When Ready	Colour
Early Laxton	Mid-July	Yellow, flushed Red
Rivers Early Prolific	Late July–August	Purple-black
Czar	Early August	Purple-black
Belgian Purple	August	Deep Purple
Gisborne's Prolific	Mid-August	Yellow
Purple Egg	Mid-August	Deep Purple
Belle de Louvain	Late August	Dark Purple
Pershore	End of August	Yellow
Victoria	August	Pinkish-red
Blaisdon Red	September	Red
Giant Prune	End of September	Reddish-purple
Monarch	Late September	Dark Purple
Pond's Seedling	Late September	Deep Red
Schwitchen	September–October	Dark Blue
Wyedale	October	Reddish Purple

VARIETIES OF PLUMS

ESPECIALLY HARDY PLUMS

Variety	Dessert or Cooking	Garden or Orchard
Belle de Louvain	Cooking	Garden or Orchard
Blaisdon Red	Cooking	Orchard
Czar	Cooking	Garden or Orchard
Denniston's Superb Gage	Dessert	Garden or Orchard
Early Transparent Gage	Dessert	Garden
Green Gage	Dessert	Garden
Gisborne's Prolific	Cooking	Orchard
Jefferson's Gage	Dessert	Garden
Oullins Gage	Dessert	Orchard or Garden
Pershore	Cooking	Orchard or Garden
Rivers Early Prolific	Cooking	Garden
Victoria	Dessert or Cooking	Garden or Orchard
Warwickshire Drooper	Dessert or Cooking	Garden or Orchard

THE BEST-FLAVOURED PLUMS

Variety	Dessert or Cooking	Season
Bryanston Gage	Dessert	September
Cambridge Green Gage	Dessert	Early September
Coe's Golden Drop	Dessert	Late September
Comte d'Althan's Gage	Dessert	Mid-September
Denniston's Superb Gage	Dessert	Mid-August
Early Transparent Gage	Dessert	Mid-August
Golden Transparent	Dessert	October
Green Gage	Dessert	August–September
Jefferson's Gage	Dessert	September
Kirke's Blue	Dessert	Mid-September
Late Transparent Gage	Dessert	End of September–October
Reine Claude de Bavay	Dessert	September
Transparent Gage	Dessert	September
Washington Gage	Dessert	Early September

PLUMS FOR GROWING IN POTS. See page 367.

GOOD MARKET PLUMS

Variety	Cooking or Dessert	Ready
Belle de Louvain	Cooking	Late August
Blaisdon Red	Cooking	September
Czar	Cooking	August
Early Laxton	Cooking	Mid-July
Giant Prune	Cooking	September
Kentish Bush (Waterloo)	Cooking	Late September–October
Monarch	Cooking or Dessert	Late September
Oullins Golden Gage	Dessert	Mid-August
Pershore (Yellow Egg)	Cooking	End of August
Pond's Seedling	Cooking or Dessert	Late September
Purple Pershore	Cooking	Mid-August
Rivers Early Prolific	Cooking or Dessert	Late July–August
Schwitchen	Cooking	September–October
Victoria	Cooking or Dessert	August
Warwickshire Drooper	Cooking or Dessert	August–September
Wyedale	Cooking	October

VARIETIES OF PLUMS

PLUMS FOR GROWING ON WALLS

North Walls		South Walls	
Belgian Purple	(C)	Coe's Golden Drop	(D)
Belle de Louvain	(C)	Denniston's Superb Gage	(D)
Denniston's Superb Gage	(D)	Early Transparent Gage	(D)
Early Transparent Gage	(D)	Golden Transparent Gage	(D)
Jefferson's Gage	(D)	Jefferson's Gage	(D)
Oullins Golden Gage	(D)	Kirke's Blue	(D)
Rivers Early Prolific	(C)	Late Transparent Gage	(D)
Victoria	(D)	Reine Claude de Bavay	(D)
		Washington Gage	(D)

East Walls		West Walls	
Angelina Burdett	(D)	Bryanston Gage	(D)
Coe's Golden Drop	(D)	Coe's Golden Drop	(D)
Comte d'Althan's Gage	(D)	Denniston's Superb Gage	(D)
Denniston's Superb Gage	(D)	Early Transparent Gage	(D)
Early Transparent Gage	(D)	Jefferson's Gage	(D)
Kirke's Blue	(D)	Kirke's Blue	(D)
Oullins Golden Gage	(D)	Oullins Golden Gage	(D)
Victoria	(D)	Victoria	(D)

PLUMS SUITABLE FOR THE VARIOUS FORMS

Bush		Standard	
Belgian Purple	(C)	Belgian Purple	(C)
Belle de Louvain	(C)	Belle de Louvain	(C)
Coe's Golden Drop	(D)	Blaisdon Red	(C)
Czar	(C)	Cambridge Gage	(D)
Early Orleans	(C)	Coe's Golden Drop	(D)
Early Transparent Gage	(D)	Czar	(C)
Giant Prune	(C)	Early Laxton	(C)
Jefferson's Gage	(D)	Early Transparent Gage	(D)
Late Transparent	(D)	Giant Prune	(C)
Monarch	(C)	Jefferson's Gage	(D)
Pershore	(C)	Kentish Bush (Waterloo)	(C)
Purple Pershore	(C)	Monarch	(C)
Rivers Early Prolific	(C)	Pershore	(C)
Transparent Gage	(D)	Pond's Seedling	(C)
Victoria	(D)	Purple Pershore	(C)
Warwickshire Drooper	(C & D)	Rivers Early Prolific	(C)
		Schwitchen	(C)
		Victoria	(D)
		Wyedale	(C)

Half-Standard		Fan	
Coe's Golden Drop	(D)	Bryanston Gage	(D)
Czar	(C)	Cambridge Gage	(D)
Early Laxton	(C)	Comte d'Althan's Gage	(D)
Jefferson's Gage	(D)	Denniston's Superb Gage	(D)
Late Transparent Gage	(D)	Early Orleans	(C)
Monarch	(C)	Early Transparent Gage	(D)
Rivers Early Prolific	(C)	Laxton's Gage	(D)
Victoria	(D)	See also plums for Growing on
Warwickshire Drooper	(C & D)	Walls above.

NOTE.—For Damson Varieties, see page 243.

PLUMS FOR EXHIBITION

Variety	Dessert or Cooking	Ready
Belle de Louvain	Cooking	Late August
Black Diamond	Cooking	Early September
Giant Prune	Cooking	End of September
Kirke's Blue	Dessert	Mid-September
Monarch	Cooking	Late September
Pond's Seedling	Cooking	Late September
President	Dessert	October

THE BEST PLUMS FOR ORCHARDS

Variety	Cooking or Dessert	Ready
Belle de Louvain	Cooking	Late August
Blaisdon Red	Cooking	September
Czar	Cooking	August
Giant Prune	Cooking	September
Kentish Bush (Waterloo)	Cooking	September to October
Pond's Seedling	Cooking	Late September
Red Myrobolan	Dessert	July
Rivers Early Prolific	Cooking	July to August
Victoria	Dessert	August
Warwickshire Drooper	Dessert	September

THE QUINCE (Cydonia vulgaris)

ORIGIN AND HISTORY

The quince is a native of southern Europe and the more temperate parts of Asia. It is recorded that it was cultivated by the ancient Greeks and Romans and is supposed to have been introduced into this country from Austria about the year 1573. It is closely related to the Pyrus, with which some botanists erroneously classified it for a time, as *P. vulgaris*. The fruit, which is very sharp and acid, makes quite a good preserve or jelly, for those who like its flavour. The principal value of the quince, however, is as a rootstock for pears (see page 281), and for this purpose certain varieties, particularly the true Angers Quince (Quince A) and the Common Quince (Quince B), are propagated vegetatively on a large scale by nurserymen. It should not be confused with *C. japonica*, the Japanese quince, which is a beautiful flowering shrub of decorative value only.

SOIL AND SITUATION

The quince thrives in moist soil, and does particularly well when planted near a pond or stream. The tree itself is very beautiful and lives to a great age, requiring very little attention when once established. This being so, it seems strange that the quince is not more frequently planted in private gardens. Its natural habit is that of a rather low, twisted tree, and it is difficult to persuade it to make a good straight standard, or to adapt its peculiarly untidy habit of growth to any of the artificial forms of tree.

The quince is particularly hardy and thrives in a sunny, open situation or against a wall, even in the colder northern districts, but it is only in the milder southern districts that it ripens its fruit in the open.

PROPAGATION

The quince may easily be propagated by means of layers, stools, or hard wood cuttings or suckers.

The stooling method is the one usually adopted for the production of stocks. (See page 39.)

PLANTING

The best time to plant is early in the autumn. Standard forms should be put in 20 feet apart, half-standards 12 to 15 feet apart, and bushes about 10 feet apart.

PRUNING

The quince should be judiciously thinned as to the main branches, and should have unproductive and straggling wood cut out. This is best done in early autumn.

GATHERING AND STORING

The fruit of the quince should be left on the tree until thoroughly ripe, and should not be gathered until the end of October, unless the autumn is unusually frosty. On no account should it be gathered when wet. The ripe fruits are strongly aromatic and when gathered they should be stored by themselves (otherwise the aroma will affect the flavour of other fruit with which they are stored) in a cool, frost-proof place on layers of straw on a shelf, until they have turned yellow. Here they will keep for from two to three months. They are then fit for use. (See also Gathering and Storing, page 108.)

MARKETING

Very large quinces are marketed in 12-lb. chip baskets, and the smaller ones in wicker half-sieves.

DISEASES AND PESTS OF THE QUINCE

INSECT PESTS

Codling Moth (see Apple, page 160), Slugworm (see Pear, page 289), and various Caterpillars (see Apple, page 155) occur on quinces but are seldom of any importance.

DISEASES

LEAF BLIGHT *(Fabræa maculata)*

The fungus causes circular, reddish-brown spots on the leaves and fruits. In severe attacks on the fruit, the spots are so close that they run together, and Brown Rot (*Sclerotinia fructigena*) often gains entry and rots the fruits. Severely-affected leaves drop prematurely. The fungus lives on the twigs through the winter, being present on roughly circular, reddish-brown areas with dark margins. To control the disease, remove any infected twigs and spray post-blossom with Bordeaux Mixture or a colloidal copper preparation as recommended for pears (see Pears).

The spray protects healthy leaves and fruits from infection, and therefore should be applied before the disease makes its appearance. The disease occasionally attacks pears and medlars, and can be troublesome on unworked quince rootstocks in the nursery.

MILDEW *(Podosphaera leucotricha)*

This sometimes attacks quinces as well as apples, and can be controlled by the same treatment (see Apple Mildew, page 168).

DISEASES AND PESTS: DIAGNOSIS TABLE

THE QUINCE

DAMAGE	PROBABLE CAUSE
Shoots and Foliage (including Blossom)	*Pests*
Leaves, opening buds and blossom attacked by small green, " looping " caterpillars	Winter Moth
Leaves spun together by small, brown, green or yellowish caterpillars, which quickly wriggle backwards when disturbed.	Tortrix Moth
Circular, reddish-brown spots on leaves and fruit	Leaf Blight
Intervenal tissue of leaves eaten by black, slug-like larvæ, leaving brown patches; leaves may turn brown and fall	Slugworm
Fruit	*Pests*
Small fruits eaten by small, green " looping " caterpillars	Winter Moth
Maggoty fruit. May drop before ripe.	Codling Moth
Circular, reddish-brown spots on fruit and leaves	Leaf Blight

Note.—Once the trouble has been diagnosed, the reader should refer to the paragraph dealing with the particular disease or pest, and should also consult the Guide to Spraying, see page 144.

VARIETIES

Some of the best-known varieties of quince are the Angers and the Common, already mentioned, the Apple-shaped, the Pear-shaped, the Bereczki, Vranja, Champion, and Portugal. The Bereczki is not quite such a good cropper as the others. The Pear-shaped and the Portugal are especially recommended for garden culture by the Royal Horticultural Society. The former is the kind in common cultivation, but its pear-shaped fruits, though plentiful, are not as large or of such good flavour as those of the Portugal.

THE RASPBERRY *(Rubus Idæus)*

ORIGIN AND HISTORY

The raspberry is indigenous to Great Britain and is often to be found growing wild in thickets and woods. In its uncultivated state the fruit is too small to be of value, but in its cultivated form it is delicious for dessert, as well as being in great demand for cooking, preserves, jellies, etc.

SOIL AND SITUATION

Raspberries do best in deep, rich, well-drained soil which holds moisture but does not waterlog. In the autumn, before planting, the soil should be dug to a depth of 2 to 2½ feet, and a liberal dressing of manure (preferably farmyard dung, cow or pig manure) should be incorporated with it. The plants are very hardy and, given satisfactory soil and good drainage, they do well in almost any situation and aspect.

FORMS OF CULTURE

The raspberry grows in the form of single canes which shoot up annually from the base of the plant, the fruit being borne on short fruit-bearing laterals of the current season which grow out from the main stem.

PROPAGATION

In these days when the virus disease known as mosaic has infected such a large percentage of the raspberry plants in the United Kingdom, the most hopeful method of raising healthy raspberry canes is to secure a nucleus of healthy plants by applying to the county advisory officer in horticulture for information as to a reliable source of supply. The healthy canes are then planted as far away as possible from any other raspberries, giving them from 6 to 8 feet between the rows and from 2 to 3 feet between the canes according to the vigour of the variety. After planting, the canes are cut back to within 6 to 9 inches from the ground. If they make very poor growth the first season, and the average height of the new cane is not above 2 feet, the whole lot should be cut down to the ground in the autumn and left to make strong canes the following season. If the average height of the new canes is well over 2 feet 6 inches, they are dug up in the winter with a sharp spade, and all canes which are well rooted are then planted out in their permanent quarters. If there are not enough canes for the space to be planted, the cane nursery will produce another batch of cane or " spawn " the following season, which will give all the new plants required. This, however, is by no means the whole story. The object of raising raspberries in this way is in order that the plants may be kept under careful inspection during their first season, and so that all canes which show the symptoms of mosaic may be " rogued " out. If raspberries are to be grown successfully, it is essential to be familiar with these symptoms and to dig up and burn the infected canes in the raspberry nursery and in the newly-planted rows two or three times during the summer.

The county horticultural officer is again the friend in need who will point out the symptoms of mosaic and show how to " rogue " the plants.

The length of life of a raspberry plantation is almost entirely governed by the health of the plants. *If kept free from mosaic,* the canes should last for nine to ten years in profitable bearing.

PLANTING

The young canes are best planted in November, though when this has been impossible, they may be planted in February. The plants should be planted singly, 2 to 3 feet apart, in rows 6 to 8 feet from one another. The top roots should be but an inch below the surface, the ground being made thoroughly firm at the time of planting. It is usual to cut down the newly-planted canes in March to about 12 inches from the soil. During the summer new canes will be produced from the base, and these will bear fruit the year after.

In gardens the canes may also be put in in clumps of three, the clumps being set from 3 to 4 feet apart.

THE RASPBERRY

In June, the bushes should be gone over, all suckers being removed, except about six of the strongest. In autumn all old canes that have borne fruit should be cut down to the ground, and burned. All weak young shoots should be cut out at the same time, about six of the strongest on each plant being left to bear fruit the following season.

Some growers believe that there is great benefit in cutting the canes of different heights when left in clumps, for as the top buds grow strongest, the fruit-bearing shoots are more equally divided and enjoy more air and light.

The only other pruning that is required consists in cutting off the sappy curved tops of the young mature canes in March to encourage the formation of laterals on which the berries are borne.

The autumn-fruiting varieties need different pruning treatment. These bear their fruit on the current season's growth, and they should have their new canes cut down to about 4 inches from the ground in February or March. The plants should be in single rows, spaced thinly in the row.

AUTUMN FRUITING

Summer-fruiting raspberries may be made to bear a crop of fruit during September and October in the following way. As soon as suckers show themselves in June, the old canes should be cut away entirely, so as to prevent summer fruiting, and by a mulch of well-rotted manure in June, encouragement should be given during July and August to such suckers as show blossom-buds, for these will bear fruit in autumn. Water should be given liberally in dry weather and liquid manure applied.

SUPPORTING THE CANES

Raspberries need some form of support, the simplest and most useful consisting of three wires strained horizontally at heights of about 2 feet, 3½ feet, and 5 feet from the ground. To these wires the canes should be tied in autumn, about 9 inches apart from each other. The new canes should not be tied up during the summer, as the wood ripens better if left untied. Raspberry canes grown on commercial plantations are often supported by either one or two double strands of coir yarn tied to crosspieces on support posts (see sketch). In this case there is no tying of individual canes. Where birds are troublesome the ripening fruit should be protected by means of fine-mesh netting.

CULTIVATION AND MANURING

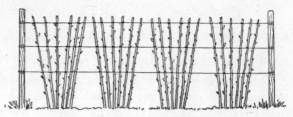

SUPPORTING RASPBERRY CANES.

The ground should be hoed in spring, but the soil should not be deeply stirred as the roots are very near the surface. In gardens a mulch of lawn mowings or old rotted dung put along the rows in May will help to keep the moisture in the soil. The best way to manure raspberries is to dig in a good dressing of dung before planting, and to give yearly applications of sulphate of potash at the rate of 2 to 3 cwt. per acre ($1\frac{1}{2}$ oz. per square yard) in winter. In alternate years nitrogen, in organic form for preference, cow manure, pig manure, or failing this, in inorganic form, is likely to be necessary in moderate dressings only.

GATHERING

Berries for dessert and immediate home use should be picked as they ripen, without the " plug." For market they should be gathered before they are fully ripe, being picked with the " plug," and for jam-making the whole crop is usually left on the plants as long as possible, being gathered in one picking, fully ripe, without the " plug."

However gathered, the fruit should never be picked when wet.

When grading fruit for market, skilled pickers go over the canes in advance of the gang and pick the choice berries, placing them direct into punnets or chip baskets as required for market. Dessert fruit is usually marketed in No. 1 or 2 punnets ; main crop fruit in 2-, 3-, or 4-lb. chip baskets (with handles). Fruit for jam-making is sent up in tubs, drums, or shallow lined wooden trays.

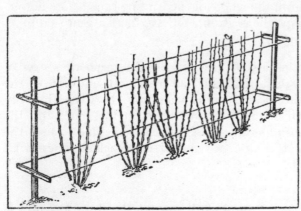

ANOTHER METHOD OF SUPPORTING RASPBERRY CANES.

DISEASES AND PESTS OF THE RASPBERRY

RASPBERRY BEETLE *(Byturus tomentosus)*. See page 264.

RASPBERRY MOTH *(Incurvaria rubiella)*

This pest is widely distributed and does serious damage to raspberries and loganberries. When the buds grow out in the spring and the resulting lateral shoots reach a length of about an inch, many of them will be found to wither and die owing to the presence of a small red caterpillar feeding within them. These caterpillars move from shoot to shoot and thus destroy a great many fruiting laterals. When fully fed they pupate in the shoots or between leaves spun together, and in June turn to moths. These are small (with a wing expanse of little more than a quarter of an inch), brown in colour, with a silvery sheen and several yellow spots on the wings. They lay their minute eggs in the blossoms. Small, pale caterpillars hatch out and feed within the berries, without, however, causing appreciable damage. When the berries ripen the half-grown caterpillars, now red in colour, leave them and drop to the ground, where they spin silken cocoons just below soil level. In these they remain until the following April, when they ascend the canes and attack the developing shoots.

Control.—On the Continent some success has been claimed for the use of tar-distillate winter washes, but, as the caterpillars spend the winter in the soil, it is doubtful whether the ground would be soaked well enough to kill them.

Attacked shoots should be pinched out and destroyed, a procedure which can be adopted in gardens. On a larger scale the best plan is to cut down the whole of the fruiting cane before flowering time. This stamps the pest out, but sacrifices a year's crop.

MINOR PESTS

Although a great variety of insects exist on raspberries, few of them, fortunately, can be reckoned as pests. In addition to the above, losses are also caused occasionally by the Cane Gall Fly (*Losioptera rubi*), which produces swellings on the cane, and the Cane Midge (*Thomasiniana theobaldi*), which sometimes causes the cane to snap off at the base. Removal of attacked canes is all that can be advised.

MOSAIC *(Virus)*

This is by far the most serious disease of the raspberry and is the cause of serious loss of growth and cropping. Being in the sap of an affected plant it is impossible to eradicate the virus or to control it by spraying. A yellow mottling of the leaves is the most characteristic symptom : affected leaves are often curled downwards. More than one virus is involved, and varieties differ greatly in their response to infection. *Baumforth's Seedling B* and *Lloyd George* are susceptible to and severely affected by one or more of the viruses, while *Preussen* is susceptible to infection but may show little or no evidence of it, or be severely affected by it. *Red Cross* shows obvious leaf-mottling but little ill effect, and *Norfolk Giant* is resistant though it deteriorates when it does become infected. The natural mode of spread of this disease in this country is at present unknown, but insects are suspected. Raspberry plants severely affected by mosaic should be grubbed, together with all their " spawn " or new canes, and destroyed. Virus-free stock should be used to start new plantations.

CANE SPOT *(Elsinoë veneta)*

The disease caused by this fungus is sometimes called " anthracnose." It is characterized by the presence of purplish spots on the young canes in early summer. As these spots get larger, their centres become grey. The leaves and leaf-stalks are affected in a similar manner, and the disease can severely disfigure the fruits. On susceptible varieties, notably *Baumforth's Seedling B* and *Lloyd George*, the spots on the canes are sometimes very crowded and run together, forming cankers that may be large enough to kill them. The new canes become infected from the fruiting ones on which the fungus has passed the winter. The best means of checking the disease is to spray, just as the buds begin to move, with lime-sulphur at 5 per cent. or Bordeaux Mixture at 10–15–100. This is a direct-action spray designed to sterilize the fungus on the fruiting canes. An alternative, or additional, method of control is to spray immediately pre-blossom with Bordeaux Mixture at 4–6–100, or a colloidal copper preparation, to protect the young canes and leaves.

BLUE STRIPE WILT *(Verticillium Dahliæ)*

In summer, the older leaves of young canes infected with this disease turn yellow and show brown discoloration between the main veins, while a broad, brownish-blue stripe is sometimes present on one side of the cane, usually towards the base. This stripe may be over a foot long. On affected fruiting canes there is no bluish stripe, but where the cane has survived, dead buds are present usually on one side of the cane and corresponding to the blue

335

stripe of the previous year. When the cane is cut across, a brown discoloration will be found on the same side as the dead buds. The fungus occurs in the soil, and infects the root-system, ultimately growing upwards in the new canes. This disease is rarely serious enough to justify special control measures but stools with dead canes should be grubbed out and burnt with all their spawn. Natural recovery frequently occurs.

CANE BLIGHT *(Leptosphæria Coniothyrium)*

This is a fungus disease that appears to be increasing in economic importance. It causes death of the fruiting canes and in recent years has frequently been seen in gardens and commercial plantings of *Lloyd George, Reader's Perfection, Newburgh* and *Norfolk Giant*. The fungus, which persists on snags left on the plants near ground level, and possibly also in the soil, attacks the young canes usually near the ground. In the first year an elliptical, purplish area, an inch or two long, is the only sign of attack, but by the second year this area has become a canker which may girdle the cane and kill it. Affected fruiting canes can then readily be seen because the leaves wilt and die. Such canes, when bent sideways, often snap off at the canker. This is discoloured brown and loosely covered by the bark, which has flaked into strips. Spores are produced in clusters of small, spherical, blackish, fungal bodies that arise on the surface of the canker, and they can infect the new canes. The disease is frequently in association with the Raspberry Cane Midge.

Control.—There is so far no known spray-treatment for this disease. All affected canes should be severed, preferably below ground level, and burnt ; merely snapping off the canes is useless because infected snags are left behind. Spawn for planting up should not be taken from affected plants, and it is inadvisable to replant the gaps. Keeping the rows clear of weeds is helpful in promoting free circulation of air around the plants.

DISEASES AND PESTS : DIAGNOSIS TABLE

THE RASPBERRY

Damage	Probable Cause
Canes	*Pest*
Swellings on canes	Cane Gall Fly
	Diseases
Purplish spots on young canes in early summer, getting larger and having grey centres	Cane Spot
Broad, brownish-blue stripe near base (see also under leaves)	Verticillium Wilt

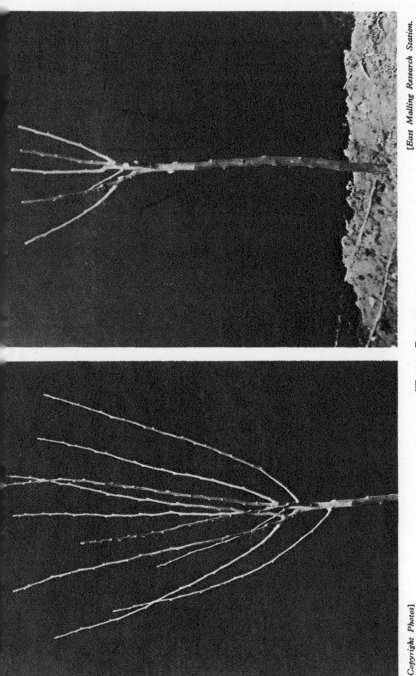

[East Malling Research Station.

WINTER PRUNING.

Apple "Cox's Orange Pippin" Bush Tree (three years old).

Before Winter Pruning and——   ——after.

G.

Y

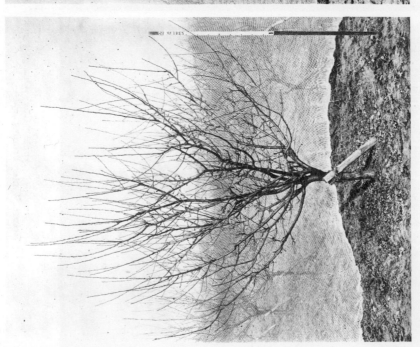

[East Malling Research Station.

WINTER PRUNING.
Apple "Cox's Orange Pippin" Bush Tree (six years old).

THE RASPBERRY

DISEASES AND PESTS : DIAGNOSIS TABLE—continued

Damage	Probable Cause
Canes Purple areas on young canes, cankers on fruiting canes. Leaves wilt and die if cane girdled. Cane readily snaps off at canker.	*Disease* Cane Blight
Foliage and Shoots Buds, when about 1 inch long, wither and die, eaten by small red caterpillars	*Pests* Raspberry Moth
Yellow mottling of leaves ; often curled downwards Older leaves show brownish discoloration between main veins, broad, brownish-blue stripe on canes, usually at base	*Diseases* Mosaic Blue Stripe Wilt
Fruit Fruit maggoty, often deformed	*Pest* Raspberry Beetle

Note.—Once the trouble has been diagnosed, the reader should refer to the paragraph dealing with the particular disease or pest and should also consult the Guide to Spraying, see page 144.

VARIETIES

Most gardeners will now be satisfied with two or at most three varieties of raspberry, a summer-fruiting kind, an autumn bearer, and possibly, for novelty's sake, a yellow-fruiting species. The introduction of the prolific *Lloyd George* variety settled for most growers the choice question, and where only one raspberry is to be grown, this is undoubtedly the best sort, its fruit being excellent, and its bearing season longer than any other. Unfortunately mosaic has been spreading rapidly in *Lloyd George* of recent years, and it is now by no means easy to get a mosaic-free stock of canes from any ordinary source. For those who prefer something else, we give particulars of some other varieties. The best autumn-fruiting kind is probably *Hailsham Berry*, and of the yellow-fruiting kind we recommend *Yellow Antwerp*.

SUMMER FRUITING

Name	Size and Shape	Season	Qualities
Baumforth's Seedling A	Medium to Large, Round	Summer	Soft, acid flavour, prolific, best for jam
Baumforth's Seedling B	Medium, Conical	Summer	Good flavour and very sweet
Brocket Hall	Large, Round	Summer	
Laxton's Bountiful	Medium to Large, Roundish, Conical	Summer	Sweet and luscious
Lloyd George	Very Large, Conical	July–Autumn	Vigorous and prolific. Frequently crops on young canes in the autumn
Newburgh	Large	Summer	Good cropper, vigorous. Subject to Cane blight

VARIETIES OF THE RASPBERRY

SUMMER FRUITING—(continued)

Name	Size and Shape	Season	Qualities
Norfolk Giant	Medium to Large, Roundish	Late Summer	Heavy cropper
Preussen	Large to Very Large, Round	Summer	Rather soft, sweet, fine flavour
Pyne's Royal	Very Large, Conical	Summer	Slightly acid. Good for jam; good quality. Makes few canes
Reader's Perfection	Medium to Large, Roundish, Conical	Summer	Prolific
Red Cross	Large, Roundish, Conical	Summer	Good flavour and prolific
St. Walfried	Long, Conical	Summer	New promising Dutch variety

YELLOW FRUITING

Name	Size and Shape	Season	Qualities
Golden Hornet	Large, Round	Mid-season	Fine flavour
Yellow Antwerp	Large, Round	Mid-season	Sweet, pleasant flavour
Yellow Superlative	Large	Mid-season	

AUTUMN FRUITING

Name	Size and Shape	Season	Qualities
Belle de Fontenay (Red)	Very Large	October–November	Prolific. Short canes
Hailsham Berry (Red)	Large, Round	October–November	Vigorous grower
Lloyd George (Red)	Large	Summer and Autumn Lloyd George can be easily converted into an autumn-fruiting variety by cutting the fruiting canes hard back to the ground in February or March	Good flavour
[(Red) November Abundance	Large	November	Good flavour
October Red (Red)	Large	Autumn	Prolific

Most of the autumn-fruiting varieties bear in October and November, but the quality of the crop depends largely on the weather during those months.

RASPBERRIES TO GROW FOR MARKET

Baumforth's Seedings A
Baumforth's Seedling B
Lloyd George
Newburgh

Norfolk Giant
Preussen
Pyne's Royal
Reader's Perfection

Red Cross

RASPBERRIES FOR JAM AND BOTTLING

Baumforth's Seedling A
Lloyd George

Pyne's Royal
Reader's Perfection

Red Cross

FRUIT GROWING

THE STRAWBERRY *(Fragaria)*

ORIGIN AND HISTORY

The wild strawberry is indigenous to many parts of Europe, including Great Britain, and is frequently to be found growing on hedge banks, on the Chalk Downs, in woods, and on uncultivated land. The cultivated fruit was introduced from Virginia and Chili early in the seventeenth century, and most of the cultivated strawberries of to-day are the result of subsequent crossings. The Alpine Strawberry came from the Continent early in the eighteenth century. To-day we have the large-fruited strawberries (early, mid-season and late), the small-fruited (Alpine) berries, and the perpetual-fruiting kinds, the last-named being the result of a cross between the large-fruiting and the Alpine Strawberries.

SOIL, SITUATION AND ASPECT

The cultivated strawberry may be considered fairly catholic in regard to soil requirements. Some varieties such as *Sir Joseph Paxton* and *Huxley* are reputed to prefer the heavier loams, whilst *Royal Sovereign* favours the medium and light loams. There is a belief among some strawberry growers that the plant thrives in soils which are slightly acid, and it is true that runners planted in old woodland sites have made astonishingly vigorous plants. Probably a good humus content in the surface is essential to the production of a shallow fibrous root-system like that of the strawberry. A sunny situation free from frost is desirable, and since the leaves of strawberry plants are inclined to scorch when sprayed with winter tar-oil washes, it is always best to plant them separate from other fruits. In gardens, the season of picking may be lengthened by planting varieties which ripen at different times, and by planting in borders with different aspects.

PROPAGATION

With strawberries, as with black currants and raspberries, the subject of propagation cannot be separated at the present day from that of virus disease. Reversion in black currants, mosaic in raspberries, " yellow-edge " and " crinkle " in strawberries, are troubles which are rampant wherever these crops are grown. All three belong to that obscure group of virus diseases that, like many human diseases, continue to puzzle the experts. The present-day stocks of the most desirable varieties of black currants, raspberries and strawberries are constantly being exposed to infection from diseases quite as fatal to their constitution as tuberculosis

339

is to man, because they are constantly being visited by insects which are carriers or "vectors" of these deadly virus diseases. Hence, before it is possible to control such diseases, it is essential to find out which are the chief carrying insects and how they can be controlled, and whether any varieties of the plants concerned are likely to be carriers of the disease without showing the usual symptoms. All these investigations are actually being carried out, but they must necessarily take time and it is unlikely that any very clear-cut results will be forthcoming just yet.

Meantime, much can be done in the way of raising healthy strawberry plants from parents which have been kept under observation and carefully "rogued" for "yellow-edge" and "crinkle" symptoms. Once again, the county horticultural officer is the man to ask for advice as to the best sources of supply of such material. If only one plant guaranteed free from virus can be obtained, it is better to start with that and build up a supply of healthy runners, rather than to risk buying in runners that may have been exposed to infection and that, although they may look healthy enough, may all go down with "yellow-edge" or "crinkle" in their first season.

Starting with a small number of healthy and vigorous parent plants, it is possible to produce new plants to stock a fair-sized garden plot in a single season. This is done by means of a process of vegetative propagation.

Raising strawberry plants vegetatively is comparatively simple owing to the habit, possessed by most varieties, of sending out long, threadlike stolons in June or July, from which young "runner" plants grow naturally at distances of anything from 6 to 12 inches apart. If these runner plants are left undisturbed, quite a number of them will throw out roots into the ground and will continue growing. If they are "hand-laid," that is to say, if they are pushed gently down into the soil and held firmly in place with a wire pin or stone, they start rooting more quickly, and, if the season is favourable, quite a number of them will be ready to plant out from July onwards in their permanent quarters. Recent experiments have shown that all the runners from a healthy parent plant will ultimately make good plants provided they all receive equally good treatment. At the same time, it is probably true that very small runner plants will suffer more than large or medium-sized ones from any hardships of weather or treatment that they may be called upon to endure during the process of transplanting, and for the first six months or so after they have been planted out.

It has been shown, for instance, that small runner plants appear to find it more difficult than larger plants to get going again after the " warm water treatment " for mite. (See page 347.)

Strawberry runners are best raised in a strawberry runner nursery bed laid down on the lines shown in the diagram. When the runners are all laid into separate little blocks like this, it is much easier to discover the parent plants from which they came, and if necessary, the whole batch of plants in the b l o c k affected can be pulled up and got rid of should they develop symptoms of virus disease.

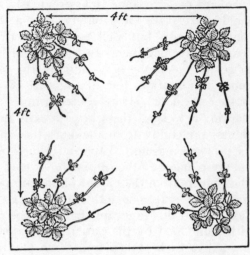

BLOCK METHOD OF RAISING STRAWBERRY RUNNERS.

ALPINE STRAWBERRIES

These grow well on any chalky or light soils and respond to generous cultural and manurial treatment. Raised from seed sown in spring or autumn, they should be planted at least one foot apart in the row, in rows of 1 foot to 18 inches apart. Fresh plants should be raised from seed every other year. Some of the best varieties are *Belle de Meaux, La Brillante, de Gaillon Blanc*, and *Cresta*.

PERPETUAL-FRUITING STRAWBERRIES

These fruit from early summer into December in favourable situations. Cultivation is the same as recommended for large fruited berries, except as regards the autumn crop of fruit which is produced on rooted runners from the main plant. This, of course, necessitates more room being allowed between main plants when making a bed, as the runners which spring from the centre plant must be pegged down around it. The main plants should be put in 2 to 2½ feet apart. The summer fruit is borne on the main plant and the runners must be pegged down and stopped as soon as a single plant has formed on each. Some growers destroy the centre or main plant before it summer fruits, to encourage the runners' development for autumn fruiting. The original bed should

341

be renewed annually in autumn, planting selected runner plants as main plants for next year.

PLANTING

The ideal conditions for planting strawberry runners are those which provide a warm soil which has been heavily manured with farmyard manure some time previously and deeply dug. Planting should take place immediately after a shower, and the soil should continue warm but well supplied with moisture for as long as possible after planting. In the west of England it may be possible to get rooted runners in July by the methods already described, under Propagation, but in the east of England the only way to make certain of getting rooted runners early enough for August planting is to layer them in pots early in July from healthy parent plants, preferably from maidens (i.e., plants which were runners the previous season). Three or 3½-inch pots filled with good potting soil are plunged to the rim in the ground close to the parent plants. The runners from the parent plants are pegged down with a hairpin or piece of wire, one into each pot, the rest of the stolon being then nipped off to ensure that the potted runner is well provided with plant food by the parent. Opinion differs as to the number of runners to be taken from each plant. Provided the parent is healthy and vigorous there is no reason why at least 12 runners should not be potted up from each. If ideal conditions for planting out are to be obtained, speedy rooting of runners is desirable. Rooting may be encouraged by earthing up round the base of the runner and even by judicious watering in very dry weather. All runners not required for planting may be cut off. Runners potted in early July under these conditions should have made sufficient roots in three to four weeks. The stolon connecting each runner with the parent plant is then cut off and the pots removed to a shady place, where they are kept moderately watered. When the site is ready and conditions for planting appear favourable, the runners are given warm water treatment (see page 347), and are then planted out without the ball of soil round the roots being broken. Distance of planting varies, the maximum for strong-growing varieties being 3 feet between the rows, and 18 inches between the plants in the row.

In the case of Alpine Strawberries, at least 12 inches should be allowed between the plants each way.

With potted runners it should be easy to complete planting by September, but with ordinary runners, if planting cannot be carried out in August or September, it is usually wise to postpone planting until March or early April of the following year, when the soil will again be warming up. The runners will then have a chance to grow on continuously with little or no check other than that inevitably given by warm water treatment (see page 347). These are counsels of perfection, which, if they can be carried out, should result in first-class plants.

In many seasons, however, planting conditions are far from ideal, nor may it always be possible to arrange for the warm water treatment. The main points are to get well-rooted runners from healthy plants, and to transplant them with as little check as possible into soil conditions conducive to rapid root growth. From this latter point of view potted runners are to be preferred, but *potted plants are no better than any others unless they come from healthy, vigorous parents free from virus, and unless they are planted in a situation which is isolated from strawberry plants that are already diseased.* Hence, under present-day conditions the wisest plan is to dig up the whole strawberry bed every three years, burn the plants, and start again with a supply of healthy runners from the best source available. Here again, as in the case of mosaic-free raspberries, advice should be sought from the county advisory officer.

Method of Planting.—Where the number of runners to be planted is comparatively small, a trowel may be used. A hole is made large enough for the roots to be well spread out, a fine covering of soil is then thrown over the roots, and the hole filled up and firmly trodden down with the heel.

When planted, the crown of the runner should be just above the surface of the ground.

When planting strawberry runners on a commercial scale, a dibber is generally used, and the roots are put straight downwards into a vertical hole, care being taken to see that they are not turned upwards. If severe frosts occur during the winter, autumn-planted runners may be partially lifted. Such plants should be trodden well in during the following March, and any gaps where runners have died should be filled up.

CULTIVATION

From March to mid-May the ground should be kept well hoed to keep down the weeds, and conserve soil moisture. In hoeing, great care should be taken to draw the soil towards rather than away from the plants, and not to go too deep with the hoe.

THE STRAWBERRY

If the strawberry bed is known to be situated in a frost-pocket and the plants are already in cropping, orchard heaters should be put out as soon as the flower trusses are showing green, and should be lit throughout the blossoming season whenever frost threatens.

POLLINATION

Tardive de Leopold is self-sterile and *Oberschlesien* is partially self-sterile. *Huxley* will pollinate either of them, but *Oberschlesien* is not a good pollinator for *Tardive de Leopold*. *Royal Sovereign* could be used for this purpose, but would be likely to go down with virus disease sooner or later because *Tardive* is a partial carrier of virus.

STRAWING

For fruiting plants, as soon as the fruit is well set and beginning to swell, clean wheat or oat straw is laid along the rows and fitted close in under the leaves of the plants in order to protect the berries from being splashed with mud when it rains. Where orchard heaters are not available and frosts are feared, strawing should be delayed until the last possible moment because straw when placed below the blossoms insulates them from the warmth of the soil while leaving them exposed to loss of heat by radiation on clear nights. After the crop has been picked, all runners are cut off from the parent plants and the straw litter is either raked up and carried off or it may be burnt over. At the time of burning, there should be a light following wind blowing down the rows. The straw litter is lit at one end of the bed, care being taken to see that the flames go straight down the row, and do not linger round any particular plant. If carefully done, burning in this way does no harm to the plants, and it is even claimed by some authorities as a useful piece of orchard hygiene which will rid the plants of certain insect pests, and may even invigorate the plants themselves.

MANURING

Experiments have shown that potassium and phosphorus are both very important for strawberries, and that nitrogen must not be given *in excess*.

Once strawberry runners have been planted, it is almost impossible to dig in organic manures without injuring the roots. Hence, the ideal practice is for really short-littered dung or shoddy to be

THE STRAWBERRY

ploughed or dug well in to the soil some weeks before the runners are planted, or even for the previous crop. Horse manure from stables where peat moss litter is used is excellent for the purpose. Since nitrogenous manures alone tend to produce excessive leaf growth and poor flavour in the berries, potash and phosphate should be given every winter by pricking in sulphate of potash at the rate of 2 to 3 cwt. per acre (1 to 1½ oz. per square yard), and either steamed bone flour or superphosphates at the rate of 4 to 5 cwt. per acre (2 to 2½ oz. per square yard).

PROTECTION AGAINST BIRDS

Birds are very fond of ripe strawberries, and in gardens it is, therefore, necessary to provide protection in the form of the usual bird scarers or netting suspended over the plants. In the latter case, the netting should be supported well away from the plants, otherwise it is liable to damage the plants and fruit.

GATHERING

Strawberries should never be gathered while they are wet, or rotting will set in very quickly. For home use the berries are picked when fully ripe. For marketing as dessert fruit they are picked just before they are fully ripe, each berry being picked with a short stalk. A good method is for each picker to carry one punnet to hold either one or two pounds of extra-selected fruit, and one chip basket to hold either 3 or 4 lbs. of selected fruit. As soon as the fruit is picked, the receptacles must be put in a shady place or the fruit may be over-ripe by the time it reaches the retailer. Ripe fruit for jam may be gathered and marketed in receptacles known as tubs and holding 56 lbs. of fruit. These may be either returnable or non-returnable packages.

Canning factories often supply flat trays for strawberries. These are stacked in lorries and taken straight from the farm to the factory.

MARKETING

Extra-selected fruits may be marketed in non-returnable punnets or in small chips holding 1 or 2 lbs., and the selected fruits for the main crop in 3- or 4-lb. chip baskets. These containers are lined either with strawberry leaves or with lining paper, or they may be bought ready-lined with greaseproof paper from the chip-basket makers or from horticultural sundriesmen. Before being despatched to market, punnets and chips are protected from dust with special

345

covers held in place by elastic bands. A convenient way of transporting small punnets in bulk is to place them in flat trays specially designed for the purpose. Cellophane covers, provided they allow for ventilation, give an added attraction to the appearance of small punnets.

In certain strawberry districts the railway authorities provide specially-fitted vans for transporting strawberries to the London markets, particulars of which are available at the local railway stations.

See also Fruit under Glass, page 402.

INSECT PESTS OF THE STRAWBERRY

Strawberries suffer from a great many pests, any of which can be very serious and some of which can easily be kept in check.

STRAWBERRY APHIS (Capitophorus fragariæ)

This pest frequently attacks the plants to such an extent that serious malformation of the leaves and stunting of the plants are caused, resulting in loss of crop and, very often, the loss of valuable plants. The insects are very pale green—so pale as to appear almost colourless—rather long-legged, and attain a length, when fully grown, of about $\frac{1}{12}$ inch. They feed on the leaves and leaf-stalks, where they multiply at a great rate, and suck the sap. From time to time winged forms appear and these spread the infestation. Not only is the Strawberry Aphis important by reason of the direct damage it does, but it is also important as a vector (carrier) of the dreaded virus diseases.

Control.—One may make sure of starting a plantation free of aphis either by warm water treatment of the runners (see page 347), or by dipping these in a strong solution of nicotine and soap. A look-out should be kept for the appearance of aphis and the plants should then be sprayed as often as is necessary with nicotine and soap or dusted frequently with nicotine dust.

TARSONEMUS MITE (Tarsonemus fragariæ)

This is a very serious pest, the importance of which has been fully realized only in recent years. The creature itself is minute, intermediate in size between its near relatives the Gall Mite of the black currant and the fruit tree Red Spider, and lives between the folds of the very youngest leaves. It is of a pallid—almost colourless hue—and lays large numbers of small, round eggs. The damage it does much resemble that caused by Aphis. Indeed, Aphis damage, Tarsonemus damage, and the symptoms of the virus disease " Yellow Edge " are so much alike that even the expert often finds it difficult to differentiate between them. The mite spreads about chiefly by crawling along the stolons from plant to plant. The use of infested runners has in the past been the means of transporting it from district to district.

Control.—Little can be done to check this pest when once it has become established, and badly-infested plants are best ploughed in. All runners for planting should be submerged for twenty minutes in warm water which is maintained at a temperature of 110° F. to kill the mites and their eggs. Suitable apparatus for

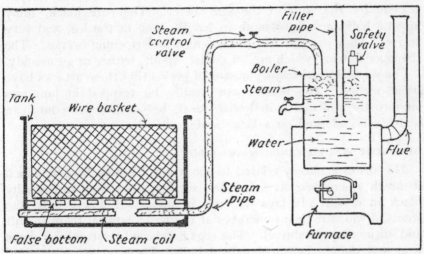

APPARATUS FOR WARM WATER TREATMENT OF STRAWBERRY RUNNERS.

carrying out this treatment can readily be obtained or devised. A suitable arrangement is shown in our diagram.

The plants are stacked in a wire-mesh or wicker basket (or even in a loosely-woven sack), and immersed in a tank of water heated by steam from a boiler or in any other convenient manner. The temperature of the water, naturally, drops somewhat when the plants are plunged into it, and it is, therefore, important that the prescribed temperature be reached as soon as possible and maintained for the full length of time.

EELWORM (*Aphelenchoides fragariæ*)

At one time almost all the little-understood troubles to which the strawberry plant is prone were laid at the door of the eelworm.

347

Latterly it has received less attention. The whitish worms, which measure some three-hundredths of an inch in length, live and breed in the plants, and if sufficiently numerous, cause the stems to swell and the flowers to develop into an abortive cauliflower-like mass.

Control.—No effective remedy can be suggested. " Cauliflower " plants should be destroyed, as they can never be expected to recover. Warm water treatment can be relied on to destroy eelworm present in runners intended for planting.

GROUND BEETLES *(Carabidæ)*

Ground beetles are beneficial insects and feed on slugs, caterpillars and the like. Unfortunately, a few species have developed a taste for the fruit of the strawberry. They are black, shiny insects, half an inch or more in length, long in the leg, and very active. They eat the skin of the green and ripening berries. The damaged berries, which are, of course, spoilt, wither or go mouldy.

Control.—No satisfactory means of preventing these attacks have been devised. The beetles can readily be trapped in jam jars let into the soil and baited with meat, but such a procedure can scarcely be adopted on a large scale.

BLOSSOM WEEVIL *(Anthonomus rubi)*

This insect is closely related to the Apple Blossom Weevil, which it much resembles. It is rather smaller, however, and wholly black in colour. It lays its eggs in unopened flower-buds, the stems of which it then punctures at the base, causing them to wilt and, ultimately, to shrivel. The eggs hatch and the resulting grubs feed and pupate in the damaged buds. Later a new generation of weevils emerges and does further damage to leaves and petioles.

Control.—Some of the beetles can be caught on tarred boards and the destruction of rubbish which might harbour them also helps. Derris dust should be applied frequently when the weevils are active ; i.e., when the blossom buds appear.

OTHER PESTS

Among other pests which sometimes occur may be mentioned a weevil (*Exomias araneiformis*), which has been found to feed on the green berries, and the caterpillars of a moth (the Strawberry Tortrix, *Peronea comariana*). The latter feed chiefly on the leaves and in some districts do a great deal of damage. They are normally kept in check by parasitic insects. Red Spider (*Tetranychus telarius*) also occurs, but is kept in check by the sulphur dusting carried

THE STRAWBERRY

out for mildew. Several root-feeding insects such as Wireworms, Chafer Beetle grubs and Leather-jackets, also occur.

DISEASES OF THE STRAWBERRY

MILDEW *(Sphærotheca Humuli)*

This is a "powdery" mildew, attacking the leaves and sometimes the berries, to which it gives a whitish, mealy appearance. The presence of the disease can readily be recognized in the plot by the up-curled margins of the leaves, usually the younger ones. The effects of attack can be serious, particularly in dry seasons, but the disease can usually be controlled by dusting two or three times with "flowers of sulphur" at seven- to ten-day intervals up to the setting of the fruits. Fruits intended for canning should not be dusted with sulphur or they will not be acceptable to the canners. Where the disease is persistent and is likely to impair the vigour of the plants, dustings can be continued after the crop has been gathered. Maiden plantations and runner beds should also be protected by dusting in summer during likely periods of infection (dry weather after recent growth has been rapid). Spraying with a 2 per cent. lime-sulphur solution before blossom and a 1 per cent. afterwards is also an effective remedy, but it is not as convenient to use as the dusting method. Burning-over the plantation in autumn tends to reduce the source of infection for the following year by destroying the fungus already present on the plants.

LEAF SPOT *(Mycosphærella Fragariæ)*

This disease has been known to cause occasional losses in this country, but it is not usually of serious economic importance. The result of attack by the fungus is the appearance on the leaf of circular spots, the centres of which ultimately turn grey, but remain surrounded by a purplish-red halo. The tufts of spores produced on the spots are whitish, and serve to spread the disease. The fungus passes the winter on the old leaves; hence, burning-over the plantation would reduce the sources of infection in this case also.

LEAF SCORCH *(Marssonina Fragariæ)*

In its early stages this disease is similar to Leaf Spot in that small, purplish spots appear on the leaves. They are more irregular than those of Leaf Spot, and do not develop a pale centre. The older leaves are usually the worst attacked, and, when severe, the

349

disease can kill them. The fungus produces spores on the spots in shiny, black blisters, which burst to free the spores. The disease is not often severe, but the variety *Sir Joseph Paxton* is very susceptible. Control as for Leaf Spot.

GREY MOULD *(Botrytis cinerea)*

This mould can be severe in persistent wet weather. The fruits, usually when nearly ripe, develop a soft, squashy rot, around the margin of which grows a copious grey fungal weft bearing spores. Under a hand-lens, the spores can be seen clustered together on stalks, and they resemble bunches of grapes. Rain-splashes from the soil are likely carriers of infection, which can thus be prevented to some extent by adequate strawing of the beds. Overcrowding of plants should be avoided, and care should be taken that they have sufficient aeration.

ROOT ROT *(Non-parasitic)*

When strawberries are planted in badly-drained, wet soils, many of the roots often rot and turn black through lack of aeration. This weakening of the root-system naturally debilitates the plants, which may then fall victims to certain fungi that are weakly parasitic on the roots. Such fungi would not prove fatal to a healthy strawberry plant, but under unsuitable growth-conditions they are likely to accelerate the death of the root-rotted plants. The remedy lies in improving the drainage and aeration of the soil.

As there are certain parasitic fungal diseases, notably Red Core (*Phytophthora*) and Verticillium Wilt that can have superficially similar effects to those caused by waterlogging, sickly plants should be shown to an expert for examination wherever possible.

VIRUS DISEASES

Attention has already been drawn (page 339) to the serious nature of virus diseases, for which, as they are carried in the sap, there is no cure except the drastic one of roguing, i.e., the removal and destruction of all affected plants as soon as they are seen. Failure to do this exposes neighbouring healthy plants to risk of infection.

YELLOW-EDGE

The outstanding cause of the failure of strawberry plantations, especially those of the variety *Royal Sovereign* in the eastern parts of the country, is this virus disease, which is characterized by

350

DISEASES AND PESTS OF THE STRAWBERRY

a dwarfed, flattened, sickly appearance in the plant, the young leaves of which are small, often cupped upwards, and have short stalks. At certain periods of the growing season these leaves have bright yellow edges, from which the common name of the disease is derived. The disease is carried from affected to healthy plants by aphides, which, when they puncture the leaf to suck the sap, transmit the virus. This gets into the sap of the plant and thus affects all the runners from it.

Control.—All affected plants and their runners must be promptly taken up and burnt as soon as the disease is seen. As a precaution, near neighbouring plants and their runners also should be destroyed. New plantings should be made only from certified virus-free stock, and should be well isolated from existing sources of infection. It must be borne in mind that the varieties *Huxley* and *Oberschlesien* are " tolerant " of the disease, i.e., they can be infected without showing any symptoms, and infected *Tardive de Leopold* often does not show them, so that these varieties are a special source of danger for *Royal Sovereign.*

CRINKLE

This is another serious virus disease, and it is specially prevalent in western parts of the country. It can be recognized by the presence of small, pale areas on the leaves, which are often wrinkled and puckered. The yellow areas become reddish or purple and eventually brown, and may at first glance resemble damage by capsids. Plants may be mildly infected, when they suffer little ill effect ; or severely infected, when degeneration is rapid.

Control.—The methods applicable to Yellow-Edge should be practised also for Crinkle. *Royal Sovereign* is very susceptible.

DISEASES AND PESTS : DIAGNOSIS TABLE
THE STRAWBERRY

Damage	Probable Cause
Plants	*Pests*
Plants wilt, fail to develop properly, or die.	Wireworm, Chafer Beetle
Evidence of insect damage to roots	Grubs, or Leather Jackets
Foliage	*Pests*
Leaves and leaf-stalks malformed, and infested with pale-green rather long-legged aphis	Strawberry Aphis
Leaves and leaf-stalks malformed, and infested by tiny almost colourless mite	Tarsonemus Mite
Stems of flower-buds wilt and shrivel ; leaves eaten	Strawberry Blossom Weevil
Leaves eaten by caterpillars	Strawberry Tortrix
	Diseases
Up-curled margins of leaves with powdery mildew	Mildew
Circular spots, centres turn grey and are surrounded by purplish-red halo	Leaf Spot

THE STRAWBERRY

DISEASES AND PESTS : DIAGNOSIS TABLE—(contd.)

DAMAGE	PROBABLE CAUSE
Foliage	*Diseases*
Irregular purplish spots scattered over leaves	Leaf Scorch
Dwarfed and flattened appearance of entire plant; small, curled, bright yellow-edged leaves on short stalks	Yellow Edge
Yellowing or reddening of leaves in small localized areas, crinkling and puckering	Crinkle
Blossom	*Pest*
Blossom develops into abortive cauliflower-like mass	Eelworm
Fruit	*Pest*
Skin of green and ripening berries eaten ; fruit withers and goes mouldy	Ground Beetle
	Diseases
Whitish, mealy appearance	Mildew
Soft, squashy rot ; grey fungus on stalks and berries	Grey Mould

Note.—Once the trouble has been diagnosed, the reader should refer to the paragraph dealing with the particular disease or pest, and should also consult the Guide to Spraying below.

STRAWBERRY. GUIDE TO SPRAYING

Time of Application	Treatment	To Control
Before planting	Warm water treatment (20 minutes at 110° F.)	Tarsonemid Mite, Aphis Eelworm and Red Spider
Early May (before flowering and as necessary after fruit picked	Sulphur dust	Mildew and Red Spider
August–September	Roguing	" Yellow-edge " and " Crinkle " viruses

SOME STRAWBERRY VARIETIES

Variety	Colour	Season	Qualities
Bedford Champion	Bright Scarlet	Mid-season	Large, oval. Heavy cropper, and market fruit
Black Prince	Dark Crimson	Very Early	Fine jam maker. Small but good flavour
British Queen	Bright Red	Mid-season	Large. Excellent flavour. Does well on chalk subsoil
Cambridge Early	Dark Red	Early	Fairly large, conical, sub-acid. Moderate vigour
Deutsch Evern	Bright Red	Early	Medium-fair quality. Good cropper. Small
Dr. Hogg	Pale Red	Late	Large, wedge-shaped. Said by some to be the best-flavoured strawberry
Givon's Late Prolific	Dark Red	Late	Large and fine flavour. Hardy and prolific
Huxley (Brenda Gautrey)	Reddish	Mid-season	Very strong grower. Good cropper. Fruit large but coarse and of leathery texture

352

CHERRY : "BIGARREAU NOIR DE SCHMIDT."

CHERRY : "BIGARREAU NAPOLEON."

VARIETIES OF STRAWBERRIES

Variety	Colour	Season	Qualities
Keen's Seedling	Crimson	Mid-season	Large. Excellent flavour. Hardy and prolific. An old variety difficult to obtain
King George V	(See Royal Sovereign)		
Laxton's Latest	Dark Scarlet	Late	Large and fine flavour. Heavy cropper on suitable soil
Little Scarlet	Light Red	Early	Small. Good flavour. Fine for jam-making. Very old variety, difficult to obtain
Lord Grenfell	Red	Mid-season	Medium to large. Hardy. Fertility moderate
Madame Kooi	Deep Scarlet	Late	Large. Poor flavour. Good for exhibition and market as preserving fruit
Oberschlesien	Varies from Pink to Scarlet	Mid-season	Large. Medium flavour. Heavy cropper
Perle de Prague	Bright Red	Mid-season	Medium to large, bluntly conical. Moderate vigour
President	Scarlet	Mid-season	Large
Royal Sovereign	Bright Scarlet	Early	Large. Good flavour. Prolific on most soils, especially light or medium. Best market sort if free from virus
Sir Douglas Haig	Deep Scarlet	Early	Excellent flavour. Good cropper
Sir Joseph Paxton	Dark Red	Mid-season to Late	Large. Good flavour. Hardy and prolific on heavy soil. Market fruit
Stirling Castle	Red	Mid-season	Small but good flavour. Used to be widely grown for jam-making and market. Difficult to obtain on account of its extreme susceptibility to virus diseases
Tardive de Leopold	Dark Red	Late	Large. Fine flavour. Strong grower
Waterloo	Very Dark Crimson	Late	Large and good flavour
Western Queen	Crimson	Mid-season	A promising new variety

STRAWBERRIES WITH THE BEST FLAVOUR

British Queen (Mid-season)
Dr. Hogg (Late)
Royal Sovereign (Early)

Sir Joseph Paxton (Mid-season to Late)
Waterloo (Late)

ALPINE STRAWBERRIES

Variety	Colour	Season	Qualities
Alpine Improved	Deep Red	Summer and Autumn	Small, Good flavour. Hardy and prolific
Belle de Meaux	Red	Late	Large and long fruits. Good flavour and cropper. Fruits until October—forms runners
Bush White (de Gaillon Blanc)	White	Summer and Autumn	Small to medium in size. Good flavour. Makes no runners. Useful for borders
Des Quatre Saisons (La Brillante)	Bright Red	Summer and Autumn	A vigorous grower
Gaillon Rouge Amélioré	Pale Red	July-October	Large fruits. Crops well. Makes no runners. Plant in borders. Excellent flavour
Cresta	Bright Red	June–November	Large. Good flavour. Vigorous—many runners

PERPETUAL FRUITING STRAWBERRIES

Variety	Colour	Season	Qualities
St. Antoine de Padoue	Bright Red	Autumn	Large. Prolific
St. Fiacre	Deep Red	Summer and Autumn	Medium. Good flavour. Hardy and prolific
St. Joseph	Light Red	Summer and Autumn	Medium. Good flavour and prolific

STRAWBERRIES RECOMMENDED FOR GARDEN CULTURE

Variety	Season	Qualities
Black Prince	Early	Small, but good flavour. Excellent for jam
Doctor Hogg	Late	Remarkable for its flavour
Royal Sovereign	Early	The earliest and best for all purposes
Sir Joseph Paxton	Mid-season	A fine main crop fruit
Tardive de Leopold	Late	A highly-recommended late variety, provided it is planted with a suitable pollinator, such as Huxley
Waterloo	Late	Excellent flavour

STRAWBERRIES FOR MARKET

Variety	Season	Qualities
Huxley(Brenda Gautrey)	Mid-season	Fruit large, but coarse, and of leathery texture
Oberschlesien	Mid-season	Pink to scarlet fruit. Large, and of medium flavour
Royal Sovereign	Early	The best market variety
Sir Joseph Paxton	Late	Flowers late and escapes frost
Tardive de Leopold	Late	Large fruit and good flavour
Western Queen	Mid-season	A promising variety of recent introduction

STRAWBERRIES FOR JAM-MAKING AND BOTTLING

Black Prince (Very Early)
Little Scarlet (Early)
Royal Sovereign (Early)

Sir Joseph Paxton (Mid-season to Late)
Stirling Castle (Mid-season to Late)

VEITCHBERRY

A new hybrid berry, obtained by means of crossing a blackberry and a November Abundance raspberry. See under Blackberry (Hybrids).

THE WALNUT *(Juglans)*

ORIGIN AND HISTORY

Walnuts were grown by the Romans, who may have introduced them to this country. The Common Walnut, *Juglans regia,* was originally a native of Persia and the Himalayan regions and is now widely grown in Europe. The Black Walnut, *J. nigra,* and the White Walnut, *J. cinerea,* natives of North America, are valued for their timber.

354

THE WALNUT

SOIL AND SITUATION

The walnut grows well in a variety of soils of fair depth, provided drainage is adequate. A moderate amount of lime or chalk is beneficial. Freedom from spring frosts is of the utmost importance, since the walnut " leafs out " or starts into growth moderately early and the tender young growth is extremely susceptible to frost.

PROPAGATION

The walnut can be raised from seed and this is how most of our English walnut trees have been produced. Seedlings, however, can never be depended on to produce nuts identical to those from the parent tree, and this fact accounts for the wide dissimilarity in the size and quality of English walnuts. Moreover, walnut trees grown from seed take from fifteen to twenty years to come into bearing, whereas grafted trees should be in cropping ten years after planting. To obtain the best results, only grafted walnut trees should be planted. One-year-old seedlings of *Juglans nigra* or of *Juglans regia*, the English walnut, have been used with success as stocks for grafting. To raise stocks from seed the ripe walnuts are gathered from beneath the tree, and are half-buried, without the husks being removed, in boxes filled with damp sand, where they are left in the open air (protected from birds and vermin) until the following March to become " stratified." They are then put out in the open in good friable soil, in drills 2 feet apart, the nuts being 6 inches apart in the row, and covered with 3 inches of soil. Here, too, they should be protected from birds, particularly rooks, and from other vermin. The seedlings are lifted in November, potted into 4½-inch pots and stood outside until February, when they are brought into the glasshouse ready for grafting. The scions are cut in January from selected trees known to bear good walnuts, well-ripened wood with a small pith area being used. The cut ends of the scions are coated with grafting-wax and stored in moist sphagnum moss until March. The seedling stocks are grafted in March under glass while still in the pots. The stock is cut to within 2 inches of soil level, and the scion inserted by the double whip and tongue method, tied and waxed with grafting wax. The pots are then plunged in coco-nut fibre in closed frames with a bottom heat of from 60° to 70° F., where they are kept moist for about three weeks. The plants are then hardened off and planted out in a nursery, where they are left for two or three years before being moved to their permanent position. This is a long and tedious process and accounts for the fact that grafted

355

walnut trees are not easily obtainable at the present time. Experiments in the budding of walnuts in the open are being carried out at East Malling.

PLANTING

Walnut trees grown as standards should be planted in autumn from 40 to 50 feet apart. A good hole should be dug to take the tree without cramping the root-system. The tap root should be cut back to within about a foot of the base and the rest of the main roots are trimmed with a long, sloping cut on the under side. Short lateral roots are left full length and spread out evenly. The earth is rammed well home to promote rapid growth of new roots.

CULTIVATION

Walnut trees do not transplant as easily as most fruit trees, and need very careful after-treatment for the first few years. The ground within a radius of 3 or 4 feet from the stem should be kept hoed in spring and summer and dug over in the winter yearly until the tree has become well-established. If it is found that the tender young shoots are killed by frost every spring when they have made a few inches growth, it would be wise to move the tree to higher ground. Special attention should be paid to careful tying, staking, and guarding against cattle and vermin.

There are three important and little-known facts about the pollination of the walnut. First, nutlets and catkins are normally borne on the same tree, the pollen from the catkins being carried by the wind to cross-pollinate the nutlets. Unless the nutlets are thus pollinated, they will drop off when the size of a pea. Secondly, on young trees nutlets are often produced for some years before catkins appear. Thirdly, although nutlets and catkins may be present on the same tree, the nutlets may not be in a receptive condition when the pollen is ripe on the catkins. Hence it follows that single isolated trees of walnuts may remain unfruitful unless and until some other tree bearing catkins is planted near them. Some varieties, such as Meylanaise, are useful pollinators because they carry catkins from an early age.

PRUNING

As little pruning as possible should be done to a walnut tree, apart from the cutting out of dead or crossing branches. Such pruning should be done in late spring or in August, all pruning wounds being pared over and covered with a good white-lead paint.

THE WALNUT

GATHERING AND STORING

Walnuts should be harvested from the ground as soon as they fall. After removing the green outer husk, the crevices of the shells must be freed from every trace of fibre as it is here that moulds begin to grow. The fibre can be easily removed by scrubbing the nuts with a soft nailbrush in water. The nuts should be removed from the water after a few moments, and spread out in single layers to dry at room temperature. Clean nuts which are well sealed may be bleached by dipping in a bleaching solution for about 3 minutes. The walnuts may then be stored in earthenware crocks filled with alternate layers of a storage medium—equal quantities of common salt and slightly damp coco-nut fibre.

The crocks should be kept in a cellar as recommended for cobs and filberts.

INSECT PESTS OF THE WALNUT

Walnuts suffer little from insect attack, the few insects that feed on them seldom occurring in sufficient numbers to matter. In addition to various species of greenfly, there occasionally occur Codling Moth (see Apple, page 160), a microscopic mite, *Eriophyes tristriatus* var. *erinea*, which causes small swellings on the leaves, and the Common Green Capsid (see Black Currant, page 234).

DISEASES OF THE WALNUT

BACTERIAL BLIGHT *(Pseudomonas Juglandis)*

The earliest symptoms of this disease are small black spots on the leaves, from which the bacteria spread to all the current year's growth. Later symptoms are lesions or long black markings on the shoots and leaf-stalks, and black spots on the nutlets. The latter may drop if badly affected. Shoots showing the lesions should be cut out in winter, and, where small trees are affected, they should be sprayed the following spring, as soon as the leaves open, with Bordeaux Mixture (6 lb. copper sulphate, 9 lb. hydrated lime to 100 gallons of water) and later as necessary.

GRAFT DISEASE *(Chalaropsis thielavioides)*

This fungus sometimes attacks the unions between stocks and scions of walnuts when they are being grafted under glass. A preventive is to paint the part of the stock to be grafted with a 1 per cent. solution of formalin before the scion is inserted. As a further means of control, the glasshouse where the grafting is

357

THE WALNUT

carried out should be sprayed with a 1 per cent. solution of formalin before the work is begun.

WALNUT LEAF BLOTCH *(Gnomonia leptostyla)*

This disease is caused by a fungus that produces brown, roughly circular patches on the leaves. Similar patches are found on the green husk which surrounds the young nut. The best way to control this disease is to collect and burn the leaves from infected trees as soon as they fall in autumn, thus destroying the fungus, and preventing reinfection of the new leaves in spring.

DISEASES AND PESTS : DIAGNOSIS TABLE
THE WALNUT
(It is chiefly young trees in the nursery that are attacked.)

DAMAGE	PROBABLE CAUSE
Branches and Stems	*Disease*
Fungus on unions between stocks and scions of grafted trees	Graft Disease
Foliage	*Pests*
Shoots and young leaves stunted and infested with aphides	Greenfly
Small swellings on leaves	*Eriophyes tristriatus*
Leaves torn and distorted, shoots stunted and may be killed	Common Green Capsid Bug
	Diseases
Small black spots; later long black markings on shoots and leaf-stalks	Bacterial Blight
Circular brown patches on leaves	Walnut Leaf Blotch
Fruit	*Pest*
Maggoty nuts	Codling Moth

Note.—Once the trouble has been diagnosed, the reader should refer to the paragraph dealing with the particular disease or pest.

VARIETIES

The following French varieties of the *Juglans regia* bear large nuts of excellent quality, and are at present under trial in this country : Franquette, Mayette, Meylanaise and Parisienne. The following English varieties are of first-rate quality : East Malling Nos. 95, 162, 202, 589, 719. The English varieties, Leeds Castle and Patching, grow in clusters and are specially valuable for pickling green early in July. All the varieties named above come into leaf comparatively late in the spring and should escape all but the most exceptionally late frosts.

WORCESTER BERRY

See under Hybrid Berries, page 204.

CHAPTER XIV

FRUIT UNDER GLASS

Fruit may be grown under glass, either planted in borders or in pots, in lean-to or span-roofed houses, the latter being the more suitable form of house for fruit-culture in pots, while some fruits, such as the melon, may be grown in frames.

THE BORDER

The border may be entirely in the house, all outside, or half in and half out. For early forcing, however, the whole border should be under glass.

A border 3 feet in depth will accommodate any kind of tree, and 3½ to 4 feet will be found quite wide enough for the first year. It may be made 18 inches to 2 feet wider each succeeding year, up to 12 to 15 feet in width, as the roots extend. This is a better plan than making the border the full width the first year, as by extending it annually new soil is supplied to the young roots, whereas if the whole border were made up together, the soil at the extreme edge would probably be stale by the time the roots reached it.

Drainage must be perfect and 9 to 12 inches of broken brick is usually rammed into the bottom of the border to ensure this.

Instructions for preparing the borders and composts to suit the various trees will be found in the following paragraphs on the cultivation of each particular fruit.

ASPECT AND SITE OF THE HOUSE

If the glasshouse is to be used for fruit, it should stand in full sunlight. Daylight and shelter from north winds are essentials.

The glasshouse may be built in either of two shapes : the span-roof, where the roof has two equal sized and equally sloping sides, or the lean-to, where the roof slopes down in one plane from one side, or from a wall. Span-roof houses are best placed with the gable ends north and south ; the light and heat from the sun can be better regulated in this way, and the houses require less attention. If one end of the house touches a wall, it should be the north end.

Lean-to houses are best and most economical when built with their highest side against a wall. This gives stability and cheapness together. Needless to say, the wall should not come on the sunny side of the house, or the latter will only be useful for shade-loving plants and ferns.

There is an intermediate form of roof known as the hip-span, which is built with one slope of the roof very much shorter than the other, and is very useful for building against a wall too low to support a lean-to. Lean-to and hip-roof houses can be built with any aspect from south to west, the east being not so good, the worst of all being north.

VENTILATION

Ventilation, from which temperature or heat cannot be divorced, is an art that can be acquired only through experience. Hardy fruits such as those referred to in this section will do well without any artificial heat. Success or failure in growing fruit under glass depends more frequently upon sound ventilation than upon any other factor. The plant will vitiate the air in a badly-ventilated house, just as a crowd of people will use up the air in a crowded room. The plant's vitality, the composition of its substance, and the functioning of its organs, are seriously affected by inadequate ventilation. Again, ventilation controls the atmospheric moisture in a glasshouse, and this in turn controls the transpiration of the plants. If the ventilation is inefficient, the atmosphere becomes saturated. The plant cannot get rid of its moisture and transpiration slows down. The young growth becomes soft and is susceptible to diseases, and wood grown under such conditions will never ripen, however the conditions may improve at a later period. Further, since ventilation and temperature are the two most important factors in the management of a glasshouse and cannot be dissociated from one another, they must be considered together and applied proportionally, always having regard to the plant, and to its condition and stage of development. Every glasshouse is to some degree a forcing house and a forcing temperature is merely a relative one. For example, we would start early peaches in a temperature of 45° to 50° F. We would ventilate the house at 50° as we are growing hard-wooded plants and the temperature must be kept low, air being given whenever it is possible. A temperature of 50° F. with ventilation during the period of growth to which we refer will produce the desired results ; while a temperature of 60° F. without air would prove fatal.

It is impossible to give a general rule that can be applied to the ventilation of all plants. The amount of air given must vary with the nature of the plant, the stage of growth and the season of the year. It is well to remember that it is extremely rare to find a crop that has been spoiled by excessive ventilation, while a hot, vitiated atmosphere in glasshouses is as common to-day as it used to be in a dwelling-house.

Except in very small houses, side ventilators are always desirable where hard-wooded plants are grown.

If the top ventilation is ample, side ventilation is of less importance, but it must be remembered that the air which escapes from the top of the house must be replaced from somewhere. The draught bogey exists largely in the imagination only.

The leaves of plants, both under glass and out of doors, though most frequently the former, are liable to become scorched, under certain conditions, just as if they had been held before a fire. Burning on vines is the result of a saturated atmosphere which has resulted from the transpiration of the plant during the night, in a closed house. The temperature of the atmosphere rises very rapidly with sunshine, while that of the leaves and shoots rises comparatively slowly. If the house remains closed, heavy condensation occurs on the cooler growth which, because of similar treatment previously, is probably soft and unhealthy. Burning and rotting will result. If the vines had been continuously and adequately ventilated, the growth would be healthy and resistant and would be unlikely to scorch should the house, on an odd occasion, remain shut too long, which should, of course, be carefully guarded against.

It is most important that the temperature of the house shall be carefully watched, especially in the morning, for the sun will often come out suddenly with surprising power, and unless the ventilation is regulated in time, the heat will very soon become intense.

In order to avoid the risk of scorching, the ventilators, in mild weather, should be opened early, beginning with a little opening, which is gradually increased as the sun becomes more powerful, and reversing the process gradually towards evening as the temperature falls.

TEMPERATURES OF THE HOUSES

It is not possible to give any definite figures for the temperature of the glasshouse. This must of necessity vary with the plants grown, and instructions in this matter will be found under the headings of the different plants. Glasshouses are, however, roughly divided into cold, cool, warm or intermediate, and hot houses,

361

and as a rough guide the following may be taken as the mean temperature:

COLD HOUSE	Summer	Day	. 55° to 60° F.
		Night	. 45° to 50° F.
	Winter	Day	. 45° to 50° F.
		Night	. 30° to 35° F.
COOL HOUSE	Summer	Day	. 60° to 65° F.
		Night	. 55° to 60° F.
	Winter	Day	. 55° to 65° F.
		Night	. 45° to 50° F.
(INTERMEDIATE) WARM HOUSE	Summer	Day	. 65° to 75° F.
		Night	. 60° to 70° F.
	Winter	Day	. 60° to 70° F.
		Night	. 55° to 65° F.
HOT HOUSE	Summer	Day	. 70° to 85° F.
		Night	. 65° to 75° F.
	Winter	Day	. 65° to 75° F.
		Night	. 60° to 70° F.

The temperature should never be allowed to fall below these lower figures in any of the artificially heated houses, and if in summer the temperature rises during the sunny part of the day, the house must at once be ventilated when the indicated maximum has been reached.

Overheating weakens the plants and encourages the incubation of numerous insect pests. As the cold house has little or no artificial heat, the temperature is apt to fluctuate, particularly in the winter.

THE UNHEATED OR COLD HOUSE

This house depends solely on the heat of the sun for its warmth. Thus its temperature varies enormously at different times of the year. It requires no artificial heat even in winter. It must, however, be remembered that glass of itself will not keep out frost and the plants grown in the cold house must necessarily be hardy and able to stand a few degrees of frost.

Much may be done by placing sacking and canvas over the glass to keep frost from the more tender plants and such hardy plants as bloom too early in the season to withstand the frost in the open.

362

VENTILATION

The cold house must have ample ventilation, but care must be taken to exclude all draughts. We should aim to get as much ventilation as possible, bearing in mind that the cold house contains half-hardy plants. The ventilators may be lowered with the falling of the sun and closed all night in really cold weather, but it must be remembered that in an unheated house, after a sunny day, condensation and stagnation may have a devastating influence on the plants.

The conservation of the heat of the day is a problem that must be studied with the greatest care, for faulty ventilation will cause the damping off of seedlings as well as the rotting of foliage. On warm summer nights, the ventilators should be kept open all night.

The great thing is to avoid extremes of temperature, especially in the spring. (See Ventilation, page 360.)

WATERING

Watering requires a good deal of care, and is best done in the morning. The foliage and atmosphere will then have time to dry somewhat before the cold night air can cause " damping-off." This applies especially to watering in autumn, winter, and spring ; in summer, the watering may be done in the evening.

In hot weather plants may be sprayed overhead and the paths and staging damped, as is usual in the warm house, but this should be done with caution and only in the hottest periods, for the majority of cold house subjects are not lovers of a damp and humid atmosphere.

SHADING FROM THE SUN

Shading is a difficult subject. Speaking generally, the less of it the better. The amount required depends largely upon the facilities available for keeping sufficient atmospheric moisture during the very sunny periods. If the house is efficiently ventilated and the ventilators are used to the best advantage, there are few plants that will not winter in a cold house, and that are not better without shading.

An unheated house should be provided with ample ventilation. Other things being equal, a plant which will not burn in the sun out of doors will not burn under glass, providing the atmosphere is not allowed to get too dry.

Actually, ordinary glass, to a certain degree, forms a barrier against the sun. It will neither burn nor blister the skin of a worker in a glass house.

If the weather is scorchingly hot, a very thin shade of whiting may be used to advantage, but this should be washed off immediately the wave has passed.

Blinds which can be let down during very bright sunshine and rolled up during dull weather, are to be preferred to any kind of permanent shading.

These blinds may also be pulled down as protection against frosts on winter nights.

A point to remember is that a plant that has been heavily shaded in the summer will winter badly.

TRAINING

Strong galvanized wire should be stretched along the roof, some 18 inches to 2 feet from the glass; it must not be closer or the foliage will be scorched by the sun, but wire can be fixed 12 to 15 inches at the front or sides of the house. The wires must be about 9 inches apart; and on these the trees will be trained.

FUMIGATION

Shut all ventilators, and cover with damp matting all broken or cracked lights and all roof ventilators which are likely to leak. Most gardeners will find the fumigating or vaporizing materials sold ready for use, with the necessary apparatus for burning, highly satisfactory; the makers give detailed instructions which should be closely followed.

Where the house is badly infested with any insect pest, it should be dealt with two or three times on successive evenings; this is almost always necessary when extirpating the red spider.

364

CHAPTER XV

FRUIT GROWING IN POTS

In certain conditions it may be impossible or inexpedient to grow the more delicate kinds of fruit trees in a suitable situation, against a wall. Where, for example, the garden is enclosed, not with walls, but with hedges, and where these hedges, for some reason of beauty or age, are required to be preserved, a difficult problem presents itself to the gardener who wishes to grow peaches, nectarines, apricots, or late pears, with the better kinds of dessert plum. Where a moderate supply of fruit only is required, and where there is some glass available, an excellent plan is that of growing the trees in pots, placing them in the open for a certain part of the year, and bringing them into the fruit-house in succession as they require shelter and warmth.

Pot trees, in a house, have the advantage over planted-out trees of providing a greater variety of fruit from a given space. A supply of apples, apricots, cherries, currants, figs, gooseberries, nectarines, peaches, pears, and plums, can be produced in one house, while strawberries of good quality can be grown on shelves where they can receive abundance of light, being introduced in March and removed outside as soon as the fruit has been gathered. Moreover, the trees in pots are portable and therefore can be removed whenever desired.

Success or failure with these trees depends entirely on the management, attention, potting, watering, syringing, top dressings, supplemented by concentrated or liquid manure, in order to sustain health and fertility. So that trees in pots entail more work than those planted out.

In a mixed house some fruits can be kept constantly in the house from the beginning of February—apricots, figs, nectarines and peaches ; while apples, pears, and plums, only need to be placed in the house to ensure the safety of the blossoms and young fruit from spring frost and can be given a favourable position out of doors from the beginning of June to the beginning of February, if desired. Currants, cherries, and gooseberries, come under the latter group of fruits, but these are best left in the house till after the fruit has been gathered. By removing those last mentioned, more light and air are admitted to the kinds first referred to.

FRUIT GROWING IN POTS

Early varieties of apricots, nectarines, and peaches, can be removed to a warm position outdoors as the trees are cleared of the fruit ; this allows space for any plums or other kinds which it may be desirable to return to the house for perfecting or preserving the fruit in unfavourable weather.

THE HOUSE

The best house for the purpose is one not less than 20 feet wide, and about 6 feet high at the sides, rising to 12 at the ridge. The " run " of the house does not very much matter, some people preferring a north to south house, others liking it to lie east and west. The latter is, perhaps, slightly preferable, as it exposes a smaller surface to the easterly winds, which are most prevalent when the fruit trees are in blossom. The doors should be in both ends, and should be double, allowing ample space for the entrance of the trees. All the sides of the house should be made to open panel-wise, as free ventilation, whatever the wind, may be necessary. Sufficient heating should be allowed to keep out frost in March and April, though, where the difficulties seem insuperable, this may be dispensed with. It has the advantage, however, of making the house far more generally useful, as it may then be used during winter for such things as chrysanthemums, while the trees are wintering outside. A floor of beaten ashes is the best.

SELECTING THE TREES

The trees selected for this purpose should preferably have been grown in pots from the time they were first budded or grafted, should be three or four years old, and must have a good show of fruit buds.

Varieties suitable for pot culture are :—

APPLES

Calville Blanche	Lady Sudeley	Patricia
Charles Ross	Laxton's Exquisite	Peasgood Nonsuch
Cox's Orange Pippin	Laxton's Fortune	Rev. W. Wilks
Ellison's Orange	Laxton's Premier	Wealthy
Irish Peach	Melba	White Transparent
James Grieve	Miller's Seedling	

APRICOTS

Blenheim	Hemstirk	Moorpark
Gros Peach	Kaisha	

FRUIT GROWING IN POTS

Varieties suitable for pot culture are :—

CHERRIES

Bigarreau Napoleon	Early Rivers	Governor Wood
Black Tartarian	Frogmore	May Duke

CURRANTS

Raby Castle (Red)	Laxton's No. 1	White Dutch (White)

FIGS

Brown Turkey	St. John	White Marseilles
Osborne Prolific		

GOOSEBERRIES

Broom Girl	Leveller	White Lion
Leader	Lord Derby	Whitesmith

NECTARINES

Early Rivers	Elruge	Lord Napier

PEACHES

Barrington	Hale's Early	Sea Eagle
Duke of Cornwall	Princess of Wales	Violette Hative
Duke of York	Royal George	

PEARS

Beurré Giffard	Doyenné d'Eté	Marie Louise
Citron des Carmes	Doyenné du Comice	Souvenir du Congres

PLUMS

Coe's Golden Drop	Early Transparent	Late Transparent Gage
Denniston's Superb	Jefferson	Reine Claude de Bavay

STRAWBERRIES

Dr. Hogg	Royal Sovereign	Sir Joseph Paxton
King George	Sir Douglas Haig	Waterloo

367

THE COMPOST

An important part of the process is the preparation of the compost in which the plants are to grow. This should be prepared in September, and have a clear month in the open, under cover, to amalgamate. It should be composed of a barrow-load of leaf-mould, one of coarse sand, one of old mortar rubbish, one of rotted manure, and five of yellow loam. This is further enriched by the addition of two gallons of bone-meal, and another gallon or so of some good fertilizer or vine manure. A bushel of quarter-inch bones is also mixed in the compost for drainage purposes.

REPOTTING

Every year, in about the middle of October, when the leaves commence to drop, the trees should be overhauled, as annual potting is not necessary. Healthy trees only need the removal of loose surface soil, also a little from the sides of the ball, with a pointed stick.

The trees should be taken out of their pots while the soil is fairly dry, so that their roots may be easily freed from it.

When a tree requires repotting, a strip of board is placed across a barrow, the tree is lifted out of its pot : the drainage crocks are loosened and fall back into the pot, which, with the crocks, is taken away to be washed and dried. The ball of roots and soil is then lifted on to the board, while the operator stands between the handles of the barrow with the head of the tree turned from him. The latter thus has free room, and there is less danger of injury either to shoots or bloom buds. The stem of the tree is held in the left hand, while with the right a short, pointed stick is used among the roots to loosen the soil as much as possible, taking great care not to break the root fibres.

The ball of roots should be shaken from time to time during this process.

When the roots are as free as possible from soil they should be carefully looked over, all woody and long fleshy roots being removed with clean cuts with a sharp knife, leaving all the useful fibrous ones untouched.

It is better, if anything, to err on the side of over-severity with the larger roots, as with strong growers such as pears and apples these long roots would soon take the tree beyond the possibility of pot culture.

The pots used should always be large enough to allow of the fibrous roots lying out horizontally in the soil, but so long as this is possible the smaller the pot the better. Pot-grown fruit trees ought never to exceed a sixteen-inch pot, and smaller sizes—the twelves and fourteens—are used extensively. While the trees are young, it will be usually found advisable to give a larger-sized pot each repotting, but with older trees this is seldom needed, the trees going back into a pot of the same size as before. Composts best suited to each kind of tree are given in the articles devoted to the culture of the individual plants.

All pots should, of course, be clean and dry, as should the crocks for drainage. A good layer of these latter is placed in the bottom of the pot, and covered with a little soil. The ball of the tree is set firmly in the centre and the upper two-thirds of the fibrous roots are held upwards with the left hand, while with the right compost is rammed down very firmly and evenly over the bottom third in the pot. A wooden rammer is used for this purpose. A few more roots are then laid out, and covered with firmly-rammed soil, and so on until the pot is almost full, a space of 2 inches being left at the top for future top-dressings.

WINTERING IN THE OPEN

The trees, when potted, should be watered well and plunged to the rims of the pots in ashes in the open. The pots being covered with a layer of litter from 6 to 10 inches in depth to exclude the frost.

This should be done not later than the first week in November, and if possible earlier by a fortnight.

They will then require little further care or attention until February, when they are moved into the house, except that in January they will need looking over, and the pruning of the pears and plums should be completed.

Before bringing in the trees, at the end of January, the orchard-house should be thoroughly cleaned, and the brick-work lime-washed.

MOVING INTO THE HOUSE

The peaches and nectarines should come into the house between February 1st and March 1st, and should be given the sunniest part of the house.

The exact date must be determined by the weather, and they should not be brought in whilst the ground is very wet, nor yet when there is hard frost. A time should be chosen when there is a spell of bright, open weather, fairly dry, and the trees brought in while it lasts.

If cherries are grown, they must be placed on the shady side. The various kinds of fruit should be grouped together in batches, and should not be placed piecemeal all over the house. The house need not be heated at all until the blossom appears, but ample fresh air is required for which the ventilating facilities of the house will be all called into play.

WATERING IN THE HOUSE

A watering with clean water is also needed occasionally. During the whole period of the indoor life of the trees, with the exception of the period in which the fruit is colouring, they should be syringed daily in all dull weather; twice daily, night and morning, on fine and sunny days, with rain-water. Early in the season only a little water is required, but as the hot weather comes on, watering must be more frequent—as often as four times a day in the middle of summer may be necessary.

FORCING

If heat is available, some of the trees can be forced: apples, cherries, pears and similar fruits may be taken into the house with a temperature of between 40° and 50° F. As little heat as possible should be used when forcing these fruits. Nectarines and peaches can endure a greater amount of heat than the fruits mentioned above, namely, 45° and 50° F.

FUMIGATION

When the blossoms of the peaches and nectarines in the house are showing pink, which is generally about the middle of March, and just about a couple of days before they open, the pears and plums are moved in. This is a good opportunity to fumigate the house, to destroy any young greenfly that there may be. These are destructive to the peach blossom.

Two successive nights should make the fumigation effective. (See also page 364.)

When the peach blossom is opening it is well to give a little heat at night, but only just sufficient to keep out possible frost. This night heat should be kept up until the fruit is set, or even, should the frosts still be hard at night, longer still. In damp weather, whilst the bloom is out, a very little heat during the day, also, will help to keep the air dry and assist the diffusion of the pollen. As soon as the fruit has set, a moister atmosphere is again necessary.

POLLINATION

The pollen question is an important one where indoor trees are concerned, owing to their isolation from insects and wind, and where an especially choice specimen or variety is being dealt with it is usually worth while to go round the trees with a small camel-hair brush or rabbit's tail and cross-pollinate by hand. Where, however, the blossom is abundant, as it usually is in orchard-houses, the best plan is to go round the house morning and afternoon and give the stem of each tree a sharp, firm blow with the side of the hand. This jerk will set the pollen flying, and is in all ordinary cases enough to secure a good supply of set fruit.

Pears, which have heavier, stickier pollen, will not fertilize in this simple way, and generally need attention with the camel-hair brush or rabbit's tail.

It is a good plan to put a plant or two of cytisus among the pear trees to attract bees, which will very materially help in the operation. Some fruit growers place a hive of bees in the house during the blossom season. This is a method worth adopting if a hive is available, but it should be removed during the time that any fumigating is being done ; it can be replaced later.

Between the setting of the fruit of the peaches and nectarines and the blossoming of the pears and plums, it is as well again to fumigate the house, the operation being of sufficient importance to warrant the removal of any precocious trees which may have broken a few blossoms into a neighbouring shed for the night whilst the smoking is in progress.

THINNING THE FRUIT

The next important step is the thinning, and this must be done with a stern hand, as almost every tree will have set far more fruit than it can possibly carry. The trees should be gone over as soon as the blossom drops, and at least two-thirds of the fruit taken out at once, leaving a final thinning to be done when the fruit has " stoned."

This last operation needs firmness again, or too much fruit will be left. Young trees should not be permitted to bear more than from ten to a dozen fruits.

PRUNING AND DISBUDDING

All fruit trees in pots need careful pruning. In the case of nectarines, peaches and plums, the main shoots are cut back by

371

about one half and laterals to within two or three buds of their base. Nectarines and peaches produce their fruit on the previous year's growth, which must therefore be preserved.

All unfruitful wood not needed for the extension of the tree should be cut out. When the young shoots have put out eight good leaves they should be pinched back to five while the shoot is still soft and immature. This will have the effect of checking the shoot only enough to throw all the buds into flower-buds except the last one, which will again shoot out, and should again be pinched back later on.

Plums are pinched back and pruned in much the same way, longer leaders and shorter side-shoots being left.

Apples, pears, cherries, currants and gooseberries are summer pruned (see pages 57 and 58) in July and August.

MANURING

When the young fruit on the trees is making good progress, the trees should be helped by feeding them. A rich compost is prepared consisting of a couple of barrow loads of turfy loam, one of well-rotted, rather sticky manure, and one of mortar rubble, pounded fine, the whole enriched with two gallons of bonemeal, and two gallons of fertilizer or vine manure. This compost is banked up round the trees to as much as three inches above the rim of the pot, being shaped and moulded with the fingers into a steep rim or dyke, steep on its outer side and sloping more gradually towards the stem, so as to afford a shallow basin or cup for watering. Between setting and stoning each tree is banked in this way with the compost, and as soon as the stoning is over weak liquid manure is used for watering instead of the plain water used before.

As much air and light as possible must be given while the fruit is ripening, and heavy fruits, as apples and pears, should be secured to the trees with bass or raffia. At this time it is essential to exclude wasps ; this may be done by placing close-meshed netting over the ventilators.

In the middle of September all the trees are moved out of the house on to a spare piece of ground, where they remain, plunged to the rim of the pots in ashes, until the overhauling or repotting again takes place. They must be shaded from the strong sun when first put out in the open, but after a week or so they will enjoy all the sun they can get. Watering must still be carefully attended to.

In securing a supply of plums, at least three times as many trees are grown as there is accommodation for in the house. One-third are taken in for blooming, while the rest are plunged in a spot sheltered alike from the east wind and the morning sun. When their fruit is three-quarters grown, that of the trees in the house is ripe, and the first lot come out, to give place to a set from outside. In this way three gatherings of plums is obtained, and the season much prolonged.

BRUISES

Care should be taken when working with tools among the branches of fruit trees, that the bark is not bruised or rubbed off by accident. Such bruises and grazes are very apt to give entry to the spores of one of the wound fungi, and canker may result, or, in the case of peaches, plums, and apricots, gumming may be caused.

Instead of repeating our remarks on heating, ventilation and the general management of the glasshouse, we refer the reader to the chapter dealing with Fruit Growing under Glass, where temperature, ventilation, and cultural requirements are discussed.

Full cultural details for all fruit grown in pots will be found in the paragraphs in the following section devoted to each particular fruit.

DISEASES AND PESTS IN THE GLASSHOUSE

Cleanliness is the most important factor in successful glasshouse work. Dead leaves and other rubbish harbour pests and diseases and, if allowed to remain, give rise to endless trouble. Fungus spores and small insects get into crevices in the timber and brickwork ; dirt and growths of green algæ accumulate on the glass, robbing the plants of valuable light. Every year, therefore, the glass should be washed, the bars scrubbed and the inside of the house thoroughly cleaned. For this soap and water have no equal, though, if the house be empty, it is wise to finish up by spraying the inside of the structure with cresylic acid or formalin.

A house that can be completely emptied periodically, if only once a year, is very much easier to keep clean than one that houses plants—particularly a mixture of various kinds—all the year round.

TREATMENT OF EMPTY HOUSES

In treating an empty house where disease has been prevalent, all benches, pipes and floors, as well as the glass, walls, and wood-work, should be well wetted with a 2 per cent. solution of formalin. It is advisable to start at the far end and finish at the door. The house should then be closed up for 24 hours and the temperature raised—to 70° F. if possible. It must then be freely ventilated until no smell of formalin remains. This may take two weeks or more, but is a wise precaution, for formalin fumes are fatal to many plants.

POTS, BOXES AND PANS

Pots, boxes and pans should be thoroughly cleaned before use. It is advisable to sterilize them, either by bringing them to the boil in water or by soaking in 2 per cent. formalin, not omitting to air them until no smell remains.

STERILIZATION OF SOIL

The sterilization of the soil of the glasshouse, so necessary for the profitable cultivation of fruits such as the tomato, is scarcely necessary for the hardier fruits that are dealt with in this volume. For pot work, however, it is advantageous to sterilize the soil, and this can readily be done either with steam or with formalin. A compost should never be sterilized as such, unless it is not required for a considerable time. Ingredients such as loam or turf should be sterilized beforehand and mixed with the other ingredients (lime, fertilizers, peat, etc.) afterwards. For steam sterilizing some form of apparatus is required in which the temperature of the soil can be raised to 180° F. and maintained there for 10–15 minutes. Many types, some electrically operated, are available, ranging from the large vertical steam boiler type down to a domestic copper.

The most elaborate precautions to ensure a clean house and clean soil can readily be brought to naught by failure to ensure that the plants brought inside are equally clean. Many of the pests that attack fruit trees and bushes out of doors can, if allowed to do so, become established in a glasshouse and give rise to a great deal of trouble. For this reason it is necessary to dip dormant trees and bushes in a tar-oil wash to prevent outbreaks of the various species of aphis, *Apple Sucker*, *Tortrix* caterpillars and the like, and in a petroleum wash to destroy *Capsid*, *Red Spider* and *Winter Moth* caterpillar. If both dips are given, the first should be allowed to dry on before the second is given. Potted strawberries should receive the warm water bath (see page 347).

PESTS

When formalin is used, one gallon of a 2 per cent. solution should be applied to each bushel of soil. This should then be covered for a couple of days and afterwards spread out to get rid of the gas.

Although many of the usual pests can be introduced into the glasshouse and there do immeasurably more damage than in their natural surroundings, there are some that are of special importance. Two species of *Red Spider* (*Oligonychus ulmi* and *Tetranychus telarius*) attack almost any fruit under glasshouse conditions, especially in an overdry atmosphere, and are difficult to eradicate. Winter cleaning and careful attention to material brought in should largely prevent attack ; fumigation with sulphur or naphthalene is a further help and, should spraying become necessary, the active stages can be killed with lime-sulphur or with Derris. A special grade of summer petroleum-oil emulsion is fatal to any stage, but the safe and successful use of this, and of lime-sulphur * too, depends largely on personal experience, and no satisfactory rules can be laid down. Various kinds of *Aphis* or greenfly may make their appearance and the Woolly Aphis can be especially troublesome. They are best dealt with by burning nicotine shreds. These usually contain about 15 per cent. nicotine and are sold with full instructions. *Woodlice* and *Earwigs* may cause annoyance. Again, nicotine fumes will be found useful. Woodlice can usually be overcome by putting down a bait composed of 1 oz. Paris Green and 1 lb. of Bran. The addition of a little dried blood increases the attractiveness of the bait. *Ants* are undesirable not only for their habit of encouraging greenfly but on account of their fondness for biting tender stems and petals. Their nests should be located and attacked with boiling water or petroleum emulsion or an emulsion of carbon bisulphide. Baits for ants are obtainable, but although sometimes very effective, are usually slow and uncertain in action. *White Fly* (*Trialeurodes vaporariorum*) is a well-known pest in glasshouses and has a wide range of host plants. The simplest way of dealing with it is to introduce the parasite *Encarsia*, which is now almost as well known as the Fly itself.

The *Mealy Bugs* and *Scale Insects* of the Vine, and those of peaches, nectarines and other fruit grown under glass, are not difficult to control if the attacks are taken in hand in good time.

* It should be noted that lime-sulphur has the effect of blackening wood-work that has been painted with a white-lead paint, but this objection does not apply to colloidal or to dispersible sulphur.

In the dormant season infested vine rods should be scraped, scrubbed with nicotine and soap solution, and sprayed with a tar-oil wash. At other seasons spraying with a petroleum-oil emulsion or with nicotine may be necessary. These pests are most easily introduced when other plants are brought in, such as potted ornamentals, and the need for care in this respect cannot be too strongly emphasized.

Thrips commonly attack leaves and flowers and can do much harm. They can usually be kept in check by spraying with water, but should more drastic action be needed a petroleum-oil emulsion or nicotine and soap will suffice.

Eelworms of various kinds infest the roots of some glasshouse plants. They are microscopic and can, as a rule, be diagnosed only by a specialist in such matters. With the possible exception of the Melon, the fruits dealt with in this volume are not likely to be affected. This is fortunate, for the soil-inhabiting eelworms can be destroyed only by the expensive method of steam sterilization.

DISEASES

Diseases are not usually prevalent in the glasshouse unless the ventilation is inadequate, when fungal *rots* (especially those caused by *Botrytis*) and *mildews* of various kinds may become troublesome. The best remedy is to pick off and burn all affected parts at an early stage, and to give as much air as possible at all times without risking damage by frost or cold winds.

It is best to avoid spraying with fungicides by such attention to good growth conditions, but where spraying is necessary, e.g., to control powdery mildews, colloidal or a dispersible sulphur is preferable to lime-sulphur.

Peach Leaf Curl is sometimes troublesome, especially where there is a draught near a door or a broken pane. Small branches and laterals can be removed and burnt, but where spraying is necessary, the trees should be treated as recommended for outdoor peaches and nectarines (see page 277), using Bordeaux Mixture or a colloidal copper preparation in preference to lime-sulphur.

CHAPTER XVI

THE CULTURE OF PARTICULAR FRUITS —UNDER GLASS

APPLES, PEARS, PLUMS, CURRANTS AND GOOSEBERRIES

These need no artificial heat and may all be successfully grown in the cold glasshouse, in the same way as described for the apricot. Cultural details are here unnecessary and the reader is referred to the chapter on Fruit Growing in Pots, page 365, and to the chapters devoted to the particular fruits.

APRICOT

The apricot will hardly bear forcing, and being more sensitive to heat than almost any of the half-hardy fruits, a confined atmosphere, or the slightest excess of heat, brings its blossoms off in showers, and so mars the prospect of fruit, so that it requires a cool house with plenty of ventilation. If planted in the border along a wall, fan-trained trees must be used, fastened to wires 6 inches apart. If the house is of sufficient height, standards or half-standard trees can be planted in the centre and sides of the house and excellent crops obtained. For pots, pyramid trees are best. Place these in 11-inch pots with good drainage, on this put a layer of half-inch bones, using a compost of three parts good turfy loam, torn into pieces the size of a walnut, one part of decayed horse manure, one part of old mortar rubble. Shorten the strong roots so that the tree can be placed in the pot, with uppermost roots one and half inches below the rim and the side roots one inch from the sides ; place some rough soil in first, ram it firmly with a stick, and press the soil well about the roots, which should be spread out evenly. Water at once, moistening the soil through to the drainage ; the pots can then be either plunged in ashes outside or stood in a cool house. The trees can be frequently syringed before and after the flowering period. During all the earlier stages of growth and until fruits have stoned, an artificial temperature of 45° F. should not be exceeded. After that stage the fruit will stand five degrees higher, but not more, for unless abundance of air is given, a temperature of, say, 55° F. may bring off the fruit. There must on no account be any closing of the house such as is practised for peaches or grapes. The apricot loves a warm day and a cool night. Attention must be given to watering and damping, an occasional syringing up to the time of the fruit changing colour is beneficial, it helps to keep away red spider, but when ripening commences, syringing should be discontinued. In dry weather damp the floor, borders, etc., instead. When the fruits are developing, an occasional watering with liquid manure will greatly assist the plants.

After the fruit has been gathered, the heat should gradually be reduced, then full air admitted regularly, and when the wood is ripe, give all the air possible for the trees planted out, and those in pots can be stood outside.

Packing and marketing are the same as for peaches and nectarines, while the pruning is similar.

DISEASES AND PESTS. (See pages 199 and 373)

VARIETIES SUITABLE FOR GROWING AS TRAINED TREES UNDER GLASS. (See page 366)

CHERRIES *(Prunus avium)*

Cherries may be grown planted permanently in a border in the cool house and trained as fans or as cordons, or they may be grown as bushes or pyramids in pots.

SOIL

This fruit thrives best in a compost of two-thirds loam and one-third old mortar rubble, wood ashes, bone-meal, and charcoal. Potting or planting should be done firmly in October, the roots being covered with at least 6 inches and not more than 9 inches of fine soil. Good drainage is essential, ample crocks should therefore be provided in the pots or, if planted out, the bottom of the border must be filled with some 9 inches of broken bricks well rammed in. After planting, give the trees a liberal watering.

TEMPERATURES

Only slight heat should be applied and that very gradually. Until the flowers open, the thermometer should not be allowed to drop below 40° F. at night, but it must not rise above 50° to 55° F. by day. Once the fruit has set the temperature may be allowed to rise to between 45° and 50° F. by night, and 55° to 60° F. by day.

Ventilation is all-important, give a free circulation of air whenever the weather outside will permit, but do not allow sudden drops and rises in the temperature.

POLLINATION

When the flowers are out, dust them over daily about noon, when the air is driest, with a rabbit's tail to ensure good pollination; this is an important point. (See page 371.) While the fruit is setting, syringe the trees twice daily in fine weather, and keep a good look out for insect pests.

As soon as the fruit has set, the trees may be assisted by the application of diluted farmyard manure or soot water. This may be varied by guano or a compound fruit manure.

When applying manure, it is important not to use it when the soil is dry. If dry, the plants should be first watered with clear water; this applies to all plants, especially to pot-grown subjects.

SUMMER PRUNING

Young shoots should be pinched back to five or six leaves to encourage good fruiting spurs, the laterals being again shortened to three or four buds in October.

The cherry easily forms fruiting spurs, and when the tree has a sufficient number of these to ensure a good but not exhaustive crop, it should be left alone, and the knife used as little as possible.

REPOTTING AND WINTERING

Once the fruit has been gathered, all possible air should be afforded the trees, those in pots being stood out in the open, in the sun, on a hard ash floor. As soon as the wood begins to ripen up, repotting should be commenced. The pots are then plunged to the rim in ashes and wintered in the open.

DISEASES AND PESTS

See Cherries in the open, page 205, and Fruit Growing in Pots, page 365.

CHERRIES—VARIETIES SUITABLE FOR GROWING UNDER GLASS

Variety	Season	Colour	Variety	Season	Colour
Early Rivers	Early	Black	Roundel	Mid	Black
Elton	Early	White	Bradbourne Black	Late	Black
Ronald's Late Duke	Late	Red	Bigarreau Mezel	Late	White
Noble	Late	Black	Reine Hortense	Early	Red
Royal Duke	Mid	Red	Impératrice Eugénie	Early	Red
May Duke	Early	Red	Triaux	Mid	Red
Bigarreau Napoleon	Late	White	Waterloo	Mid	Black

FIG (*Ficus carica*)

The fig is an excellent fruit for forcing, and very easy to grow, and under glass most varieties will easily produce two or three good crops in the year. The first crop is borne on the shoots of the previous year, the second on the growth of the current year, and the third on the sub-laterals which spring from the current year's shoots. The third crop, however, unless the plants are in expert hands and are started very early, is rarely of much value, and to avoid unduly weakening the plants, amateur growers usually prefer to pick this off before it develops. When doing this, however, care must be taken to remove only those fruits that would partially develop and would not remain dormant through the winter ; the smaller fruits towards the points of shoots must on no account be removed, as these produce the first crop of fruit for the following year. A clever grower will get his third crop off every time. Success depends largely upon starting the trees sufficiently early, correct practice and perfectly matured wood. To get three crops of figs, the first crop must be ripe in May, and for such early work the plants must be started early in December and are more easily controlled in pots. Plants started in January will yield their first crop in June, the second in August, and the third crop is then too late to be of much value and is best treated as described above. A temperature of from 75° F. to 80° F. during the day is necessary and it must not be allowed to fall below 60° F. at night. Any form of house is suitable for forcing figs, but if the figs are to be grown in pots, the span-roofed house will be found the most suitable. Ample light is essential.

COMPOST AND PLANTING

Figs are usually propagated by means of cuttings, taken from one-year-old wood, 4 to 6 inches long and inserted in pots in September, but the amateur may prefer to buy his plants from the nurseryman. They should be bought in 6- to 8-inch pots already shaped as bushes or fan-trained trees. As figs are very vigorous growers and " gross " feeders, the roots must be confined or the plants will run to wood and produce little fruit. Small pots should therefore be used and the plants remain in the pots and not be planted out in the glasshouse border.

Good drainage is essential and the compost should consist of fairly rich fibrous loam, broken mortar rubble, and burnt earth. The addition of a little lime every second or third year is very helpful.

WATERING

Until the plants break into active growth, but little moisture is required, but once moving, ample moisture must never be lacking, even in winter, or the fruit will shrivel up and drop. During the ripening periods, the water must be withheld somewhat or the fruit may crack. If this happens, ventilation should be more freely given and the floor of the house be sprinkled instead of the foliage being syringed.

PRUNING

Fig trees planted under glass may be trained as fans as described on pages 75 and 76, allowing ample room between the fan ribs for training in new fruit-bearing shoots.

Pruning appears much more simple if one keeps in mind the fact that the spring crop of fruit develops from the tiny fruit that have remained dormant on the young wood during the previous winter, and that the second crop comes on the young shoots which grow while the spring crop is maturing. The third crop comes on a young shoot which grows while the second crop is maturing. This is the shoot which carries at the point the dormant fruit which forms the spring crop. Care must be taken not to cut these points back, and so reduce the spring crop in the following year. For this reason the points of these shoots must not be cut off, but as soon as it is possible to decide which fruit forming the third crop will ripen, and which are sufficiently undeveloped to remain dormant, say, the size of large peas, the intervening fruit which will be too late to ripen and too far advanced to remain dormant should be picked off. Having decided upon the shoots that may, with ample room, be left for fruit production, the remainder may be removed by disbudding, and the fruiting shoots should be stopped beyond the fruit.

THINNING

As soon as the fruits are the size of a pea, they should be thinned out so that, on an average, not more than three remain on each shoot. Once the fruit commences to ripen, syringing should be discontinued and more ventilation given. About nine weeks after the first crop has been gathered, the second should be nearly ripe.

GATHERING

The fruit is gathered as it ripens for dessert, or if for market, just before it is ripe. Choice selected early fruits are sent up in small wicker "handles" containing four figs. The later crop is marketed in trays containing a dozen or in boxes holding up to four dozen figs. Early fruit is always the most profitable.

REPOTTING AND WINTERING

After all the fruit has been gathered, fruit grown in pots should be taken out and stood in the open on a bed of hard ashes. When the leaves begin to turn in colour, the trees should be repotted, if necessary, and before the frosts become severe the pots should be plunged to the rim in ashes and then covered with 6 to 9 inches of litter to exclude all frost. Where the trees are planted permanently in the borders in the house, as free a circulation of air as possible should be given, except when there is danger from frost ; never give such ventilation as to cause the temperature to drop suddenly.

For Diseases and Pests and Varieties, see page 246.

DISEASES AND PESTS : DIAGNOSIS TABLE

THE FIG (Under Glass)

DAMAGE CAUSED	PROBABLE CAUSE
Branches and Twigs	*Pests*
White, mealy-looking patches	Mealy Bug
Encrusted with scale-like formation	Scale
	Fungus
Twigs die off, patches and cracks in bark, red dot-like fungus	Canker
Foliage	*Pests*
White, mealy-looking patches	Mealy Bug
Leaves turn yellow, then silvery, falling early	Red Spider
Wilt and curl, infested with whitish fly	White Fly
Blossom	*Pests*
Injured and infested with blackish-grey insects	Thrips
Fruit	*Pests*
Damaged	Ants
Eaten	Wasps
Stolen	Mice

GRAPE *(Vitis vinifera)*

The grape is said to be a native of Asia Minor, particularly of the country to the south of the Caucasus and of the Caspian Sea. The introduction of the grape into this country is generally credited to the Romans, during the reign of the Emperor Augustus about 10 A.D. It is certainly one of the oldest of domesticated fruits, and it is a well-known fact that the food values of fresh grapes and fresh figs, reckoned in calories, are higher than those of any other of the fruits cultivated generally in northern climes.

382

By careful selection of suitable varieties, grapes of a high quality may be grown in glasshouses of the simplest construction. In suitable situations really excellent grapes can in most seasons be obtained without any artificial heat at all, though, of course, where this is available, much better results may be counted on.

FORM OF HOUSE

The best form of house is in general that known as the lean-to, providing that a wall facing south is to be had. For a cool vinery much is to be said in favour of a three-quarter-span against a south wall. Otherwise a span-roof house must be used, in which case the house should run from north to south, so as to obtain the maximum amount of sunshine. The situation chosen should be a high one, so that there may be no possibility of stagnant water in the borders. Where artificial heat is provided it is desirable to have much more piping than is usually afforded, since thus it is unnecessary to heat the pipes to excess in order to get the average temperature to the required degree.

The requirements of the grape vine, however, are such that it is not possible to grow it successfully in a glasshouse with numerous other plants. Only those plants which are grown out of doors in summer and need little heat in winter, such as the Chrysanthemum, should be kept in the vinery.

SOIL AND SITE

The border in which the vines are to be planted should be dug out to a depth of from $2\frac{1}{2}$ to 3 feet, because although the vine is not very particular as to soil, it is very particular as to drainage. The borders should, where space is available, be about 10 feet wide. Still, where choice can be had, there is no doubt that the grape vine thrives best when the sub-soil is of chalk or limestone.

A suitable compost is composed of five parts of turfy loam, one part wood-ash charcoal and burnt garden refuse, one part stable manure, one part of old mortar rubble and broken brick and about 1 lb. of broken-up bones added to every barrow load. The soil should be thoroughly mixed and trodden firm before planting.

In the case of quite small houses a narrow border about 2 feet wide may be constructed on lines similar to those suggested immediately within the front wall of the house. In this border the vines are to be planted, and their roots should be able to make their way into a wide, similarly-prepared border outside. In the case of wide, span-roofed houses, beds may be prepared on similar lines anywhere within the house.

PLANTING

The vines are best planted 3 to 4 feet apart, if grown as single stems, 1½ to 2 feet from the front wall, and about 1 inch deeper in the soil than the old planting mark. A good time to plant indoors is early in January, when the canes should be cut back to about 18 inches long. As vines for planting are usually purchased in pots, they should, before planting, be washed free of all soil. This allows the roots to be spread out evenly. The extent to which they should be shortened depends upon the height of the glass in front of the house. It is best to cut back to ripe wood. Choose a time when the soil is not too adhesive. See that the soil is carefully filled in amongst the roots, and cover the surface roots with about 4 inches of soil ; then tread the plant in. If the vines are planted in the front of the house they have a clear run up the wall and then up the slope of the roof to the back.

An eye struck in the spring will be well developed in a 6-inch pot to go out in the late autumn. Or it may be transferred into a 10-inch pot and carried over for planting in the following year. They should not remain in the pot sufficiently long for the roots to become matted. At the same time, the ball of earth should, when carefully removed from its pot, remain practically coherent until slightly squeezed by the hand. This should be done at the moment of planting, in order to break up the soil about the roots a little and so bring about a more ready extension of the rootlets into the adjacent soil. Before removing the plants from the pots, holes should be dug at the required intervals, ready to receive them. The surface of the ground should be covered with about 3 inches of short manure as soon as planting has taken place. Although the soil should be well broken up it should be made firm as soon as the plants are in position.

TRAINING, PRUNING AND DISBUDDING

During the first year, the main shoot only should be allowed to grow to its full length. Side shoots may be run out to 2 feet to encourage root action ; they should then be stopped. These side shoots will be cut off in the winter pruning. The leading shoot, if the vine is well grown, will reach the top of the house during the second year, and at the winter pruning it should be cut back to a point where it is well developed, and the wood is ripe and hard. This will be at about 6 to 8 feet from the ground. The following year's leader will ripen to the top of the house, where

PRUNING AND TRAINING THE GRAPE VINE.

1. A vine spur before pruning. 2. After pruning. 3. A vinery cleared and pruned in readiness for starting, and showing the tops of the vines bent down to ensure an even flow of sap.

—after thinning.

Grape : " Black Hamburgh."

Bunch before thinning and—

it may be cut back and definitely stopped on the top wire. After the first year of growth, side shoots are allowed to form on the wood that has been cut back the previous winter; these laterals are pruned to one bud from the base to form spurs. When the main shoot is sufficiently strong and has reached the top of the house, no young growth is allowed to form at the top of the main stem, but is rubbed off to promote vigour in the fruiting spurs below; these are annually cut back to one bud shooting outwards. Only one shoot is desired from each of these spurs, therefore, when the young shoots push out in spring, the most vigorous one only is retained, the others being pinched off. The inexperienced gardener, however, should wait until the small bunches of fruit are visible on these shoots; then he should select the best bunch and discard all the other shoots. When a rod has not been fruiting well, it is a good plan to train in another shoot from the bottom to take its place, the old rod being cut out when the young growth has reached the

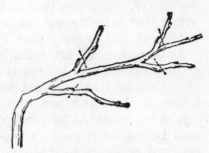

PRUNING THE GRAPE VINE.

In winter, prune the side shoots made the previous summer to within one bud (shooting outwards) of the base. Cut back the main shoot annually to about 2 feet from the start of the current year's growth.

top of the house. The young shoot should be cut back to hard, ripe wood and then be treated as advised for the young vine.

The above method of training is applicable when several vines are grown in one house. Where only one vine is planted, instead of training one shoot to run vertically up the glass, two shoots are grown horizontally, running in opposite directions to each other, and are pruned as for the single vertical stem. Laterals are allowed to form from the upper side of these stems and are trained vertically upwards at intervals of 3 to 4 feet, these eventually being pruned and trained as for the single main shoot. The vines should be tied to wires, fixed 9 inches apart, and kept 18 inches from the roof-glass. The rods frequently produce shoots from their tops before any young growth has formed near the base. To encourage this lower growth, the rods must be unfastened from the wires and should have their heads bent down towards the ground. This will arrest the flow of sap and young growth will soon form at the base. When the laterals all up the rod are in an even state of growth, the rods may again be tied to the wires in an upright position. Vines should not be allowed to bear grapes the first year. If the vine is a strong one, a few bunches of fruit may be taken off during the second year, but not until the third season should anything like a crop be allowed to mature. At this time each lateral may be permitted to carry one bunch.

The rule against overcropping must be rigidly enforced. Flavour, size and colour will be sacrificed if the vine is overloaded. There is no known cultural practice that will adjust the balance. The weight of fruit that a vine will mature to perfection varies with the variety. Generally the less fine flavoured will colour the greatest weight, but in such cases the result is to make what a connoisseur would call bad, worse. (See Thinning, page 388.)

As an unlimited extension is undesirable, when a lateral has produced two leaves beyond the bunch, the end should be nipped off. Laterals that have not borne fruit should be left the same length as those that are fruiting. Sub-laterals that result from this stopping should be pinched back to one leaf. After fruiting each lateral is cut back to one-half its length when the bunch is cut, and in winter to the basal bud close to the main rod. The next spring three or more laterals will shoot from this bud, and the strongest of these should be retained for fruiting, while the others must be pinched off so that the shoot bearing the grapes may be as vigorous as possible.

TEMPERATURES

Newly-planted vines should be allowed to become well established before any unnecessary heat is employed, but it is only in an exceptionally good summer that well-ripened wood can be obtained without some fire-heat. The economy of fuel is not worth the loss of time. Indeed, the best results can never be obtained in an unheated house. The finish of a grape, its flavour and colour, provided the vines are properly grown and not overcropped, depend upon warmth and sun. Choice grapes such as *Cannon Hall* and *Muscat of Alexandria* are not worth growing without fire-heat. Temperatures must vary with the requirement of the variety growing. *Hamburgh* and *Muscat*, for example, started in January in a temperature of 50° to 55° F., with the increase that the sun, as the season advances, will give, will progress together through the increased night temperature of 60° with the day temperature of 70° until just before the bunches come into flavour. Then, however, the difference in the variety begins to assert itself. The *Muscat* prefers a temperature 10° higher than the *Hamburgh* after this, and must be indulged to that extent if the crop is to approach perfection. Another example may be taken from late *Colmar*. For winter grapes *Colmar* may be allowed to start with the weather in an unheated house, but the period without artificial heat is very short. The grapes must be ripe by the first of October. After that time there is not sufficient sun to complete the ripening and the grapes will not keep if not ripe. It is quite possible to get a good berry even though the fire-heat has been stinted, and with the aid of a few chilly nights some colour may be obtained, but grapes are not eaten for the sake of their appearance, although because of their appearance, sometimes they are not eaten.

When the fruit is required in July or August, the temperature may be raised to a minimum of about 55° F. early in March, and from the middle of April onward, the temperature from sun-heat alone may be allowed to rise to 70° to 75° F., a night temperature of about 55° F. being afforded. From the time the young leaves are fairly developed until the grapes are in flower, a night temperature of 55° to 60° F. should be given.

When grapes are in bloom, the night temperature should not fall below 60° F. In the case of *Muscats*, not below 70° F. Some very successful growers maintain 80° F. at night during the setting period of *Cannon Hall Muscats*. It is the practice in some nurseries to fertilize this last-mentioned grape with a rabbit's tail. We have never found artificial pollination necessary at any time. The trouble with most grapes is that they set too freely. Those varieties that are shy will set as much fruit as they will carry if the borders are sufficiently wet and a reasonable amount of atmospheric moisture is maintained. A dry house and a dry atmosphere are inimical to vines in bloom.

The two most necessary factors making for successful grape culture are moisture and ventilation. The air in the house must be fresh and sparkling—what is known as "buoyant" among grape growers—and this can be secured only by efficient ventilation and by keeping the soil moist and by syringing the foliage frequently as soon as growth starts and until the flowers open. The house should be well ventilated at all times, but especially when the sun is shining brightly, since otherwise the berries may be scalded and the leaves scorched.

Ventilation should always be started just before the sun rises, and should be increased as the temperature rises, until noon. With the setting of the sun and with an eye on the temperature the ventilation should be diminished, and the house should be finally closed just before the maximum evening temperature is reached. During very hot weather, and when the grapes are beginning to colour, a little top ventilation should be afforded at night. Should the weather be cold and dull while the grapes are ripening, heat should be given, but ventilation should be provided. Except when the grapes are colouring, when the heat must be somewhat reduced and more air given, the floor and walls should be freely damped during the hot weather. When the grapes are colouring, however, a good damping twice a week is sufficient. As soon as the grapes are well coloured, more ventilation may be given and the heat must be reduced to the minimum.

The different varieties of grape vary in the amount of heat they require. The *Muscat of Alexandria*—a finely-flavoured yellow fruit—needs the highest temperature of all. As soon as the crop has been gathered, the heat should be reduced to that degree which will ensure the frost being kept out, ample ventilation being given.

As the laterals grow, they must be gradually bent down, a little at a time, before they touch the glass, and should be first loosely tied to the wires with raffia, being later more securely fixed when the wood has toughened and they have become more used to the position. Great care must be exercised when the loose tie is put on because a shoot will tie down with perfect safety when the sun is shining, but the cool of the night will stiffen the shoot and it will break off hours after it was tied down. The shoots must be evenly distributed over the wires so that each receives ample sun and air. Water when the vines are " starting," shortly before the flowers open, while the fruit is stoning, liberally while the grapes are swelling, and after the fruit has been harvested.

THINNING

As soon as the bunches have set their berries, it should be decided how many bunches are to be left, and how many grapes on each bunch. It has been estimated that each foot of rod of a well-matured vine should bear about 1 lb. weight of grapes. Thus a fully-established vine about 20 feet long, of such a variety as *Muscat of Alexandria* or *Black Hamburgh*, should not be allowed to bear more than about twenty bunches, averaging 1 lb. a bunch, whilst of such varieties as *Trebbiano* or *Grosse Guillaume* not more than sixteen bunches, each averaging $1\frac{1}{4}$ lb. in weight, are as much as it should be permitted to hold. No lateral should be allowed to carry more than one bunch, and the bunches retained should

388

be compact and neat in form, not long, straggling ones. Surplus bunches should be removed as early as possible, and on the bunches that are allowed to remain the grapes should be thinned out at an early stage, so as to make shapely bunches.

Grape thinning is an art which is quickly acquired, but hard and fast rules, particularly as to spacing, cannot be set down on paper. Even if the size of the berry were accepted as a guide for spacing, the ultimate issue is affected by the long or short shank varieties. *Colmar* gives a big berry, has a short shank, and requires double the space that should be given to *Alicante*, which is a smaller berry but a thicker setter. *Alexandria*, on the other hand, with a berry of size about midway between the former two, has a long shank and an oblong berry. Neither *Colmar* nor *Alicante* can be used for comparison in such a case. The thinner must thin with the facts and peculiarities in mind, otherwise the muscats will be flappy, shapeless bunches. It is a good plan to get on to a few of the earliest bunches in good time and so accustom the eye to the results. Generally, terminal berries should be retained, shoulders must be left well-furnished and the whole of the thinning done within the frame of the bunch. The centre especially should be thinned. Failure to thin the bunches sufficiently will result in flattened berries in the centre of bunches when ripe. This occurs particularly in the case of *Colmar*. On the other hand, over-thinning will result in slack bunches of mature fruit. Experience will soon teach the grower how to secure the desired result. Grape-thinning scissors and a forked stick some 10 inches long to separate the grapes should be used, as on no account must the grapes be touched by the hand. Care must be taken not to injure the grapes.

SUPPORTING THE " SHOULDERS "

With some varieties that produce large, heavy berries it is necessary to support the top two branches with raffia looped to the wires ; this relieves the pressure on the lower fruit and should be done before the berries become very heavy. For market work, bunches of this type and size are seldom required and it is the usual practice at the time of thinning to cut off such shoulders as would require support, with the object of reducing the weight of the bunch. Varieties bearing smaller and lighter berries are better without this support. After thinning has been completed, the border should be dressed with a layer of farmyard manure 2 to 3 inches in thickness, or with a dressing of any good fertilizer, since farmyard manure is difficult to obtain.

FRUIT CULTURE UNDER GLASS

PROPAGATION

The grape vine is grown on its own roots, as is the case with the majority of soft fruits, and may be propagated either from buds or dormant cuttings in January. The amateur, however, is advised to leave this work to the professional, since better results are obtained when a vine is bought in autumn or winter.

To propagate, several eyes or buds, that is, short pieces of the previous year's side growth some 2 inches in length, each with one good bud upon it, and having a slanting cut ½ an inch long directly under the bud, are planted in January horizontally with the bud just above the soil in small pots, in a compost consisting of loam with one third leaf-mould and a liberal addition of sand. The pots are placed in a mild hot-bed and the soil is kept moist and shaded. The eyes start growth quickly under these conditions, and should then be moved to a cooler, but light position. As soon as the roots have well filled the pot, the plants should be repotted singly into 6-inch pots. As the vines grow, they must be carefully staked, and by midsummer the plants will be about 6 feet in height. They should be moved into 8-inch pots, then again into 10-inch pots, being kept in the open from September to November, and planted in the house in January.

INARCHING OF VINES

This is a process whereby new and vigorous shoots may be grafted on to an old and perhaps useless vine. Two growing shoots in close proximity (the plant bearing the scion or graft is usually potted-up and stood close to the stock on which it is to be grafted) are selected and a thin strip, some 3 inches long, is cut away from the stems of each shoot. The shoots are then bound firmly together with raffia or soft cloth so that the cut surfaces come into contact and so that the outer side or bark of one shoot coincides with that of the other stem ; on both sides if the shoots are of similar diameter, or on one side at any rate should there be a difference in the thickness of the stems. Cover the graft thickly with clay or grafting wax to exclude the air. The union should be complete in six weeks or so, when the portions of the old vine above the graft may be cut back. When the graft is quite firm, usually the following autumn, it may be severed from its mother vine and will in future be supported by the roots of the formerly useless vine. Inarching is best carried out when the vines are in vigorous growth.

390

BOTTLE-GRAFTING

Bottle-grafting is similar in its principles to inarching, but does not necessitate having the root bearing the graft or scion in close proximity to the stock. Bottle-grafting is most successful if effected when the vine is just coming into growth. The graft must be cut from its parent in the previous autumn and should be stored buried to half its depth in earth in a cold, but frost-proof position. A few days before the operation is to be effected, that is, when the vine breaks into growth, place the graft in the vinery so that both graft and stock may assume the same state of growth. The stems are grafted together as described under inarching, but the lower end of the graft is placed in a bottle of rain water, so suspended that its weight shall not be borne by the graft. The bottle must not be removed until the graft is finally established and has grown to a fair length.

STORING GRAPES (See Storing Fruit, page 115)

CUTTING, GRADING AND PACKING

Ripe bunches of grapes only should be cut, one at a time, as they become ready, cutting with each bunch (except in the case of early *Hamburghs*) 2 to 3 inches of the lateral from which the stalk springs. In the case of early *Hamburghs*, however, this seems detrimental to the subsequent development of the vine, and the main stalk itself should be cut close to the lateral, without injuring the latter. Each bunch must be carefully examined and any imperfect or diseased berries snipped out. The bunch is then graded direct into its prepared package for market. These packages (see Marketing) are usually ready padded and papered and placed on a movable stand in the vine-house. In grading, the size and shape of the bunch are important points, also the colour and size of the grapes themselves, and the general quality of the fruit. Some black grapes, such as *Alicante*, must be quite black when ready; the others, such as *Hamburghs* and *Colmar*, show reddish tints when fully ripe. They are usually graded as : " Extra Selected " (symmetrically-shaped bunches of 1 lb. or over of fully-coloured, even-shaped, large-sized berries) ; " Selected " (symmetrically-shaped bunches of ¾ lb. or over of good-sized, uniformly-mature berries) ; and " Medium " (bunches of ½ lb. or more of sound, ripe grapes). Great skill and care is necessary in packing. All packages should be carefully padded with wood wool and lined with tissue. (White in the case of black grapes, and pink for other kinds.) Some growers send the fruit to market in shallow baskets, unpadded, the bunches being secured in position by means of string, 8 to 10 lb. in a basket. The grapes must be comfortably tight in their baskets and not be allowed to shake about. Muscats are frequently sent up two or three bunches in a handled basket.

MARKETING

Grapes are sent to market chiefly in returnable flat baskets, containing a shallow tray and oval cross-handle baskets (Nos. 6, 8, 10 and 12). A package that has gained favour in recent years is the " Climax " chip basket (non-returnable), with curved ends, and this is to be recommended especially when sending up a few early " Selected " bunches. All packages should be clearly marked " GRAPES " and labelled with full details.

GRAPES
Indoor Varieties

Name	Colour	Size	Season	Qualities
*Black Alicante (Mixed vinery)	Black	Large, oval	Late October to March	Of good flavour if lightly cropped, otherwise much inferior to Colmar
*Black Hamburgh (Hot or cool house)	Black	Large, roundish	May–November	Vigorous and productive. Excellent flavour. Forces well For Pots
Buckland Sweetwater (Mixed vinery)	Amber	Large, round	Early	Does not keep well. Must be started early. Cool house
*Cannon Hall Muscat (Hot house)	White	Very large, good	Later than Alexandria	Excellent flavour. For Pot culture
Foster's White Seedling (Cool house)	White	Large, round	May–November	Vigorous and productive. Inferior flavour to Muscat of Alexandria. Cool house
Gros Colmar (Warm house)	Black	Large, round	Late August to February	Poor flavour. Very sweet, requires heat to finish
Gros Maroc (Warm house)	Black	Large, round, oval	Late	Vigorous and productive. Showy fruit but poor flavour. Flavour like that of a sloe
Lady Downes (Mixed vinery)	Black	Large, roundish-oval	Late	Keeps well
Mrs. Pearson	White	Good	Late	Excellent flavour
*Muscat of Alexandria (Hot house)	Amber	Large, oval	Early and Late	Superior flavour, but requires more heat than Black Hamburgh, etc. For Pot culture

* Best grapes to grow for market.

DISEASES AND PESTS

The chief insect pests of the vine are the mealy bug, red spider, and thrips. As these are mainly glasshouse pests the reader is referred for their control to the section on Diseases and Pests in the Glasshouse, page 373.

POWDERY MILDEW (Uncinula necator)

This is the most common fungus disease of indoor and outdoor vines in this country. Its chief characteristic, like that of the powdery mildews as a class, is the presence of a white, mealy fungus growth over affected leaves, shoots, flowers, and fruits. The disease is common in heated vineries in spring, when equable ventilation is difficult, and the vines are making quick growth. Sometimes over-dryness of the roots will induce mildew, both in indoor and outdoor vines.

Control.—The disease can usually be avoided on indoor vines by adequate moisture and ventilation. Dusting with sulphur powder or spraying with a colloidal or dispersible sulphur preparation will check infection.

SHANKING *(functional)* is common in overcropped or underfed grapes : in fact, among all those that are waterlogged or improperly grown in some way. The fruit develops well for a time, when the stalk begins to shrivel and becomes discoloured, while the berries themselves shrink up and grow sour and uneatable. Thorough remaking and enrichment of the vine border, together with the avoidance of overcropping, will get rid of the tendency.

For Crown Gall, see page 169.

DISEASES AND PESTS : DIAGNOSIS TABLE

GRAPES

Symptoms	Probable Cause
Branches and Twigs	*Pests*
White, mealy patches	Mealy Bug
Scales on bark	Scale Insects
Foliage	
White, mealy patches	Mealy Bug
Leaves turn yellow, then silvery-grey and fall early	Red Spider
Spotted, infested with small, blackish or yellow insects	Thrips
Leaves infested with whitish fly	White Fly
Patches eaten out of leaves	Vine Weevil
Leaves spun together, eaten by caterpillars	Tortrix Moths
	Fungi
White, mealy mould	Grape Powdery Mildew
Buds and Young Shoots	*Fungi*
White, mealy mould	Grape Powdery Mildew
Blossom	*Pests*
Infested with small, blackish or yellow insects	Thrips
	Fungi
White, mealy mould	Grape Powdery Mildew
Fruit	
White mealiness	Mealy Bug
White mealy mould	Grape Powdery Mildew
Berries, shrivel	Shanking

393

MELON *(Cucumis Melo)*

The melon, which is closely related to the cucumber, is said to be a native of the milder parts of Asia. It was originally introduced into this country from Jamaica in 1570, and has long been cultivated under glass. *C. Melo*, at one time known as the Musk Melon, is quite a different variety from *C. Citrullus*, the Water Melon, so largely imported from abroad. The latter's cultivation is rarely attempted here.

The home-produced melon is much superior to its imported rival, possessing a far better flavour. It is distinguished from the imported melon by its skin, which may be either green or yellow.

Melons are best grown in houses heated by hot-water pipes. But in most gardens, frame culture will necessarily be resorted to, and in frames, carefully managed, melons of the highest quality can undoubtedly be grown. The cultivation is somewhat similar to that of the cucumber, but it should be remembered that, whereas the cucumber is picked in the green stage, the melon is of value only when it is fully ripened. Consequently, a high temperature is needed, and it is hopeless to attempt to ripen the melon after the month of October. A firmer soil and less water are needed in the case of the melon than in the case of the cucumber. Also, a stronger light and more air are necessary for the successful growing of the former. Stiff loam, with an admixture of a little old mortar rubble, makes an excellent compost.

PREPARING THE BED

Not less than a two-light frame should be employed, and a three-light frame is to be preferred, as it is easier to maintain an even heat with a larger body of fermenting material. For a three-light frame six loads of farmyard manure should be laid in a heap, and turned two or three times in the course of a fortnight, so as to let out a little of the fire. Fresh manure is necessary, and it is important that fermentation should be in active progress. At the end of the fortnight the manure should be pressed down firmly with the fork, but not trampled upon, and it should be covered with about six inches of good, ordinary garden loam with an admixture of a little old mortar rubble, sand and a few handfuls of crushed charcoal. The top of the bed should be brought up to within 24 inches of the glass to afford the plants full sun. This should bring us to about the end of March. Melons are better grown on heaps of soil, each heap amounting to about two pecks of compost. A hole is opened in the centre of the heap and the soil rammed down firmly and hard. When stable manure is unobtainable, the bed may be heated by means of a hot-water pipe system or by electricity.

SOWING

Seed may be sown in the bed itself, or young plants may be raised in a pot, in a temperature of about 70° F. early in March, being planted out, 2 feet apart, as soon as an even temperature of about 80° F. may be counted upon.

Double as many seeds should be sown as plants ultimately required.

As the fumes generated by the hot-bed are liable to injure the young seedlings, for the first few days the lights should be left very slightly open to allow the gases to escape. Cover the lights with matting or sacking at night to exclude frost, gradually reducing the covering as the weather becomes warmer.

PRUNING

Very little pruning is necessary, the cutting and slashing so commonly resorted to being very harmful. If grown in a frame, the main shoot should be pegged down on to the soil and stopped when about 2 feet in length. Three or four laterals should be permitted to form. These should be trained evenly over the bed, being pinched back when sufficient flowers are visible.

No plant should be allowed to bear more than four fruits, and these should be kept off the earth by means of a tile or slate.

In a house the plant should be allowed to grow up as a single cordon supported by a cane until it reaches the wires, being stopped back when 4 feet high. Laterals will be thrown out and should be trained along horizontal wires 10 inches apart, being stopped when some 18 inches long. The female flowers have small, globular growths at their base, and four or five of these on each plant require " setting." This is done by picking the male flower, which has no globular formation at its base, removing the yellow petals, and by pressing the pollen-covered stamens into the female flower. The best time to do this is early in the morning when the sun is shining and the plants are dry. The female flower will close, and in a few days' time will commence to swell. A dry atmosphere is not essential while the fruits are setting. While the fruit is ripening, it is essential to allow the shoots from beyond the fruits to thrive, in order that nourishment may be drawn out to the fruit; all unnecessary side growth, however, must be stopped to avoid crowding. Only one fruit must be allowed on a lateral.

WATERING AND VENTILATION

During the early periods of growth, the plants must never be allowed to be dry at the root, in bright weather the leaves should be syringed with water; preferably in the morning and again when closing the house for the night. Tepid water should always be used. When the flowers open, less water may be given, but the plant must never be allowed to suffer for want of it. Spider, fly, thrips and mildew are all associated with scarcity of water. Water at the roots should be given, and the plant should not again be syringed overhead until the fruits begin to swell. In watering melons, great caution must be used in supplying only the quantity wanted, as an excess of water at the roots only tends to increase the size and deteriorate the quality of the fruit. The kind of structure the plants are grown in will have some effect on the quantity of water they will require. In lofty pits or houses, where the foliage attains a large size, and where a much drier atmosphere is obtained than in frames and low pits, more water will be necessary and the whole surface of the soil should be frequently sprinkled. During the whole period of growth, air should be liberally afforded, a careful eye being, of course, kept on the temperature, which should not fall below 60° F. at night, or below 70° F. by day. Should the thermometer rise above 85° F. while the sun is shining, a little more ventilation should be afforded until the temperature has dropped. It will be difficult to maintain these temperatures when frames are used, but much may be done by covering the lights closely with mats and sacking on cold nights. Throughout their whole lives melon plants require free ventilation and an abundance of light, and this is especially true during the period of fruit ripening. Once their roots are established, they cannot have too much sun. It is almost impossible to give a melon too much heat. After the fruit has commenced to ripen, a temperature of 90° F. will enhance the flavour.

RIPENING THE FRUIT

Fruit sown in March takes some four months from the time of sowing to ripen, later-sown fruit will only require three months. As soon as the fruits begin to swell, fertilizers may be applied or tepid liquid manure may be given at intervals. As the fruits swell, more water, which must be tepid, is needed until they begin to ripen, when the syringing and water supply must be diminished and more air given, but the plants must never be allowed to flag.

Three melons on a plant are as much as can be expected to do well ; never more than four should be allowed to remain. Pinch off all the rest and every unnecessary growth. It is important that the plants shall not be allowed to ramble after the fruit has begun to swell, for this will require the whole strength of the plants. Three or four laterals in addition to those carrying the fruits are sufficient, and these after the first stopping, at, say, the fourth leaf, should be stopped again at the first leaf that appears.

The fruit is heavy, and when the size of a tennis ball, arrangements should be made for supporting it by means of small wooden " rafts," or nets, suspended from the wires. Ample sun is required during the ripening period. The fruit takes some four or five weeks, occasionally more, from the time of setting to the time of ripening, which is indicated by the stalk appearing to separate from the fruit. Melons should be cut and used on the day this takes place or very soon after, and a melon should be dead ripe before it is cut.

Melons, while ripening their fruit, are liable to crack when exposed to moisture or when water is applied too freely to their roots. This is more likely to happen with the higher-flavoured ones owing to the thinness of their skin. But a melon that has not been deprived of sufficient water when it required water, will not crack when it is ripening. In ordinary frames some difficulty will be found in keeping the air sufficiently dry. To prevent this, in moist weather air must be left on at night, both back and front, to admit of a slight circulation. By turning over linings, a little extra heat should be thrown into the bed to keep the temperature up. Where, however, melons are grown with the assistance of hot-water pipes, an atmosphere can be maintained which will fully carry out the ripening process of this delicious fruit even in unfavourable weather.

SECOND AND THIRD CROPS

As soon as the fruit is cut—if it is intended that the plant shall bear a second crop—prune back the shoots to where the fresh growth commences. Two or 3 inches of fresh loam should be spread over the surface of the bed, which should at the same time have a good soaking with manure water in order to assist the plants to make fresh growth. An additional stimulus at the same time should be given to the roots by means of slightly increased bottom heat. It is never worth while, except in extraordinary circumstances, to attempt a second crop on old plants.

Where artificial heat is available, by planting a strong young plant as soon as the fruit has been gathered from the old one, three crops of melons may often be obtained in one season. Seed sown in January will bear fruit in June, the plants put in at this time will ripen their fruit in August, and the last crop should ripen off by October.

VARIETIES

Green-fleshed.—Emerald Gem, Monarch and Ringleader.

Scarlet-fleshed.—Blenheim Orange, Cantaloup, Golden Beauty, King George and Superlative.

White-fleshed.—Hero of Lockinge and Universal.

These all do well in the glasshouse.

Munroe's Little Heath and *The Earl's Favourite* are fairly hardy, and may be successfully grown on hot-beds in a frame.

GATHERING AND MARKETING

There is only one important rule about gathering melons. Never be tempted to cut one off until it is ripe. Marketing is equally simple. Melons of quality are usually packed in shallow handle baskets with moderately coarse wood-wool to support them. They are good travellers and need only to be prevented from rolling about. Sizes vary immensely, so that the number in a basket varies according to size. Very big fruit will be placed two in a basket, and the smaller up to six together. The scarlet-fleshed variety usually sells better than the green or white-fleshed varieties.

DISEASES AND PESTS

The melon, when carefully attended to, is not subject to a lot of trouble. But a sharp look-out must be kept for aphides, wood-lice and red spider. Eelworms may attack the roots and cause the plants to wilt and die off without any apparent cause.

The two chief diseases to which the melon is subject, Canker (sometimes called Foot Rot), caused by a bacterium that rots the base of the main stem near ground level, and Downy Mildew, caused by a fungus that gives rise to greyish patches on the foliage and may be severe enough to prevent proper ripening of the fruit, are each largely brought about by too moist conditions. Good ventilation is the best safeguard against attack, and it will check either disease if noticed in the early stages. Excessive "free moisture" should be avoided, though the plants need plenty at the roots. The plants may safely be lightly dusted with copper-lime dust to prevent the spread of infection.

Diseased plants should be destroyed as soon as the fruit is gathered and the frame thoroughly cleaned and fumigated.

For Pests, see Diseases and Pests in the Glasshouse, page 375.

PEACHES AND NECTARINES (*Prunus Persica* [Peach] and (*P. P. var. nucipersica* [Nectarine]*)

Under glass the cultivation of these fruits is essentially similar to their outdoor culture.

The house must be kept very cool until the first or second week in February, when a temperature of 45° to 50° F. should be given. The border must be watered, and on fine days the trees should be syringed twice daily with lukewarm water. After ten days, the temperature should be raised by about ten degrees. Ample ventilation should be given when outside conditions are suitable. A temperature of 50° to 60° F. and plenty of air should be given during the flowering season. In order to ensure pollination, the flowers must be dusted over about noon with a soft camel-hair brush or a rabbit's tail. No syringing should be done while the trees are in bloom, but should be continued daily with soft water as soon as the fruit has set, when the temperature should be raised to 65° F. The ground should also be sprinkled with water while the fruits are forming and swelling ; but no syringing and damping should be done while the fruit is ripening. Not more than one fruit for every 12 inches square of wall space should be allowed.

SOIL AND PLANTING

Next to the grape, the peach and nectarine have been the fruit most generally grown under glass in this country, and it is certainly one of the most profitable crops, for the success of which it is essential to see that the soil is suitable and well drained, it being most important that the roots do not come in contact with water that is either percolating through or stagnant. If the soil is poor and sandy the trees will not find nourishment to enable them to support a good crop, yet as it can afterwards be enriched by suitable composts, it is preferable to soil that is too adhesive. Clay soils are most unsuitable, and the most difficult to deal with, in fact, neither the peach nor the nectarine should ever be planted in such. The best method is to remove the whole of the clay and substitute a suitable compost, or if this is too expensive an item to undertake at once, it is best to provide sufficient good soil for planting the trees and additional suitable soil can then be substituted for the bad soil, in advance of the root-growth, of course. Soil that is removed should be replaced by some good mellow, turfy loam of a substantial, but not of a binding nature. If it is strong and adhesive, then add some mortar rubble and burnt earth.

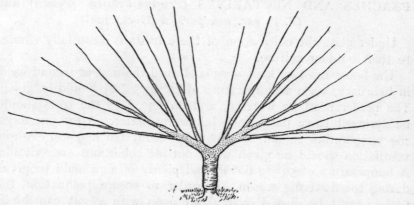

FAN-TRAINED TREE AT END OF FOUR YEARS' GROWTH.
For early training, see pages 75 and 76.

The types of trees to be planted depend on the positions for which they are required. For the front of the glasshouse dwarf trees trained on wires 12 to 15 inches from the glass ; better-flavoured peaches and nectarines are obtained from trees that are grown not far from the glass.

The best season for planting is the autumn, but if it should happen that the planting cannot be done before vegetation commences in the spring, the trees should be lifted and heeled in in a cool, shaded place to retard growth till the final planting can be performed.

FORMS OF TREE FOR PLANTING UNDER GLASS

In high houses fan-trained heads on half-standard or standard stems according to the height of the back walls may be used. The most usual form, however, is the low stemmed fan tree as described on page 76. Oblique cordons trained at 45 degrees were popular

400

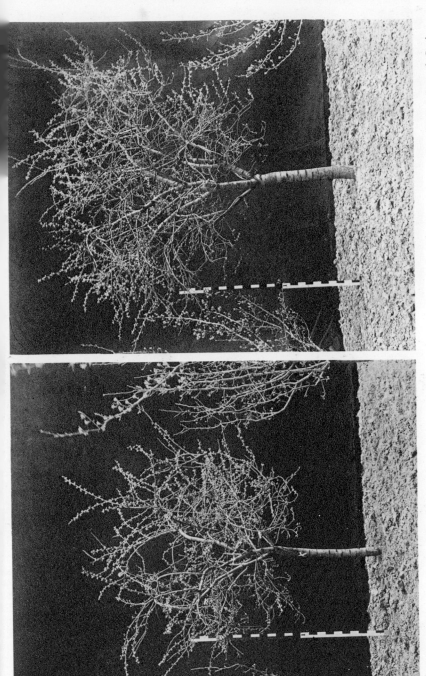

INFLUENCE OF STOCK ON GROWTH OF TREE.

"Victoria" Plum (thirteen years old) on Common Plum Stock.   "Victoria" Plum (thirteen years old) on Myrobolan Plum Stock.

NECTARINES.

PEACHES IN BLOSSOM, AND FIGS.

at one time, but the difficulty of keeping up a regular supply of well-spaced replacement shoots for next year's crop makes the pruning of peach cordons rather a ticklish job.

PRUNING, DISBUDDING AND PINCHING

The same procedure should be carried out on trained peaches indoors as is described on page 272 for wall-trained trees in the open.

Fruit Thinning.—This is done in the same way as described for open-air peaches on page 272.

RIPENING THE FRUIT

As the fruit approaches the ripening period, it should be fully exposed to the sun and given as much ventilation as possible. The shoots should be kept laid in closely, obstructing leaves being removed, and a mulch of manure given. Syringing should cease as soon as the fruit begins to colour, as a drier atmosphere is needed at this period. Some growers suspend nets supported by short stakes beneath the trees to catch any falling fruit, with some soft material in the net to soften the fall. But fruit should be picked before it falls. If the trees have been well grown, the fruit will not fall before it is quite ripe. Netting of a fine mesh is also used successfully to keep off the attacks of flies and wasps. Strong shoots that have been stopped and that have thrown out laterals should be thinned to the number required to cover the allotted space so that the wood may be thoroughly ripened in the sun. Once the fruit is gathered, the roots must be given ample water, and the border dressed with lime. The foliage should be syringed and ventilation freely given.

For methods of planting, training, pruning, etc., see page 271.

GATHERING AND MARKETING

In picking a peach considerable art is required. The fruit must be ripe before it is gathered. A peach that is picked only partly ripe is deprived of all its bouquet and half its sweetness. Although ripe, if it has been well grown, it will still be attached to the tree with a considerable degree of tenacity, and because it is ripe, its delicate bloom and tender, succulent substance are readily injured by the slightest uneven pressure. The fruit must be gripped by every muscle in the hand. The palm must be in close contact with the peach, the fingers and thumb each exerting the minimum of necessary pressure all round the fruit that will remove it from the plant. When the fruit is picked, it must be placed in shallow boxes lined with cotton-wool or very soft wood-wool. These are carried into the packing shed, where the fruit is graded with as little handling as is absolutely necessary and placed in shallow boxes, usually twelve fruit in a box. The fruit is well supported with wool so that it will not move when travelling, but is sufficiently exposed to allow buyers to appreciate the quality. Grading is carried out, having regard to size and colour. A good colour is the best indication of a good flavour. Although this is not an absolutely invariable rule, colour counts more in a peach than anything else.

DISEASES AND PESTS. See pages 277 and 373.

PEACHES SUITABLE FOR FORCING UNDER GLASS

Early	Mid-Season	Late
Dr. Hogg	Royal George	Barrington
Duke of York	Violette Hative	Princess of Wales
Duchess of Cornwall		Sea Eagle
Hale's Early		

NECTARINES SUITABLE FOR FORCING UNDER GLASS

Early	Late
Early Rivers	Pineapple
Elruge	River's Orange
Lord Napier	Spenser

STRAWBERRY (*Fragaria*)

Forced strawberries are usually the first of the new fruit of the year.

Strawberries are forced in pots in the glasshouse. In forcing them half the battle can be won by getting runners as early as possible and growing them on for all they are worth. Runners should be taken from maidens growing in the open and which were planted the previous year. All the bloom should be picked off the plants from which runners are to be taken, and the runners should be pegged down to the soil in sunken 3-inch pots in June. Time is one of the most important factors. The little plant has to be grown and matured, with a well-ripened crown, within about three months. As soon as the roots are showing well round the ball on the 3-inch pot, the plants should be potted into 6-inch pots.

COMPOST AND POTTING

A strawberry revels in a strong loam, and pasture of this nature, dug 5 or 6 inches deep, and chopped fine, not sifted, makes an excellent potting soil for a 6-inch pot. This soil is better used

402

freshly dug. Add *well*-rotted dung and a 6-inch pot of good, fine bonemeal to each barrow load of soil. If the soil is well chosen, i.e., is not too heavy and adhesive, brick rubble and lime can be dispensed with. Pot very firmly and keep the " ball " well down. The crowns will form upwards. Keep the soil one inch down from the rim of the pot. Strawberries are thirsty subjects in August, and in the forcing house. These plants will grow very fast, but they will do their best work towards the end of September. Space them out as they increase in size. Light and air must get all around them. Ultimate success depends upon a well-grown, well-ripened crown.

With the fall of the year, water may be eased off ; but the plant must never be dry while it is growing. By the middle of October the plants will have finished their work, and soakings of rain, which were invaluable in September, will not be helpful in the winter.

WINTERING

The plants may be turned on their sides, or placed in a cold house or frame, preferably the former. A plant that is to be forced must be properly rested. *For this reason the dormant period is of as much importance as the growing.* Frost plays a very important part in the scheme. There is a diversity of opinion amongst growers as to the value of frost in such cases, but in the experience of many advanced growers, eight or ten degrees of frost at the end of October or beginning of November on the plants that are to be forced early is invaluable. It fixes a definite and early date to the resting stage and the plants start better and grow stronger as the result.

It stands to reason that the roots, protected only by the thin walls of the pot, will not resist frost, and the pots must of necessity be protected with litter. If the winter is severe the plants are better removed to a cold house.

TEMPERATURE AND VENTILATION

Bottom heat for a strawberry plant is unnecessary and useless. It is a full hardy plant, and will stand intense frost, and thrives best in a cool soil.

If the plants are brought into the forcing house on the first of January, a very good time for starting the work, a night temperature of 45° F. with a day temperature of 50° F. for the first fortnight should be the maximum. This may be increased during the next fortnight by five degrees, allowing a further rise of five degrees during sunshine. Air is of great importance and the ventilators should never be closed when these temperatures can be maintained with them open. These temperatures may be sustained until the plants bloom, when a minimum day temperature of 60° F. increasing to 70° F. with the sunshine and ample air, and a night temperature of not less than 55° F. will be correct. It might be well to mention here that the brightness of the fruit and the quality of the colour, depend immensely upon temperature and a liberal supply of water. A strawberry grown too slowly or slightly short of water—not necessarily actually dry—will be dull and seedy. The flavour of the fruit depends largely upon sunshine. The water supply must be ample. If the plant really suffers once from dryness it will almost invariably mildew. The strawberry in its native element lives near the ground. Soaked by the dews, it sets its fruit abundantly.

The atmosphere should be kept reasonably moist. It is not necessary to make a special effort to keep a dry atmosphere during the pollination period. Ample ventilation will do all that is required. An arid atmosphere is, indeed, fatal to fertilization. Rabbit tails need seldom be resorted to at this period of the year.

Spider will not attack the plant if the house is clean and the plant is not deprived of water at the roots.

Plants placed out of reach against the glass are invariably neglected at some time or other. They are much better grown on stages.

THINNING AND RIPENING

Should more than twelve berries have formed on any plant, they must be thinned out, only the largest and best shaped berries being retained. Once the fruits commence to swell, weak liquid manure should be applied once a week. As soon as the fruit begins to turn colour, the temperature must be gradually lessened, freer ventilation should be given, and syringing and the application of manure water must stop.

The berries may be prevented from becoming soiled by contact with the soil by each being supported on a short prong of wood pushed into the soil below the berry.

For Diseases and Pests, and Varieties, see pages 349 and 352.

INDEX

INDEX

INDEX

409

INDEX

INDEX

INDEX

TYPICAL
FRUIT STORAGE
BUILDING...

Designed, Fabricated & Erected

BY

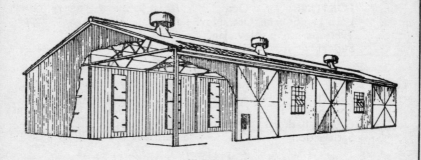

THE ENGLISH

BRIDGE & STRUCTURAL

ENGINEERING CO., LTD.,

ARNOLD ROAD   LONDON   S.W.17

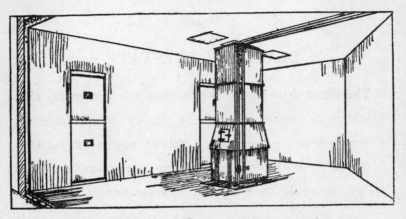
3

5

CONFIDENT GARDENING
ASSURED

BY THE USE OF ONE OR MORE OF THE

FAMOUS "CORRY" AIDS

CORRY'S WHITE FLY DEATH
CORRY'S SLUG DEATH
CORRY'S LIME SULPHUR WASH
CORRY'S QUASSIA EXTRACT WASH
CORRY'S DERRIS DUSTING POWDER
CORRY'S DERRIS INSECTICIDE
CORRY'S DERRIS LIQUID EXTRACT
CORRY'S NICOTINE POWDER
CORRY'S PYRETHRUM POWDER
CORRY'S ANT AND WOODLICE POWDER
CORRY'S WASP NEST DESTROYER
CORRY'S FRUIT TREE GREASE
CORRY'S CHESHUNT COMPOUND
CORRY'S BORDEAUX MIXTURE
CORRY'S NAPHTHALENE
CORRY'S TENAX GRAFTING WAX
CORRY'S LAWN SAND
CORRY'S "FOWLER'S" TOBACCO POWDER
CORRY'S SUMMER CLOUD
CORRY'S RED SPIDER DEATH
CORRY'S WOOLLY APHIS DEATH
CORRY'S RABBIT TREE PROTECTOR
CORRY'S D.D.T. (5% GEIGY) POWDER
CORRY'S D.D.T. (20% GEIGY) EMULSION
CORRY'S 40% FORMALDEHYDE
CORRY'S READY GREASED BANDS
CORRY'S WEED DEATH
CORRY'S WORM KILLER, ETC.

Sold by all Seedsmen and Horticultural Dealers

CORRY & CO., LTD., SHAD THAMES, LONDON, S.E.1

FRUIT IN PERFECTION

To grow good crops of any fruit free from blemishes and loss caused by Insect and Fungus attacks, special control measures are essential.

Our Research Department directs all its energies to the elucidation of Pest Control problems and its work is to Invent measures to assist growers to combat all avoidable blemish and loss of crop.

Our work, always up-to-date, is at the service of all growers.

Ask us for information and leaflets

Continuous work on Pest Control since 1900 has resulted in a vast store of accumulated knowledge and experience which we willingly place at your service.

BUGGÉ'S INSECTICIDES LTD.

SITTINGBOURNE, KENT

SPECIALISTS IN D.D.T. FORMULATIONS
(LIQUIDS, EMULSIONS, WETTABLE POWDERS, DUSTS, ATOMISTS.)

7

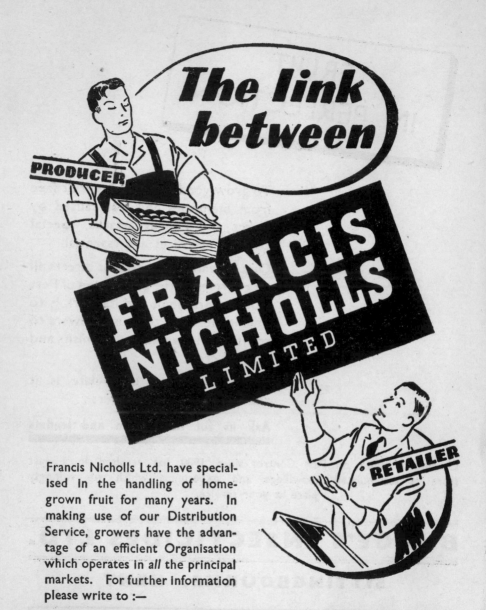